AQA
GCSE
Food Preparation and Nutrition

Anita Tull
Garry Littlewood

Illuminate Publishing

Published in 2016 by Illuminate Publishing Ltd,
P.O. Box 1160,
Cheltenham, Gloucestershire
GL50 9RW

Orders: Please visit www.illuminatepublishing.com
or email sales@illuminatepublishing.com

British Library Cataloguing in Publication Data
A catalogue record for this book is available from
the British Library

ISBN 978-1-908682-78-9

Printed by: Standartu Spaustuvė, Lithuania

08.16

The publisher's policy is to use papers that are
natural, renewable and recyclable products
made from wood grown in sustainable forests.
The logging and manufacturing processes are
expected to conform to the environmental
regulations of the country of origin.

Every effort has been made to contact copyright
holders of material produced in this book. If
notified, the publisher will be pleased to rectify
any errors or omissions at the earliest opportunity.

Proofreader: Geoff Tuttle
Design: Nigel Harriss
Layout and all original artwork:
GreenGate Publishing, Tonbridge

Cover image: © Valentina G/Shutterstock

Approval message from AQA

This textbook has been approved by AQA for
use with our qualification. This means that
we have checked that it broadly covers the
specification and we are satisfied with the
overall quality. Full details of our approval
process can be found on our website.

We approve textbooks because we know
how important it is for teachers and students
to have the right resources to support their
teaching and learning. However, the publisher
is ultimately responsible for the editorial
control and quality of this book.

Please note that when teaching the GCSE
Food Preparation and Nutrition course (8585),
you must refer to AQA's specification as
your definitive source of information. While
this book has been written to match the
specification, it does not provide complete
coverage of every aspect of the course.

The authors and publisher wish to thank the following:

Gill Maitland, **Karen Worger** and **Claire Hart** for their ideas, encouragement, advice
and input from the very beginning.

Adrian Moss and **Mark Regan** for many of the food preparation and cooking photos
that were taken as stills from the fantastic films they produced in support of this book
(shoutoutstudio.co.uk)

Yvette Farrell, the star of our food preparation and cooking films and film stills,
and who provided the location and equipment for the filming in the Forest of
Dean, Gloucestershire (hartsbarncookeryschool.co.uk). A big thank you also to
Alice Jackman for the important part she played in the making of the films.

Phil Wattis for many of the science illustrations that were taken as stills from the
superb animations he produced in support of this book (phlip.co.uk).

Karen Wallace and **Matthew Warren** at GreenGate Publishing Services for the
incredible job they have done editing, typesetting and helping to manage this book
through to publication (www.ggate.co.uk).

Cath Saunders of Balcarras School, Cheltenham, for her valuable advice at the
planning stage.

Nick Tull for taking a number of great photos used to illustrate the book.

Benjamin Bradbury, **Abigail Brownlee**, **Kelly Dunnington**, **Rebecca Higginbottom**,
Benjamin Mould and **Ruksaad Zannar** of Huntington School, York, for allowing their
work to be included in the Non-Exam Assessment chapter.

Dedication

To Nick for being a totally supportive, patient and encouraging husband throughout
the whole process of writing the book.

Contents

Introduction

This student textbook has been especially written for the **AQA GCSE Food Preparation and Nutrition** qualification that you are taking, and matches the course specification produced by AQA. GCSE Food Preparation and Nutrition is an interesting, creative and stimulating course for students of all abilities. Throughout this course the focus will be on developing practical cookery skills and a strong understanding of nutrition.

The book has been designed to help you to develop your knowledge and understanding of the subject, and successfully work your way through the theory and practical aspects of the course, so you gain understanding and confidence. This book has been written to help you to achieve your potential in both the written examination and the Non-Examination Assessment.

Aim of the Food Preparation and Nutrition course

The aim of this new and exciting GCSE course is to teach you all about food in its widest sense and help you to learn and develop a wide range of food preparation skills. It has been developed to help you understand:

- what food is composed of, why we need it and how it affects our long-term health
- how food can be prepared and cooked skilfully and safely to produce delicious and nutritious meals for different people and situations
- what happens to the ingredients in food when you prepare and cook them
- where food comes from and how it is produced and sold
- which foods different cultures eat throughout the world
- how the food choices people make affect the health and well-being of themselves, their families and the people who produce the food
- how the food choices people make affect the health and well-being of the global environment and its natural resources
- how you can become an informed and thoughtful consumer of food.

Completing the Food Preparation and Nutrition course

When you have completed this course you should be able to:

- show your knowledge and understanding of nutrition, food, food preparation and cooking
- apply your knowledge and understanding of nutrition, food, food preparation and cooking to different situations and tasks
- plan, prepare, cook and present a variety of dishes, using a range of appropriate skills and techniques
- analyse and evaluate different aspects of nutrition, food, food preparation and cooking, including food that you and others have made.

You will be assessed and graded according to how you complete:

- a written examination, taken at the end of the course (worth 50% of your final marks and GCSE grade)
- two Non-Examination Assessment (NEA) tasks (worth together 50% of your final marks and GCSE grade), taken during the final year of the course.

The last two chapters in this book are about the two NEA tasks and the written examination.

How to use this book

The book is set out in the same order as the course specification, which is divided into these sections:

- Food, Nutrition and Health
- Food Science
- Food Safety
- **Food Choice**
- **Food Provenance (where food comes from)**

It is important for you to realise and remember that all of these sections are linked to each other, so you should not treat them as completely separate pieces of information. There is much to learn but most of this will involve 'learning-through making'. For example, if you take a topic such as eggs, there will be something to learn and know about eggs in each section, and you will also experience putting some of this knowledge into practice when you use eggs in your practical work, as shown below:

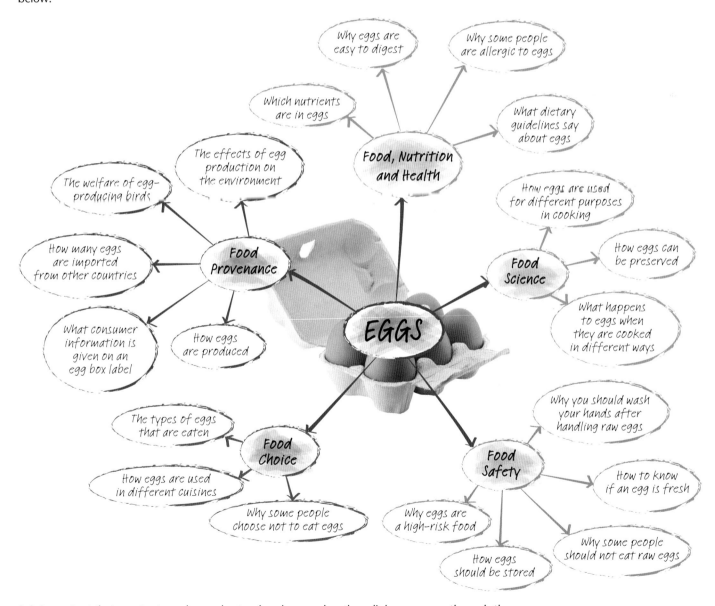

It is important that you try to make, understand and remember these links as you go through the course.

Features to help you

Throughout the book, there are a number of features to help you to study and progress through the course, which are shown below.

Good luck on your course. We hope that you will enjoy learning more about food and will feel confident in your ability to understand why food is so important and how to prepare and cook a range of delicious meals!

Key terms: these give you the definitions of the key terminology (words) in each of the topics that you need to know and use

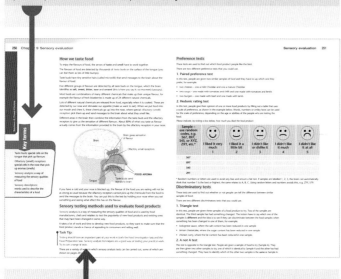

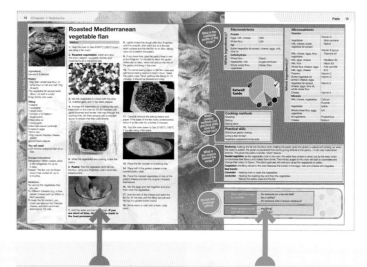

Task Tip: these give you some tips about information, resources, further research and skills that maybe useful in your studies.

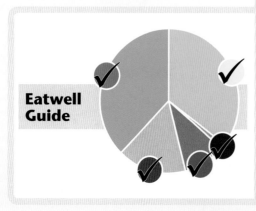

Recipes: a variety of recipes, related to particular topics, are provided. Each recipe gives the ingredients and method for making it. To help you link these to the various sections of the specification, you will find at the end of the recipes a chart showing the nutritional profile of the recipe as well as an Eatwell Guide logo, indicating by the use of tick symbols, which sections of it are provided by the ingredients in the recipe. The cooking methods and practical skills used and the science behind the recipe are also given. To help you understand and develop your meal planning skills, you may also be asked how you could vary and/ or modify the ingredients or cooking method in the recipe for different situations.

Stretch and challenge activities: these are activities in which you will need to find out more about a topic and practise being able to answer questions at a higher level, showing your detailed knowledge and understanding.

Study tips: these will give you tips on how to develop your understanding, recall and revision skills for different topics throughout the book.

Photographs and drawings: there are many of these throughout the book. They are included to help you further understand and visualise a topic, particularly what happens when ingredients are prepared and cooked (food science), produced and processed.

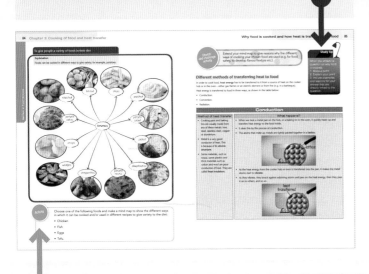

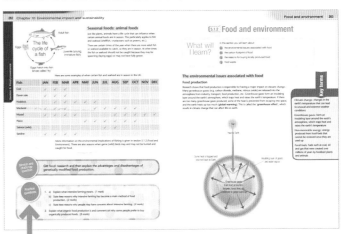

Activities: a range of activities are given throughout the book. Some of these are practical activities you can do in class, some are theory based. They are designed to encourage you to think more widely about a topic and work with other people and discuss, analyse and evaluate what you find out.

Practice questions: these are end-of-topic questions, written in different styles and with a range of command words. They are designed to give you opportunities throughout the course to practise and improve your techniques for answering questions.

Student digital book

A digital version of this student book is also available if your school has access to our Digital Book Bundle of student and teacher resources. You can view this digital version via a tablet or computer at school, at home or on the bus – wherever it suits you. Please note that the digital book is not approved by AQA.

There are extra features in the student digital book that support your studies. For each topic in this book there are:

- **Films:** Demonstrate all the key cooking techniques and skills you need for the course, with the relevant science clearly highlighted.

- **Animations:** Help make the science behind cooking techniques easier for you to understand.

- **Lifelines:** Present easy-to-read key points for each topic and are great for revising and helping you to understand what you are learning.

- **Quizzes:** Check and reinforce your understanding on a topic with interactive, self-marking quizzes.

- **Weblinks:** Take you to to websites helpful for your studies.

Chapter 1 Nutrients

1.1.1 Protein

What will I learn?

In this section you will learn about:

- the definition of protein
- the **functions** of protein in the body
- the main **sources** of protein in the diet
- the effects of a **deficiency** or an **excess** of protein in the diet
- the **amount** of protein needed every day for different life stages.

Key terms

Amino acids: the 'building blocks' that join together to make protein molecules

Essential amino acids: amino acids that the body cannot make by itself and must get ready-made from food

Biological value: the number of essential amino acids that a protein food contains

Protein complementation: eating different LBV protein foods together in order to get all the essential amino acids that the body needs

What is protein?

Protein is a **macronutrient** that is needed by all animals, including humans.

Protein molecules are made up of individual 'building blocks' called **amino acids**. There are at least 20 different amino acids and they can be found in any number or combination in different proteins.

When we eat foods containing proteins, our body breaks up (**digests**) the protein molecules into individual amino acids and makes new protein molecules for our body to use.

Why are proteins important?

Some of the 20 amino acids *cannot* be made in the body and have to come ready-made from the foods we eat. These are called **essential amino acids**, and there are eight of these needed by adults and children, and at least 2 extra ones needed just by children because they are growing.

Protein foods that contain *all* of the essential amino acids are called **high biological value** (HBV) **proteins**. This means that they are of great value to the body, because it does not have to make these amino acids from the food we eat.

Protein foods that are missing *one or more* of the essential amino acids are called **low biological value** (LBV) **proteins**. If you eat a mixture of LBV proteins together, the essential amino acids that are missing in one will be provided by another LBV protein, so you will get all the amino acids you need. This is called **protein complementation**.

Functions of protein in the body

Protein has **three main functions** in the body:

1. **To make the body grow** from a baby into an adult and, when it has stopped growing, to make certain parts of the body continue to grow (e.g. hair, finger nails and toe nails).

2. **To repair the body** when it is injured or recovering from an operation or illness, and replace certain parts of the body regularly, such as skin cells and red blood cells.

3. **To give the body energy**, although the body prefers to get most of its energy from foods containing carbohydrates and fats, rather than protein.

Also, many important natural substances in the body are made from proteins, including:

hormones – make you grow and reproduce

enzymes – digest your food

antibodies – help your immune system fight infections from bacteria and viruses.

Main sources of protein in the diet

Protein is found in animal foods including meat, fish, poultry, milk, cheese and eggs and also in plant foods, including beans, peas, lentils, nuts and cereals.

High biological value protein

Main sources

Meat, poultry, fish, shellfish, eggs, milk, dairy foods (e.g. cheese, yogurt, quark, fromage frais), soya beans, quinoa

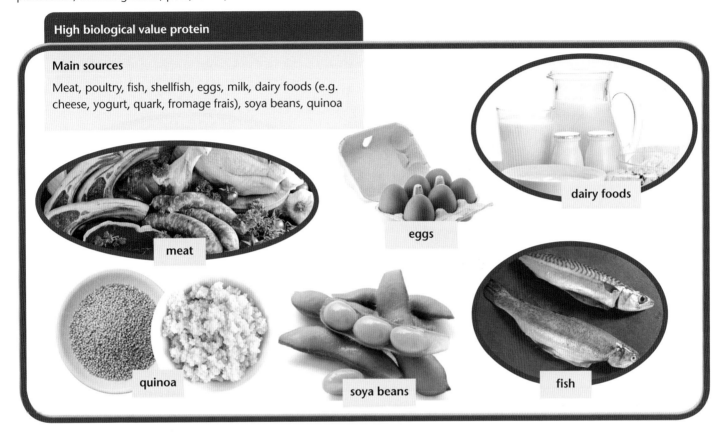

meat   eggs   dairy foods

quinoa   soya beans   fish

Low biological value protein

Main sources

Lentils, peas, beans (except soya beans), cereals (e.g. wheat, rice, oats, barley, rye, millet, sorghum), nuts, seeds, gelatine

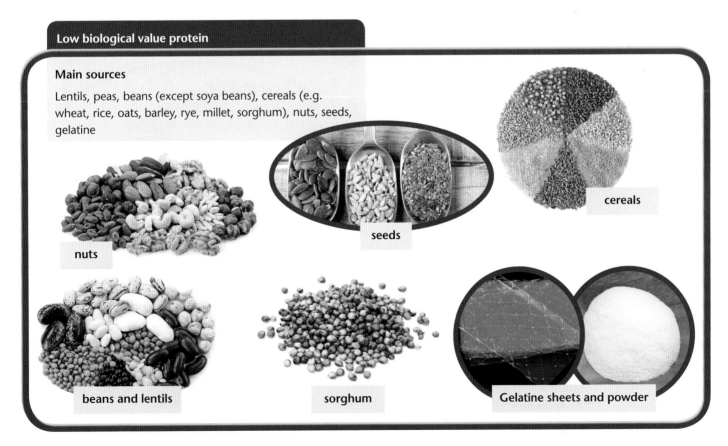

nuts   seeds   cereals

beans and lentils   sorghum   Gelatine sheets and powder

Protein alternatives

- These are manufactured products that are used as alternatives to meat.
- They all have a high protein content and often a low fat content.
- They have little flavour on their own, but readily take up other flavours.
- These proteins are often consumed by vegetarians and are used in a wide range of recipes in place of meat or fish.

Tofu (soya bean curd) – made from treated soya milk, sold as soft (silken), firm or smoked

Tempeh – made from fermented whole soya beans

TVP (textured vegetable protein) – made from soya bean flour (after the soya oil has been removed), sold as chunks or mince

Mycoprotein (e.g. Quorn®) – made from a high protein fungus (myco = fungus), sold as chunks, fillets or mince

Examples of protein complementation

Beans on toast

Rice and bean salad

Vegetarian tortilla wraps

Lentil soup

Nut butter on bread

Rice dessert set with gelatine

Activity

Copy and complete this mind map for proteins.

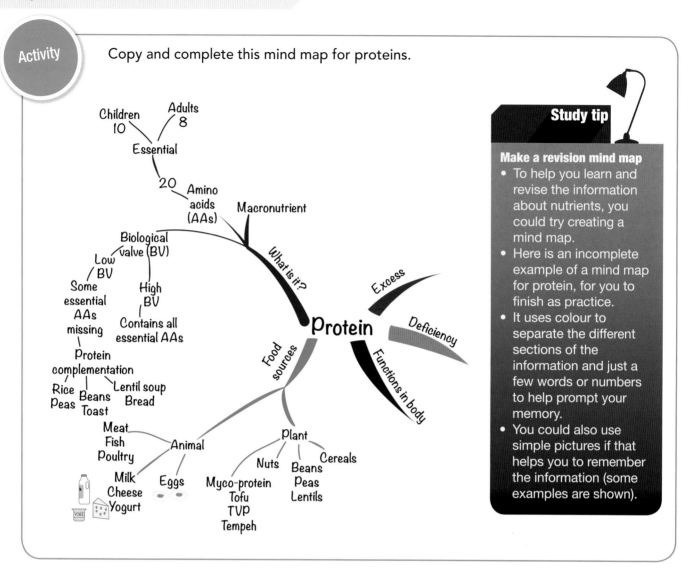

Study tip

Make a revision mind map
- To help you learn and revise the information about nutrients, you could try creating a mind map.
- Here is an incomplete example of a mind map for protein, for you to finish as practice.
- It uses colour to separate the different sections of the information and just a few words or numbers to help prompt your memory.
- You could also use simple pictures if that helps you to remember the information (some examples are shown).

Effects of a **deficiency** of protein in the diet

Children and adults have a high requirement for protein, so if their diet is deficient in protein, they will show a range of symptoms, including:

Effects of a deficiency of protein	Why does this happen?
Children will not grow properly and may never reach their full height.	The body cannot grow to the height it is meant to be without the right quality and quantity of 'materials' (nutrients) that it needs, including protein.
They may lose some of their hair.	Hair is made of protein. People can live without hair, so if there is a deficiency of protein, the body will use any protein it does get for something more important.
Their skin and nails will be in poor condition.	Skin and nails contain protein and if there is a deficiency of protein, they will not be maintained properly and will weaken.
They will easily develop infections.	Protein is needed for the immune system to protect us from infections. If there is a deficiency of protein, the immune system will weaken and infections will take hold.
They will not be able to digest any food properly.	A deficiency of protein causes changes in the digestive system, which means various nutrients cannot be absorbed into the body.

Effects of an **excess** of protein in the diet

Protein contains different chemical elements, including nitrogen. Too much nitrogen in the body is dangerous, so it is removed from the body in the urine, which is excreted.

If the diet contains too much protein, the liver and kidneys have to work harder to get rid of the nitrogen. This puts them under stress and could cause them to be harmed.

Amount of protein needed every day for different life stages

This is the amount of protein needed by different groups of (healthy) people every day:

Age/gender		Grams of protein per day
Children	1–3 years	14.5
	4–6 years	19.7
	7–10 years	28.3
Teenagers (male)	11–14 years	42.1
(female)	11–14 years	41.2
Teenagers (male)	15–18 years	55.2
(female)	15–18 years	45.0
Adults (male)	19–50 years	55.5
(female)	19–50 years	45.0
(male)	50+ years	53.3
(female)	50+ years	46.5
Pregnant women		an extra 6g
Women lactating (breastfeeding) for up to 4 months		an extra 11g
Women lactating (breastfeeding) for over 4 months		an extra 8g

The figures given for the amount of nutrients needed to maintain good health in the majority of people in the population are called **Dietary Reference Values** (DRVs).

On page 8 is a recipe to show how HBV protein can be incorporated into a main meal.

Practice questions

1. Different people need different amounts of protein.

   a) Describe why most teenage boys need more protein than most teenage girls. *(3 marks)*

   b) Explain why women who are breastfeeding a baby need extra protein. *(3 marks)*

2. a) Identify which one of the following dishes is an example of protein complementation.

       A. Cheese on toast   C. Beans on toast

       B. Apricot jam on toast   D. Poached egg on toast.

   b) Explain your answer in part a). *(5 marks)*

3. a) State what is meant by a protein alternative. *(3 marks)*

   b) Comment on why protein alternatives are useful to people who have decided to change from eating meat to a vegetarian diet. *(3 marks)*

   c) Compare the nutritional value of red meat, fish, soya and mycoprotein. *(4 marks)*

Fish pie

Method:

1. Potato topping
- Peel and chop the potatoes into small chunks.
- Place in a pan of cold water, bring it to the boil and gently boil for 15–20 minutes until the potatoes are soft.
- Drain the water away and mash the potatoes with the butter/vegetable fat spread and 50ml of milk until they are smooth.
- Season with salt and pepper.

2. Fish
- While the potatoes are boiling, prepare the fish.
- Wash the fish in cold water and place it on some greaseproof or baking paper inside a steamer pan.
- Carefully place the steamer over a pan of gently boiling water, and put the lid on the steamer.
- Do not let the water in the steamer completely evaporate.
- Steam the fish until it breaks up easily and comes away easily from its skin (about 10–15 minutes depending on the thickness of the fish).
- **If you do not have a steamer, there are two other ways you can cook the fish:**
- 1. Make a kitchen foil casing, put the fish in it, seal it up and bake it in the oven (Gas 4/180°C; 170°C if you are using a fan oven) for 15–20 minutes.
- 2. Poach the fish in the milk in a pan for a few minutes until it is cooked.
- Carefully remove the fish and place it on a board or plate. Break the fish into small pieces with a knife and fork and remove any skin. Check carefully and remove any bones.

3. Prepare the sauce
Either:

All-in-one microwave method:
- In a mixing bowl, put the flour.
- Gradually add the milk, mixing it to make it smooth with a wooden spoon or balloon whisk.
- Add the butter.
- Place the bowl into the microwave oven and set the timer to 1 minute.
- When it stops, stir the sauce thoroughly and microwave again for 1 minute – stir the sauce again.
- Repeat this 4–5 times until the sauce has thickened and is smooth and glossy.
- Take it out of the microwave.

Or:

Béchamel (roux) method:
- In a small saucepan, melt the butter on the hob – do not let it burn.
- Add the flour and continue heating it, stirring it all the time with a wooden spoon, for 1 minute (roux).
- Remove the pan from the heat.
- Gradually add the milk to the roux, stirring well each time to avoid any lumps forming, until all the milk has been added.
- Put the pan back on the heat and, stirring all the time, heat the sauce until it boils and thickens – the sauce should coat the back of the wooden spoon and be smooth and glossy in appearance.
- Remove the pan from the heat.

4. Assemble and finish the fish pie:
- Mix the peas or sweetcorn into the sauce. If they are fresh (i.e. not canned or frozen) they will need to be boiled in water for about 5 minutes until tender before they are added to the sauce.
- Chop the dill leaves with either kitchen scissors or a knife.
- Place the fish in the bottom of an ovenproof dish.
- Scatter the dill leaves over the fish.
- Pour the sauce over the fish and mix gently with a fork.
- Spread the mashed potato evenly over the fish and sauce. You could use a piping bag and star nozzle to pipe the potato on to give a different finish.
- If you are using a tomato, slice it thinly and arrange the slices neatly on top of the potato.
- Sprinkle the top with the grated cheese.
- Either: place the pie in the oven (Gas 5/190°C; 180°C if you are using a fan oven) for approximately 20 minutes until the top is browned.
- Or: place the pie under a hot grill for a few minutes until the top is golden brown.

Ingredients:
(serves 6 people)

Topping:
700g potatoes
60g butter or vegetable fat spread
50ml milk
Seasoning
30g grated cheddar cheese
1 tomato – sliced (optional)

Fish:
500g haddock or other white fish (e.g. pollock, whiting, hake, cod)
100g peas or sweetcorn
A small bunch dill (optional)

Béchamel sauce
50g unsalted butter or vegetable fat spread
50g plain flour
600ml milk

Storage instructions:
Refrigerator: allow to cool then cover and store in the refrigerator (0°C to below 5°C) for up to 3 days. Reheat only **once** until at least 70°C ('piping hot').
Freezer: allow to cool then chill in refrigerator. Place in a suitable container or cover carefully with suitably strong foil or plastic and freeze for up to 3 months.

Variations:
Try using other vegetables instead of or mixed with the potato (e.g. carrot, sweet potato, butternut squash, parsnip, swede, turnip, yam).
To save time and money, canned fish (e.g. tuna) can be used instead of fresh fish. As canned fish is already cooked, you just need to drain the oil or water from it, break it up with a fork and add it to your dish with the peas or sweetcorn, then add the sauce and complete the recipe as shown.

What is the nutritional profile of this recipe?

Which ingredient(s)?

Macronutrients

Protein

Fish, milk, cheese	HBV
Peas, sweetcorn, flour	LBV

Fat

Butter, cheese

Carbohydrate

Flour, potatoes	Starch
Onion	Sugars (intrinsic)
Peas, sweetcorn, tomato	Dietary fibre

Micronutrients

Which ingredient(s)?

Vitamins

	Vitamin A:
Tomato	Beta carotene
Milk, cheese, butter	Retinol
	Vitamin B group:
Milk, cheese, peas	Thiamine B1
Milk, cheese	Riboflavin B2
Milk, flour	Niacin B3
Milk, cheese, peas	Folic acid B9
Milk, cheese, fish	B12
Tomato (a little)	Vitamin C
Milk, cheese, butter	Vitamin D
Milk, cheese, butter	Vitamin E
Cheese	Vitamin K

Minerals

Milk, cheese, fish	Calcium
Fish	Fluoride
Milk, cheese, fish	Iodine
Flour	Iron
All ingredients	Phosphorus
Cheese	Sodium

Which cooking methods and practical skills does this recipe use?

Cooking methods

Boiling vegetables
Bake or steam fish
Microwave option for sauce
Bake or grill fish pie

Practical skills

Béchamel sauce
Fish preparation
Knife skills – vegetables and fish
Piping option for mashed potato

Eatwell Guide

What is the science behind this recipe?

Gelatinisation of starch for Béchamel sauce and cooking of boiled potatoes.
Denaturation and coagulation of protein in fish.
Melting of fat in cheese, and denaturation and coagulation of protein.

Heat transfer

Convection	Heating oven to bake fish and completed fish pie
	Boiling potatoes
	Steaming of fish
Conduction	Heat passing through the foil to bake the fish and the baking dish into the completed fish pie.
Radiation	Grilling option for completed fish pie.
Conduction	Microwave option for Béchamel sauce making.

Stretch and challenge activity

How could this recipe be modified ...	... for a vegetarian (does not eat fish)?
	... for a coeliac?
	... for someone who is lactose intolerant?
	... to increase the fibre content?
	... to reduce the fat content?

What variations could you make to ...	... the sauce?
	... the potato topping?
	... the type of fish?
	What would you serve with the fish pie?

[1.1.2] # Fats

2.

What will I learn?

In this section you will learn about:

- the definition of **fat**
- the **functions** of fat in the body
- the main **sources** of fat in the diet
- the effects of a **deficiency** or an **excess** of fat in the diet
- the **amount** of fat needed every day for different life stages.

Key terms

Fat: macronutrient that supplies the body with energy

Oils: fats that are liquid at room temperature

Fatty acids: parts of a fat molecule

Triglyceride: fat molecule

Monounsaturated fatty acid: fatty acid found in solid fats and liquid oils

Saturated fatty acids: fatty acids found mainly in solid fats

Unsaturated fatty acids: fatty acids found mainly in liquid oils

Visible fats: fats in a food that you can see (e.g. fat on meat)

Invisible fats: fats in a food that you cannot see (e.g. butter in pastry)

What is fat?

Fat is a **macronutrient** that is needed by all animals.

Fats are **solid** at room temperature.

Fats are called **oils** when they are **liquid** at room temperature.

Fats and oils have the **same basic chemical structure** and provide the **same amount of energy** (9kcals/37kJ per gram).

Chemical structure of fats

This is the basic chemical structure of a fat/oil:

Fat **molecules** are made of one unit of **glycerol** and three **fatty acids**, like this:

glycerol — Fatty acid 1
— Fatty acid 2
— Fatty acid 3   This molecule is called a **triglyceride**.

Fatty acids are either **saturated** or **unsaturated** (**monounsaturated** and **polyunsaturated**).

Foods with a lot of **saturated fatty acids** in them are often called '**saturated fats**'. They include butter, lard, suet, block vegetable fat, ghee, the fat in meat, palm oil, coconut and chocolate.

Foods with a lot of **unsaturated fatty acids** in them are called '**unsaturated fats**' or '**polyunsaturates**'. They include plant oils such as olive, rapeseed, sunflower and corn; oily fish, avocado pears, nuts, seeds and some vegetable fat spreads.

Solid **vegetable fat spreads** can be made from liquid vegetable oils.

Essential fatty acids

When we eat foods containing fat, our body breaks up (**digests**) the fat molecules they contain and makes new fatty acids and fat molecules specifically for our body to use. Two fatty acids *cannot* be made in the body and have to come ready-made from the foods we eat. These are called **essential fatty acids** and are needed by adults and children. They are mainly found in oily fish, plant and seed oils, eggs and fresh meat.

Functions of fat in the body

Fat has **four main functions** in the body:

1. To provide a **store of energy** in the adipose tissue under the skin.
2. To **insulate** the body from the cold and help it to stay warm.
3. To **protect** bones and the kidneys from damage by providing them with a protective cushion of fat.
4. To give the body **fat soluble vitamins A, D, E and K** (see pages 22–23).

Main sources of fat in the diet

When we talk about the nutritional aspects of fat, it is referred to as just 'fat'. You also sometimes see the word 'lipid' used to refer to fat. In food preparation, it is referred to as either 'fat' or 'oil'.

Fat found in foods is either present as solid fat or liquid oil. Some of these are easy to see (e.g. the fat on a piece of meat or the oil in a can of tuna). These are called **visible fats** and **oils**.

In many foods, however, it is difficult to see the fats and oils they contain because they are combined with other ingredients in the food, and therefore it is not easy to know how much fat and oil you are eating. These are called **invisible fats** and **oils** and are found in foods such as cakes, pastries, potato crisps, biscuits, chocolate, nuts, etc.

Study tip

Remember
Fats and oils have the same basic chemical structure and the same energy value.
The difference is whether they are solid or liquid at room temperature.

Types of fat

Solid animal fats

Main sources

Visible animal fats: butter, lard, suet, ghee, fat on meat

Foods containing ***invisible*** animal fats:

- cheese
- butter in cakes, biscuits and pastries
- meat products (e.g. sausages, corned beef, salami)
- meat (in between muscle cells)
- many processed ready meals and take-away foods.

Solid plant fats

Main sources

Visible plant fats: white vegetable fats, vegetable fat spreads (old name = margarines), coconut cream, cocoa butter

Foods containing ***invisible*** plant fats:

- many processed foods (ready-made curries, ready-meals and fast foods that have been fried in hydrogenated vegetable fat (solid fat that has been made in a factory from vegetable oils), e.g. fried chicken, fish and chips)
- chocolate (including white chocolate)
- pastries, cakes, biscuits, doughnuts and breads made with hydrogenated white vegetable fats and vegetable fat spreads.

Section 1: Food, Nutrition and Health

Liquid animal oils

Main sources

Visible animal oils: cod liver oil, oily fish (e.g. mackerel, sardines)

Foods containing *invisible* animal oils:

- milk, cream
- egg yolk
- oily fish (e.g. sardines, salmon, herring).

Cod liver oil capsules

Liquid plant oils

Main sources

Visible plant oils: nut and seed oils (e.g. sunflower, rapeseed, sesame, corn, olive, almond)

Foods containing *invisible* plant oils:

- seeds, e.g. pumpkin, sunflower, sesame, groundnuts (peanuts)
- nuts, e.g. walnuts, almonds, pecans, cashews
- fruits, e.g. olives, avocado pears
- vegetable fat spreads, blended butter spreads
- fried foods, e.g. doughnuts, chips, chicken nuggets
- many processed foods, ready-meals and take-away foods (e.g. curries, ice cream, salad dressings, sauces, dips such as hummus).

Effects of a **deficiency** of fat in the diet

A deficiency of fat is rare in the UK.

Effects of a deficiency of fat	Why does this happen?
If carbohydrate intake is also reduced, body weight will be lost.	The body will use the store of energy from the fat cells and it will not be replaced.
The body will chill quickly.	There will not be enough fat to insulate the body from the cold.
The body will bruise easily and the bones will hurt if they are knocked.	There will not be a thick enough cushion of fat (adipose tissue) to prevent damage to blood vessels and bones.
The body will not receive enough vitamins A, D, E or K.	These vitamins are found in foods that contain fat.

Effects of an **excess** of fat in the diet

- Fat provides the body with energy (9kcals/37kJ per gram).
- Foods that contain fat are therefore **energy dense** (see page 60).
- If the energy from fat eaten in foods every day is not all used in physical activity, it will be stored by the body under the skin in adipose tissue and elsewhere in the body (e.g. around the intestines (visceral fat)). Consequently, the body will gain weight and could become obese (see pages 70–71).
- Eating a lot of foods that contain high levels of **saturated fatty acids** has been linked to the development of **coronary heart disease (CHD)** in some people (see pages 71–72).

Amount of fat needed every day for different life stages

The amount of fat we need is calculated as a **percentage of our total daily energy** intake, rather than by weight. This is the amount of fat recommended by health experts for different groups of (healthy) adults every day:

Type of fat	% of food energy per day
Total fat of which:	**No more than** 35%
Saturated fatty acids	11%
Monounsaturated fatty acids	13%
Polyunsaturated fatty acids	6.5%
Trans fatty acids	No more than 2%

On page 14 is a recipe that contains a variety of visible and invisible fats and oils.

Many foods contain invisible fat and are energy dense

Study tip

To help you to understand which foods contain fat, have a look at a variety of ingredients lists on different food labels and see if you can identify the visible and invisible fats and oils they contain. Remember that the words 'lipid' and 'triglyceride' are sometimes used instead of the word 'fat'.

Ingredients:
(serves 6–8 people)

Pastry
150g plain wholemeal flour, or
   white flour or half and half (75g
   of each)
75g vegetable fat spread (solid
   block, not soft in a tub)
8 tsp (40ml) cold water

Filling
1 pepper
1 courgette
1 small onion
1 tomato or 2 medium
   mushrooms
2 tbsp olive oil
1 clove garlic
a few basil leaves (optional)
2 medium eggs
150ml milk
100g mature cheddar cheese,
   grated
ground black pepper

You will need
a 23–25cm ovenproof flan tin or
   dish.

Storage instructions:
Refrigerator: When cooled, store
   in the refrigerator for up to
   5 days.
Freezer: The flan can be frozen
   once it has cooled for up to
   4 months.

Variations:
Try varying the vegetables that
   you use.
Try different cheeses (e.g. a blue
   veined cheese such as Stilton,
   or Red Leicester).
To lower the fat content, you
   could use reduced fat Cheddar
   cheese, and semi-skimmed,
   skimmed or 1% milk.

Roasted Mediterranean vegetable flan

Method:

1. Heat the oven to Gas 6/200°C (190°C if you are using a fan oven).

2. Roasted vegetables: Wash and dice the onion, pepper, courgette, tomato and mushrooms all to the same size.

3. Mix the vegetables in a bowl with the olive oil, crushed garlic and ½ tsp black pepper.

4. Arrange the vegetables on a baking tray and roast them in the oven for 25–30 minutes until lightly browned and tender. Half way through the cooking time, stir them around with a wooden spoon to ensure that they cook evenly.

5. While the vegetables are cooking, make the pastry.

6. Pastry: Rub the vegetable block fat into the flour, using your fingertips, until it looks like breadcrumbs.

7. Add the water and mix to a dough. **If you are short of time, this could be made in the food processor.**

8. Lightly knead the dough with your fingertips until it is smooth, then roll it out on a floured work surface and line the flan tin or dish, taking care not to stretch the pastry.

9. If you have time, give the pastry time to rest in the fridge for 15 minutes to allow the gluten molecules to relax, which will reduce the risk of the pastry shrinking in the oven.

10. Put some baking paper in the flan case and add some baking beans to hold it down. Bake the pastry case 'blind' (without the filling) for 15 minutes. It should be cooked and crisp.

11. Carefully remove the baking beans and paper. If the base of the flan looks undercooked, return it to the oven for a further 5 minutes.

12. Turn the oven down to Gas 5/190°C (180°C if you are using a fan oven).

13. Place the flan tin/dish on a baking tray.

14. Place half of the grated cheese in the cooked pastry case.

15. Place the roasted vegetables on top of the grated cheese and add the roughly chopped basil leaves.

16. Mix the eggs and milk together and pour them over the vegetables.

17. Add the rest of the cheese and bake the flan for 25 minutes until the filling has set and the top is a golden brown colour.

18. Serve warm or cold with a fresh, crisp salad.

What is the nutritional profile of this recipe?

Which ingredient(s)?

Macronutrients

Protein
| Eggs, milk, cheese | HBV |
| Wheat flour | LBV |

Fat
Butter/vegetable fat spread, cheese, eggs, milk, olive oil

Carbohydrate
Wheat flour	Starch
Vegetables, milk	Sugars (intrinsic)
Whole wheat flour, vegetables	Dietary fibre

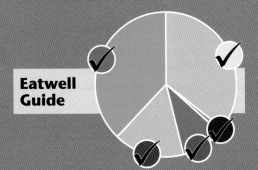

Eatwell Guide

Which ingredient(s)?

Micronutrients

Vitamins
	Vitamin A:
Vegetables	Beta carotene
Milk, cheese, butter, vegetable fat spread	Retinol
	Vitamin B group:
Milk, cheese, eggs, flour, vegetables	Thiamine B1
Milk, eggs, cheese	Riboflavin B2
Milk, flour	Niacin B3
Wheat flour, cheese, eggs	Folic acid B9
Milk, eggs, cheese	B12
Peppers	Vitamin C
Butter/vegetable fat spread, cheese, eggs	Vitamin D
Vegetable fat spread, cheese, eggs, olive oil, whole wheat flour	Vitamin E
Cheese	Vitamin K

Minerals
Milk, cheese, vegetables	Calcium
–	Fluoride
Vegetables	Iodine
Whole wheat flour, eggs, vegetables	Iron
All ingredients	Phosphorus
Cheese	Sodium

Which cooking methods and practical skills does this recipe use?

Cooking methods
Roasting
Baking
Baking blind

Practical skills
Shortcrust pastry making
Lining a flan tin/dish
Vegetable preparation/knife skills

What is the science behind this recipe?

Shortening: rubbing the fat into the flour when making the pastry gives the gluten a waterproof coating, so when the water is added, the gluten is prevented from forming long strands in the pastry – it can only make short strands. This gives the pastry a tender, 'short' texture.

Roasted vegetables: as the vegetables cook in the oven, the water they contain is driven out by the heat, which concentrates their flavour and makes them shrink. The intrinsic sugars in the onion will start to caramelise and change their colour to brown. The starch granules will swell and cause the vegetables to soften.

Coagulation: the filling will set in the oven because the protein in the eggs, milk and cheese will coagulate.

Heat transfer
Convection	Heating oven to roast the vegetables
Conduction	Heating the roasting tray and then the vegetables
	Baking the pastry case and the flan

Stretch and challenge activity

How could this recipe be modified ...	... for someone on a low-fat diet?
	... for a coeliac?
	... for someone who is lactose intolerant?

| What variations could you make to ... | ... the filling? |
| | ... the pastry? |

Practice questions

1. a) State three uses of fats and oils in cooking. *(3 marks)*

    b) State three foods that contain invisible fats or oils. *(3 marks)*

    c) Identify the similarities and differences between a fat and an oil. *(4 marks)*

2. a) Explain why the pastry used for the vegetable flan in the recipe above is called 'short crust'. *(2 marks)*

    b) Why is it important to keep all the ingredients cool when making pastry? *(1 mark)*

    c) Outline why short crust pastry must be carefully handled. *(1 mark)*

    d) Outline what happens to the ingredients when the pastry is baked. *(3 marks)*

    e) Comment on why it is not advisable for people to regularly eat a lot of pastry products. *(2 marks)*

3. a) State three foods in which you would find a lot of saturated fats. *(3 marks)*

    b) Explain why someone with a family history of heart disease might be advised to limit their intake of foods that contain high levels of saturated fats. *(3 marks)*

1.1.3 Carbohydrates

What will I learn?

In this section you will learn about:

- the definition of carbohydrate
- the **functions** of carbohydrate in the body
- the main **sources** of carbohydrate in the diet
- the effects of a **deficiency** or an **excess** of carbohydrate in the diet
- the **amount** of carbohydrate needed every day for different life stages.

Key terms

Photosynthesis: the process where green plants trap energy from the sun and form carbohydrates

Sugars: group of carbohydrates that taste sweet

Monosaccharides: group of sugars that are made of one sugar molecule

Disaccharides: group of sugars that are made of two sugar molecules

Polysaccharides (complex carbohydrates): group of carbohydrates that are made from many sugar molecules joined together, but do not taste sweet

What is carbohydrate?

Carbohydrate is a macronutrient that is needed by all animals. It is made by green plants during a process called **photosynthesis**.

Functions of carbohydrate in the body

Carbohydrate has two main functions in the body:

1. To give the body energy: carbohydrates are the main source of energy in our diet.

2. To help the body get rid of waste products: dietary fibre is a type of carbohydrate that helps us to produce soft, bulky faeces (solid waste), which are easy to pass out of our body when we go to the toilet.

Main sources of carbohydrate in the diet

There are two groups of carbohydrates: **sugars** and complex carbohydrates.

Sugars

Sugars are a group of carbohydrates that taste sweet. Plants produce two different types of sugars during photosynthesis:

Monosaccharides, which are made of one sugar molecule. There are three monosaccharides: glucose, galactose and fructose.

Disaccharides, which are made of two sugar molecules joined together. There are three disaccharides: sucrose, lactose and maltose.

Complex carbohydrates

Complex carbohydrates do not taste sweet. Plants produce several types of complex carbohydrates during photosynthesis. They are called **polysaccharides**. Polysaccharides include starch, pectin, dextrin and dietary fibre (also called non-starch polysaccharide – NSP).

Animals (including humans) make a polysaccharide called glycogen in their bodies from the carbohydrates they eat.

Type of carbohydrate – sugars: Monosaccharides

Main sources

Glucose: ripe fruits and vegetables (e.g. apples, onions, beetroot, parsnip, sweet potato). Also available in drinks, tablets and powders.

Fructose: fruits, vegetables and honey. High fructose corn syrup (HFCS) is used as a sweetener in many processed foods and carbonated soft drinks.

Galactose: milk from mammals.

Glucose

Fructose

Galactose

Type of carbohydrate – sugars: Disaccharides

Main sources

Maltose: cereals such as barley, also available as a syrup (malt extract), added to commercially made breakfast cereals, biscuits, hot drink powders, confectionery.

Sucrose: extracted from sugar cane and sugar beet and used in cooking and many processed foods, drinks and confectionery. Commonly known as 'sugar' (e.g. caster, granulated, brown, demerara, icing and golden syrup).

Lactose: milk from mammals and products made from it (e.g. yogurt, evaporated milk, cheese).

Maltose

Sucrose

Lactose

Type of carbohydrate – Complex carbohydrates: Polysaccharides

Main sources

Starch: cereals (e.g. wheat, rice, oats, barley, maize [corn]) and cereal products (e.g. breakfast cereals, pasta, bread, cakes, pastry, biscuits); starchy vegetables (e.g. potatoes, yams, sweet potatoes, parsnip, pumpkin, butternut squash, peas, beans, lentils); seeds, quinoa.

Dietary fibre/non-starch polysaccharide (NSP): wholegrain cereals and cereal products (e.g. breakfast cereals, bread, pasta, flour); fruits and vegetables, especially with skins left on (e.g. peas, beans, lentils); seeds, nuts.

Pectin: some fruits (e.g. oranges, citrus fruit peel (lemons, oranges, limes), apples, apricots, plums, greengages) and some root vegetables (e.g. carrots).

Dextrin: formed when starchy foods (e.g. bread, cakes, biscuits) are baked or toasted. Commercially prepared dextrins are used as thickening agents in salad dressings and sauces.

Starch

Dextrin

Pectin

Dietary fibre/non-starch polysaccharide (NSP)

Study tip

There are many types of sugars that you are probably not aware of when buying food. When looking at the ingredients lists, an ingredient ending in 'ose' (e.g. maltose) is usually a sugar.

Effects of a **deficiency** of carbohydrate in the diet

A deficiency of carbohydrates is rare in the developed world.

Effects of a deficiency of carbohydrate	Why does this happen?
Lack of energy/ tiredness (fatigue)	If insufficient carbohydrate has been eaten, the level of glucose in the blood (the blood sugar level) will drop and the cells throughout the body will not have enough energy.
Weight loss	If this situation continues, the body will start to use the energy stored in its fat cells (adipose tissue and visceral fat) so the person will lose weight over a period of time.
Severe weakness	The body must make sure that the brain and vital organs receive energy, so once all the fat stores are used up, the body will start to break down the protein that makes up muscles in order to obtain energy.

Effects of an **excess** of carbohydrate in the diet

- If the diet contains more carbohydrate (and therefore more energy) than the body needs and uses, it will be converted into fat and stored in the body. This could lead to obesity if the surplus stored energy is not used up in physical activity.

- **Refined and processed** carbohydrate foods (e.g. sugar and sugary foods, sweetened soft drinks, white bread, biscuits, potatoes, white rice) are quickly broken down and absorbed in the body. This causes a rapid rise in the level of sugar in the blood. If the diet contains lots of these types of foods and drinks and they are eaten frequently throughout the day, over a period of time, this will put stress on the pancreas, an organ in the body that produces a hormone called insulin. Insulin allows glucose to enter body cells so that they can use it to produce energy. Eventually the pancreas may stop working properly or the cells will become resistant to the insulin and the person may develop Type 2 diabetes (see page 76).

- Eating certain types of sugars frequently throughout the day can lead to tooth decay. Sugars that have been released from foods, such as fruit, during food processing (e.g. in fruit juices (especially concentrated juices)) or added to foods by manufacturers, cooks and consumers to sweeten them (e.g. the sugar used in cooking, honey, syrups and unsweetened fruit juices) are the most likely to cause tooth decay (see pages 73–74). These sugars are called **free sugars**.

- Sugars that are found naturally in foods such as apples, plums, carrots, onions and milk are less likely to cause tooth decay. These sugars are called **intrinsic sugars**.

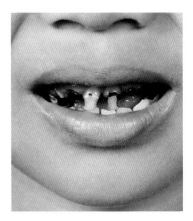

Free sugars can cause tooth decay

Amount of carbohydrate needed every day for different life stages

The amount of carbohydrate we need is calculated as a percentage of our total daily energy intake, rather than by weight (except for dietary fibre/NSP). The energy value of carbohydrate is: 1g of pure carbohydrate provides 3.75kcals/16kJ or energy. This is the amount of carbohydrate recommended by health experts for different groups of (healthy) people from age 2 years upwards every day:

Type of carbohydrate	% of food energy per day
Total carbohydrate: *most of which* should come from starch, and natural *(intrinsic)* sugars	50%
Free sugars (sugar added to foods and drinks by manufacturers, cooks and consumers to sweeten them during processing; and sugars in honeys, syrups and unsweetened fruit juices)	***No more than 5% of total carbohydrate intake.** This means: • no more than 19g/day (approximately 4 teaspoons) of free sugars for children aged 4–6 • no more than 24g/day (approximately 5 teaspoons) for 7–10 year-olds • no more than 30g/day (approximately 6 teaspoons) for children from age 11 and adults
Non-starch polysaccharide/dietary fibre	***Adults: at least 30g each day** ***Children:** 2–5 years: 15g each day 5–11 years: 20g each day 11–16 years: 25g each day 16–18 years: 30g each day

*These are the recommendations of the Scientific Advisory Committee on Nutrition (SACN) in their report published in 2015.

Task Tip:

This is the website address of The Scientific Advisory Committee on Nutrition Report (2015) on recommendations for carbohydrates: https://www.gov.uk/government/publications/sacn-carbohydrates-and-health-report

On page 20 is a recipe that contains a variety of carbohydrates.

Section 1: Food, Nutrition and Health

Courgette, onion and cheese muffins

Method:

1. Preheat the oven to Gas 6/200°C (190°C if you are using a fan oven).

2. Peel and finely chop the onion.

3. Wash then cut off the ends of the courgette and grate it into a mixing bowl with the cheese and the onion.

4. Add the flour, oil, milk and beaten egg and season with ground black pepper.

5. Mix the ingredients together with a spoon to form a batter.

6. Divide the batter equally between the muffin cases using two spoons.

7. Bake for 20 minutes, until well risen and golden brown in colour.

8. Serve warm or cold. Could be served with soup or stews.

Ingredients:
(serves 12 people)
225g self-raising flour
 (wholemeal or white)
50ml oil
175ml semi-skimmed milk
1 egg
100g cheddar cheese
1 small courgette (skin left on)
1 small onion
black pepper

You will also need:
12 muffin cases
muffin tin

Storage instructions:
Allow to cool, then place in an airtight tin or plastic box for up to 3–5 days.

What is the nutritional profile of this recipe?

Which cooking methods and practical skills does this recipe use?

Cooking methods
Baking

Practical skills
Vegetable preparation
Batter making

What is the science behind this recipe?

Which ingredient(s)?

Macronutrients

Protein	
Egg, milk, cheese	HBV
Flour	LBV

Fat	
Oil, egg yolk, cheese, milk (a little)	

Carbohydrate	
Flour, onion, courgette	Starch
Onion, courgette, milk, cheese	Sugars *(intrinsic)*
Onion, courgette, wholemeal flour if used	Dietary fibre

Micronutrients

Which ingredient(s)?

Vitamins		
		Vitamin A:
Courgette, egg yolk, milk		*Beta carotene*
Milk, cheese		*Retinol*
		Vitamin B group:
Cheese, milk, courgette, white flour		*Thiamine B1*
Eggs, milk, cheese		*Riboflavin B2*
Milk, eggs		*Niacin B3*
–		*Folic acid B9*
Cheese		*B12*
–		Vitamin C
Eggs		Vitamin D
Wholemeal flour, oil		Vitamin E
Cheese		Vitamin K

Minerals	
Milk, cheese, flour	Calcium
–	Fluoride
Milk and cheese	Iodine
Egg yolk, wholemeal flour	Iron
All ingredients	Phosphorus
Cheese	Sodium

Raising agent: CO_2 gas produced by baking powder in the flour will expand on heating and raise the mixture.

Coagulation of egg and cheese protein to help set the mixture.

Gelatinisation of starch in the flour and vegetables to help set the mixture.

Caramelisation of intrinsic sugars in the onion.

Heat transfer
Conduction of heat from the oven through the muffin tin to the muffins.
Convection of heat in oven.

Eatwell Guide

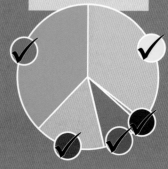

| How could this recipe be modified ... | ... for a coeliac?
... for someone who is lactose intolerant?
... to lower the fat content?
... to increase the fibre content? |
| What variations could you make to ... | ... the vegetables?
... the overall flavour?
What could you serve the muffins with? |

Practice questions

1. Discuss why it would be better for young children to eat an apple rather than a drink of apple juice. Give reasons for your answer. *(5 marks)*

2. a) State the name of the process by which plants make carbohydrates. *(1 mark)*
   b) Carbohydrates are classified into two main groups – what are they? *(2 marks)*
   c) State the names of two monosaccharides. *(2 marks)*
   d) State the names of two disaccharides. *(2 marks)*
   e) State the names of two polysaccharides. *(2 marks)*
   f) Identify which carbohydrate the body uses for energy production during respiration. *(1 mark)*

3. In their report published in 2015, the Scientific Advisory Committee on Nutrition (SACN) has recommended that people should reduce the amount of free sugars they consume to 5% of their total carbohydrate each day.

   a) Discuss why they have made this recommendation and explain what problems there might be in putting this into practice. *(6 marks)*

   b) Comment on how people can reduce their free sugar intake when buying their food, cooking and serving everyday meals for themselves and their families. *(6 marks)*

4. Look at the Nutritional Facts and the ingredients list for this breakfast cereal.

Crispy Crunchies

Ingredients list: Wholegrain toasted wheat flakes, sucrose, rolled whole grain oats, rapeseed oil, maltodextrin, glucose, dextrose, fructose, salt

Nutrition information:

Nutrient	Per 100g	Per serving (30g)
Energy	2092 kJ/500kcal	627kJ/150kcal
Fat	11g	3.3g
of which:		
Saturates	0.4g	0.1g
Monounsaturates	0.6g	0.18g
Polyunsaturates	0.3g	0.09g
Carbohydrate	82g	24.6g
of which:		
Sugars	48g	14.4g
Starch	30g	9g
Fibre	4g	1.2g
Protein	3.0g	0.9g
Salt	0.4g	0.12g

   a) Identify the different sugars on the ingredients list. *(4 marks)*

   b) The breakfast cereal contains 14.4g of sugar per portion. Comment on whether you consider this to be a suitable amount of sugar for a child. *(3 marks)*

   c) Discuss whether or not you consider this cereal to be a healthy choice for a child. Use the data from the label to explain your answer. *(3 marks)*

1.1.4 Vitamins

What will I learn?

In this section you will learn about:

- the definition of vitamins
- the **functions** of vitamins in the body
- the main **sources** of vitamins in the diet
- the effects of a **deficiency** or an **excess** of vitamins in the diet
- the **amount** of vitamins needed every day for different life stages.

What are vitamins?

- Vitamins are **chemical substances** that are naturally found in a wide range of unprocessed plant and animal foods.
- Vitamins promote health and help prevent disease.
- They are needed by our bodies in small amounts every day for a variety of different jobs. This is why they are called **micronutrients**.
- Some vitamins can be stored in the body. Without vitamins our body would show signs of a **deficiency disease**. The symptoms of a deficiency disease vary, depending on the vitamin that is missing from the diet.

Vitamins are classified into two main groups: **fat soluble vitamins** and **water soluble vitamins**.

- Each vitamin is given a **chemical name** and also a **letter** to distinguish it from the other vitamins.

The table below shows the **chemical names** of the different vitamins, the main **food sources** of them, their **function(s)** in the body, and the effects of a **deficiency** or an **excess** in the body:

Key terms

Fat soluble: vitamins that are found in foods containing fats

Water soluble: vitamins that are found in foods with a high water content

Main sources of vitamins in the diet

Fat soluble
Vitamin A

Chemical name/main food sources	Effects of a deficiency or excess in the body	Why does this happen?
Retinol **Retinol:** whole and semi-skimmed milk; cheddar cheese; butter; eggs (yolk); liver, kidney; oily fish (e.g. sardines, mackerel); vegetable fat spreads (added by law). **Beta carotene** **Beta carotene** (converted to retinol in the body [liver]): dark green leaves of cabbage, spinach, kale, lettuce; peas; orange/yellow/red vegetables and fruits (e.g. carrots, apricots, mango, papaya, peppers, tomatoes, sweet potatoes, butternut squash, pumpkin, beetroot).	**Deficiency:** • Retinol is stored in the liver, so these stores have to be used up before any signs of deficiency occur. • Children do not grow properly. • The skin and mucus membranes become dry and infected. • **Night-blindness** – people cannot see in dim light. • Can lead to total blindness and permanent damage to the eyes. **Excess (this is rare):** • Too much vitamin A can be toxic (poisonous) to the body. • Too much vitamin A may damage the development of an unborn baby.	• To grow, children need all nutrients in the right amounts. • Bacteria and viruses can enter the body more easily and the body's immune system is weakened. • Insufficient visual purple is produced in the retina. • The eyes become dried, scarred and infected. • Excess vitamin A will build up in the liver and will start to poison the body. • Pregnant women are advised not to take vitamin A supplements or eat vitamin A-rich foods to avoid the risk of harming their unborn baby.

Function in the body

- Keeps the skin healthy.
- Enables us to see in dim light by producing a substance called visual purple in the retina when light levels are low.
- Helps children to grow.
- Produces mucus for the mucus membranes in the body (e.g. mouth, digestive system, respiratory system (bronchial tubes and lungs)).
- Beta carotene is an antioxidant (see page 27).

Vitamin D

Chemical name/main food sources	Function in the body
Cholecalciferol Most comes from the reaction of **sunlight** on the skin, which causes vitamin D to be made under the skin. Oily fish (e.g. salmon, sardines, herrings, mackerel); meat and meat products; eggs; butter; liver; vegetable fat spreads (added by law); fortified breakfast cereals (added by manufacturer).	• Enables the mineral calcium to be absorbed from the small intestine during digestion. • Helps calcium to be deposited in the bones and teeth.

Effects of a deficiency or excess in the body	Why does this happen?
Deficiency: • Children: their bones and teeth will not strengthen and the bones in the legs will bend under the weight of the body. This condition is called rickets. • Adults: their bones may start to weaken and break easily. This is called **osteomalacia**. **Excess (this is rare):** • If too much vitamin D is taken, it will lead to excess calcium being absorbed, which could lead to damage to the kidneys and other organs, especially in babies and young children.	• If there is not enough calcium laid down in the bones, they cannot support the body properly. • Calcium will be removed from the body for other uses (a natural process) and, if it is not replaced, the bones will lose their strength.

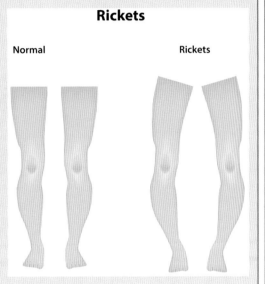

Rickets

Normal   Rickets

Vitamin E

Chemical name/main food sources	Function in the body	Effects of a deficiency or excess in the body
Tocopherol Mainly found in plant foods, especially soya, corn oil, olive oil, nuts, seeds, wheatgerm, vegetable fat spreads.	Vitamin E is an antioxidant (see page 27).	A deficiency or excess is rare.

Vitamin K

Chemical name/main food sources	Function in the body
Phylloquinone Plant and animal foods especially green, leafy vegetables, liver, cheese, green tea (also made in the large intestine by bacteria).	Vitamin K is part of the process that enables the blood to clot when the body is injured, to prevent further loss of blood.

Effects of a deficiency or excess in the body	Why does this happen?
Deficiency: • This is very rare in the UK, but sometimes occurs in new-born babies, so they are given a dose of vitamin K when they are born.	Babies can sometimes lose some blood internally during the birth process.

Section 1: Food, Nutrition and Health

Water soluble
Vitamin B1 (thiamine)

Chemical name/ main food sources	Function in the body	Effects of a deficiency or excess in the body	Why does this happen?
Thiamine Meat, especially pork, milk, cheese, eggs, vegetables, fresh and dried fruit, wholemeal bread, fortified breakfast cereals (added by manufacturer), added to all flour (except wholemeal) by law.	Enables energy to be released from carbohydrate in body cells during respiration.	**Deficiency:** Leads to a condition called **beri-beri** in which the nerves and muscles are affected and there are problems with memory, concentration and heart rate.	Energy is needed by the nerve cells, which control how the muscles and brain work. A lack of thiamine will result in insufficient energy being released to enable the nerve cells to work properly.

Vitamin B2 (riboflavin)

Chemical name/main food sources	Function in the body	Effects of a deficiency or excess in the body
Riboflavin Found in many foods, especially milk and milk products, eggs, fortified breakfast cereals (added by manufacturer), rice, mushrooms.	Enables energy to be released from carbohydrate, fat and protein in body cells during respiration.	**Deficiency:** • Rare. • May result in sores at the corners of the mouth because it is needed to help maintain healthy skin.

Vitamin B3 (niacin)

Chemical name/ main food sources	Function in the body	Effects of a deficiency or excess in the body	Why does this happen?
Niacin Beef, pork, wheat flour, maize flour, eggs, milk (cow). Can be made from an amino acid called tryptophan in the body.	Enables energy to be released from food in body cells during respiration.	**Deficiency:** Results in a deficiency disease called **pellagra**, which has three symptoms: • Diarrhoea • Dermatitis (sore, dry and cracked skin) • Dementia (loss of memory, confusion, cannot speak properly). 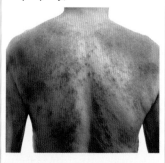 Dermatitis caused by pellagra	A lack of niacin prevents the brain and nervous system from working properly.

Vitamin B9 (folate)

Chemical name/main food sources	Function in the body	Effects of a deficiency or excess in the body	Why does this happen?
Folate (called folic acid when added to foods and used in supplements). Not found naturally in many foods. Best sources are green leafy vegetables (e.g. Brussels sprouts, broccoli, kale, spinach); yeast extract (e.g. Marmite); peas, chickpeas, asparagus; wholegrain rice; fruits such as oranges and bananas. Added to some breads and breakfast cereals.	• Works with vitamin B12 to make healthy red blood cells. • Helps to reduce the risk of developing central nervous system defects, such as spina bifida, in unborn babies.	**Deficiency:** • Can lead to a type of anaemia called **megaloblastic (means 'large cells') anaemia**, where the red blood cells become enlarged. • May lead to defects in the spinal cord in unborn babies.	• Without the folate, red blood cells do not develop to the correct size and grow very big. • This prevents them from passing through narrow blood vessels (capillaries). • Research is still needed to find out all the causes of spinal cord defects.

Vitamin B12 (cobalamin)

Chemical name/main food sources	Function in the body	Effects of a deficiency or excess in the body
Cobalamin Does not occur naturally in plant foods. Found in liver, meat, fish, cheese, fortified breakfast cereals (added by manufacturer), yeast.	• Works with folate to make healthy red blood cells. • Keeps nerve cells healthy.	**Deficiency:** • Vitamin B12 can be stored in the liver for 2 or more years. • Vegans (who do not eat any animal food) have to be careful that they do not become deficient and may take a special B12 supplement to prevent this. • A deficiency leads to a type of anaemia called **pernicious anaemia**.

Why does this happen?

Vitamin B12 is absorbed in the small intestine and can only do this if special cells in the stomach produce a particular protein that enables it to be absorbed. If these special stomach cells are damaged or do not work properly, the B12 will not be absorbed.

Vitamin C (ascorbic acid)

Chemical name/main food sources	Function in the body
Ascorbic acid Most comes from fruits and vegetables, especially citrus fruits (e.g. oranges, lemons, limes and grapefruit), blackcurrants, kiwifruit, guavas, Brussels sprouts, cabbage, broccoli, potatoes (especially new ones). There is also a small amount in milk and liver.	• Needed to help the body absorb the mineral **iron** in the small intestine. • Needed to maintain **connective tissue** which binds the body cells together in the skin, blood vessels, muscles, etc. • Vitamin C is an important antioxidant (see page 27).

Effects of a deficiency or excess in the body	Why does this happen?
Deficiency: • Some vitamin C can be stored in the body for a few months. • Iron is not absorbed, which leads to **iron deficiency anaemia**. • Bleeding from small blood vessels under the skin and in the gums leads to red spots under the skin and loose teeth. • Wounds take a long time to heal and scar tissue may break open. • This all leads to the disease called **scurvy** and can result in death.	• Iron is needed to make haemoglobin in red blood cells (see pages 32 and 75). • Connective tissue starts to break down, which allows the blood to leak out and weakens the tissue in the gums that holds the teeth in place. • Connective tissue cannot be made properly to heal a wound and it starts to break down, which can open up scars.

Study tip

Remember

There are many different vitamins that we require to maintain health and prevent disease. The vitamins in this section are the ones that you are required to study for the AQA specification. There are other B vitamins.

Activity

Using the vitamin table, produce a set of revision/ flash cards to help you learn the information. Remember to include the function of each vitamin in the body, main sources and the effects of deficiency and excess.

Amount of vitamins needed every day for different life stages

Vitamins are needed in tiny but significant amounts. These are the measurements that are used for them:

Milligrams – mg (1mg = 1/1000 of a gram)

Micrograms – µ (often written as mcg) (1µ = 1/1,000,000 of a gram)

These are the amounts of different vitamins needed by different groups of (healthy) people every day:

Age/gender		Vitamin									
		A	D	E	K	B1	B2	B3	B9	B12	C
Children	1–3 years	400mcg	#	–		0.7mg	0.6mg	–	70mcg	0.5mcg	30mg
	4–6 years	500mcg	#	–		0.9mg	0.8mg	–	100mcg	0.8mcg	30mg
	7–10 years	500mcg	#	–		1.0mg	1.0mg	–	150mcg	1.0mcg	30mg
Teenagers (male)	11–14 years	600mcg	#	–		1.2mg	1.2mg	–	200mcg	1.2mcg	35mg
Teenagers (female)	11–14 years	600mcg	#	–		1.0mg	1.1mg	–	200mcg	1.2mcg	35mg
Teenagers (male)	15–18 years	700mcg	#	–		1.5mg	1.3mg	–	200mcg	1.5mcg	40mg
Teenagers (female)	15–18 years	600mcg	#	–		1.2mg	1.1mg	–	200mcg	1.5mcg	40mg
Adults (male)	19–50 years	700mcg	#	4mg	0.001mg for each kg body weight (all adults)	1.4mg	1.3mg	17mg	200mcg	1.5mcg	40mg
(female)	19–50 years	600mcg	#	3mg		1.2mg	1.1mg	13mg	200mcg	1.5mcg	40mg
(male)	50+ years	700mcg	^	4mg		0.9mg	1.3mg	17mg	200mcg	1.5mcg	40mg
(female)	50+ years	600mcg	^	3mg		0.8mg	1.1mg	13mg	200mcg	1.5mcg	40mg
Pregnant women		700mcg	*	–		0.9mg	1.4mg	13mg	300mcg	1.5mcg	50mg
Women lactating (breastfeeding) for up to 4 months		950mcg	*	–		1.0mg	1.4mg	13mg	260mcg	1.5mcg	70mg
Women lactating (breastfeeding) for over 4 months		950mcg	*	–		1.0mg	1.4mg	13mg	260mcg	1.5mcg	70mg

Key to table:

– No figure available.

No figures have been set for vitamin D for these groups as it is assumed they will receive all they need from a balanced diet and exposure to sunlight.

^ The Department of Health recommends that people over 65 years who do not go out in sunlight very much should take a daily vitamin D supplement of 10mcg.

* The Department of Health recommends that pregnant women and those who are breastfeeding should take a daily vitamin D supplement of 10mcg.

Effects of food preparation and cooking on vitamins

Water soluble vitamins (vitamin B group and vitamin C) are easily damaged or lost during preparation and cooking. Vitamins B1 (thiamine) and B2 (riboflavin) are damaged by heat and dissolve into the water that food is cooked in and are lost. Vitamin B2 is also damaged by being exposed to light. Vitamin C is very soluble in water and is very easily damaged by heat and exposure to the air.

The loss of these vitamins can be minimised by following a few simple practices when preparing and cooking foods such as fruits and vegetables:

Storing foods:

1. Store foods away from heat and light.
2. Store them for the minimum amount of time possible.

Preparation of vegetables and fruits:

1. Cut, grate or squeeze fruits and vegetables as near as possible to the time you want to cook, serve and eat them.

   Reason: cutting, grating and squeezing fruits and vegetables exposes the vitamin C they contain to the air and to natural enzymes in the fruit or vegetable, which result in it being destroyed.

2. Avoid buying damaged or bruised fruit or vegetables as some of the vitamin C will have been destroyed by enzymes that have been released.

Cooking vegetables:

1. Use only a small amount of water to cook them in. Boil the water first, then add the vegetables and cook for the minimum amount of time until they are just tender.
2. Save the water the vegetables are cooking in and use it for gravy or soup (to use the vitamins that have dissolved in it).
3. Serve the vegetables straightaway – keeping them hot will damage more of the vitamins.
4. Steaming vegetables reduces the loss of vitamins as they do not come in direct contact with the water.

Antioxidants

Every day our bodies are exposed to lots of different chemicals from the air, water, food and pollution. Some of these chemicals pick up oxygen in the body and become reactive '**free radicals**'. Free radicals can cause damage to the cells in our bodies, which could lead to inflammation, heart disease or cancer in some people.

Antioxidants help to prevent these chemicals from picking up oxygen so that they cannot damage the body's cells. **Vitamins A, C and E are all antioxidants**. One of the reasons we are encouraged to eat plenty of fruits and vegetables is because they contain good amounts of these antioxidant vitamins and can therefore help prevent people from developing these health conditions.

On page 28 is a recipe to show the use of antioxidant vitamins in a salad.

On page 29 is a recipe to show the use of fat soluble and water soluble vitamins in a pâté.

Prepare vegetables carefully to minimise vitamin losses

Key term

Antioxidant: vitamins that help protect the body from developing heart disease and some types of cancer

Crunchy watercress and orange salad

Ingredients:
(serves 4 people)
2 oranges
bunch or bag of watercress
30g pumpkin seeds (either whole
  or the pale green kernels [insides
  of pumpkin seeds])

Dressing:
2 tbsp olive oil
freshly ground black pepper

Storage instructions:
Refrigerator: cover and store in
  the refrigerator (0°C to below
  5°C) for up to 2 days.

Method:

1. Carefully and thoroughly wash the watercress and allow it to drain.

2. Wash the oranges and finely grate the zest of one of them.

3. Carefully cut the skin and white pith from the oranges with a sharp knife. **Save the juice that is produced**.

4. Cut the segments from the oranges and put them in a bowl. Remove any seeds or membrane that separates the segments. If the segments are large, you can cut them in half.

5. Dressing: mix the olive oil with 1 tbsp of the orange juice, some ground black pepper and 1 tsp of grated orange zest.

6. Put the pumpkin seeds into a frying pan (without oil) and heat them gently, shaking them around in the pan until they start to toast and 'pop'. Add a little salt and pepper if you wish. Take them off the heat to cool slightly.

7. Mix the watercress, orange segments and dressing together in a bowl and tip into a serving dish. Scatter the pumpkin seeds and the remaining grated orange zest on top.

8. Serve as an accompaniment to other salads and main meals.

What is the nutritional profile of this recipe?

Which ingredient(s)?

Macronutrients

	Protein	
	–	HBV
	Pumpkin seeds	LBV

Fat

	Olive oil, pumpkin seeds	

Carbohydrate

	Pumpkin seeds	Starch
	Oranges	Sugars *(intrinsic)*
	Watercress, oranges	Dietary fibre

Which ingredient(s)?

Micronutrients

Vitamins

		Vitamin A:
	Watercress, oranges	Beta carotene
	–	Retinol
		Vitamin B group:
	–	Thiamine B1
	–	Riboflavin B2
	–	Niacin B3
	Watercress	Folic acid B9
	–	B12
	Watercress, oranges	Vitamin C
	–	Vitamin D
	Pumpkin seeds, watercress, olive oil	Vitamin E
	Watercress	Vitamin K

Minerals

	Watercress	Calcium
	–	Fluoride
	Watercress	Iodine
	Watercress, pumpkin seeds	Iron
	All ingredients	Phosphorus
	–	Sodium

Which cooking methods and practical skills does this recipe use?

Cooking methods
Dry frying the seeds

Practical skills
Fruit preparation/knife skills
Making a dressing

What is the science behind this recipe?

Heat transfer
Conduction Heating the frying pan to dry fry the pumpkin seeds

Eatwell Guide

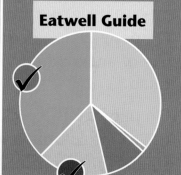

Stretch and challenge activity

How could this recipe be modified ...

... to increase the fibre content?
... to increase the protein content?
... to turn it into a main course dish?

What variations could you make to ...

... the dressing?
... the vegetables/fruit used?
... the type of seeds used?

Smoked mackerel pâté

Method:

1. Melt the butter in a small pan over a gentle heat or in a microwave oven for a few seconds. Leave it to cool slightly.

2. Remove the skin and bones from the fish and break it into small flakes with a knife and fork.

3. In a mixing bowl, put the fish, melted butter, crème fraiche/cream cheese/soured cream or yogurt, the zest and juice of the lemon and ¼ tsp black pepper.

4. Mix everything together thoroughly with a fork or spoon.

- If you want the pâté to have a smoother texture, you could use a food processor or stick blender.

5. Pile the mixture into a serving dish, cover and leave it to chill in the refrigerator.

6. Serve with toasted bread, and garnish with a lemon slice, some chopped parsley or a sprinkling of paprika.

Ingredients:
(serves 4 people as a starter)
1 medium fillet of smoked mackerel (ready to eat)
25g butter
50g crème fraiche or cream cheese or soured cream or plain yogurt
½ lemon
black pepper to season

Storage instructions:
Refrigerator: cover and store in the refrigerator (0°C to below 5°C) for up to 2 days.
Freezer: place in a plastic food box and freeze for up to 3 months. Defrost thoroughly before eating.

What is the nutritional profile of this recipe?

Which cooking methods and practical skills does this recipe use?

Cooking methods
Melting butter

Practical skills
Fish preparation/knife skills

What is the science behind this recipe?

Heat transfer
Conduction Heating the frying pan to melt the butter

Which ingredient(s)?

Macronutrients

Protein	
Mackerel, crème fraiche/cream cheese/soured cream/plain yogurt	HBV
–	LBV

Fat	
Butter, mackerel, crème fraiche/cream cheese/soured cream/plain yogurt	

Carbohydrate	
–	Starch
–	Sugars *(intrinsic)*
–	Dietary fibre

Micronutrients

Vitamins	
	Vitamin A:
–	Beta carotene
Mackerel, butter, crème fraiche/cream cheese/soured cream/	Retinol
	Vitamin B group:
Crème fraiche/cream cheese/soured cream	Thiamine B1
Crème fraiche/ cream cheese/soured cream	Riboflavin B2
–	Niacin B3
Mackerel	Folic acid B9
–	B12
Lemon	Vitamin C
Mackerel, butter, crème fraiche/cream cheese/soured cream	Vitamin D
–	Vitamin E
–	Vitamin K

Minerals	
Crème fraiche/cream cheese/soured cream/plain yogurt	Calcium
–	Fluoride
Mackerel	Iodine
–	Iron
All ingredients	Phosphorus
Mackerel	Sodium

Eatwell Guide

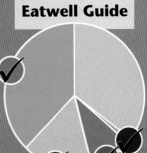

Practice questions

1. You are preparing the following main meal for four people:

   • Roast chicken.

   • Boiled new potatoes.

   • Carrots.

   • Broccoli.

   • Cabbage.

   • Gravy.

   • Fresh fruit salad.

   • Yogurt.

   Explain, with reasons and examples, how you would minimise the loss of vitamins from the food as you prepare, cook and serve the meal. *(10 marks)*

2. a) State why pregnant women, young women and elderly people might need vitamin supplements. Give reasons for your answers. *(6 marks)*

   b) Discuss why it is advisable to seek medical advice before taking or giving vitamin supplements. Give reasons for your answers. *(3 marks)*

1.1.5 Minerals

What will I learn?

In this section you will learn about:

- the definition of minerals
- the **functions** of minerals in the body
- the main **sources** of minerals in the diet
- the effects of a **deficiency** or an **excess** of minerals in the diet
- the **amount** of minerals needed every day for different life stages.

What are minerals?

Minerals are **chemical substances** that are naturally found in a wide range of plant and animal foods. They are needed by our bodies in small amounts every day for a variety of different jobs. This is why they are called **micronutrients**. Some minerals can be stored in the body.

Without minerals the body would show signs of a **deficiency disease**. The symptoms of a deficiency disease vary, depending on the mineral that is missing from the diet.

There are many minerals that are needed by the body. Three of these are described in the table below, which shows the main **food sources** of them, their **function(s)** in the body, and the effects of a **deficiency** or an **excess** of them in the body.

Study tip

Remember

There are many different minerals that we require to maintain health and prevent disease. The minerals in the following table are the ones that you are required to study for the AQA specification. There are others including potassium, selenium and zinc.

Calcium

Function in the body

- Calcium is the main mineral in the body.
- It is laid down in the teeth and bones (with other minerals) to make them strong. This process is helped by taking load-bearing, physical exercise.
- A large percentage of the minerals are laid down in the bones during adolescence.
- Vitamin D is needed to enable the calcium to be absorbed from food during digestion.
- It is needed to make the nerves and muscles work properly.
- It is needed to enable the blood to clot over a wound following an injury.

Main food sources

Milk, cheese, yogurt and other milk products; green leafy vegetables; fish with softened bones (e.g. canned fish); enriched soya drinks; it is added to most types of flour by law.

Effects of a deficiency or excess in the body

Deficiency:

- If there is not enough calcium, the bones and teeth will weaken and bend under the weight of the body.
- If the cause of this is a lack of vitamin D (which is needed to enable calcium to be absorbed into the body), the deficiency is called **rickets** in children and **osteomalacia** (which means 'bad bones') in adults.
- The muscles and nerves will not work properly.
- Blood will not clot properly over a wound after an injury.

Excess (this is rare):

- If too much calcium is absorbed into the body (perhaps because of too much vitamin D), some of it will be deposited in organs such as the kidneys, which will stop them working.

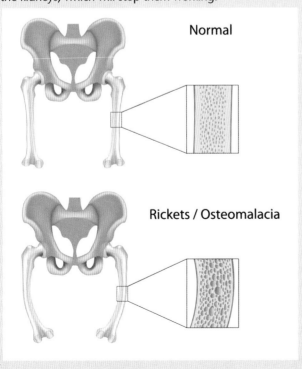

Normal

Rickets / Osteomalacia

Why does this happen?

- As we grow, our bones get stronger as calcium and other minerals are laid down in them. Eventually the bones reach their **peak bone mass** when they have the maximum amount of minerals and are at their strongest and most dense (about 30 years of age).
- If there is not enough calcium reaching the bones, they will never reach peak bone mass and are more likely to weaken and break, especially as a person gets older.

Osteoporosis

- Osteoporosis (means 'porous bones') is a natural ageing process that usually becomes apparent in old age, but can happen earlier in life.
- Once bones reach peak bone mass, very gradually over a number of years, minerals are removed from them and not replaced.
- Eventually, the bones become porous and therefore weak and likely to break easily, as shown in this photo, where the darker section shows how the minerals have been lost from the bone.

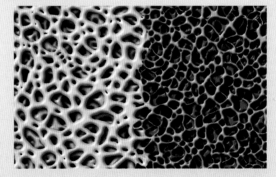

- In some people osteoporosis is severe and they have a lot of pain and bone weakness.
- The rate at which minerals are lost from the bones can sometimes be slowed down by making sure that there is enough calcium and vitamin D in the diet and staying physically active.

Iron

Function in the body

- Iron is needed to make **haemoglobin** in red blood cells to carry oxygen to all body cells.

- Vitamin C is required to enable iron to be absorbed from food during digestion.

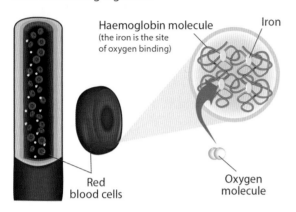

Haemoglobin molecule (the iron is the site of oxygen binding)

Iron

Red blood cells

Oxygen molecule

Main food sources

Red meat, kidney, liver; wholemeal bread, added to wheat flour (except wholemeal) by law; green leafy vegetables (e.g. watercress, spinach, cabbage); egg yolk; dried apricots; lentils; cocoa, plain chocolate; curry powder; fortified breakfast cereals (added by manufacturer; see page 285).

Effects of a deficiency or excess in the body

Deficiency:

- Leads to **iron deficiency anaemia**, which has several symptoms including tiredness, lack of energy, weakness, pale skin complexion, weak and spilt nails.

- Unborn babies build up a store of iron in their bodies during the last 3 months before they are born, so it is important that pregnant women have enough iron in their diet to allow for this.

Excess:

- Too much iron is poisonous to the body and could happen if someone takes too many supplements.

Why does this happen?

Oxygen is needed by body cells, along with glucose, to produce energy during respiration. If there is a deficiency of iron, there will not be enough oxygen available for the cells to produce enough energy.

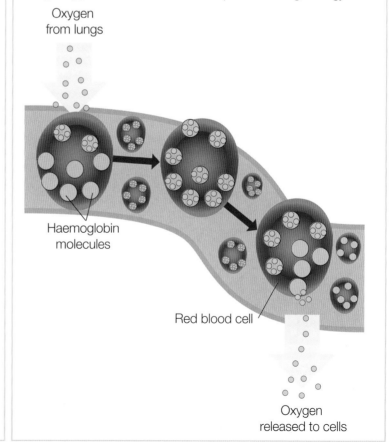

Oxygen from lungs

Haemoglobin molecules

Red blood cell

Oxygen released to cells

Sodium

Function in the body

- Sodium controls the amount of water in the body.
- It also helps to control nerves and muscles.
- It helps the body to use energy.

Main food sources

Salt (**sodium** chloride) and any foods that have salt added to flavour or preserve them such as cheese, yeast extract, stock cubes, gravies and seasonings, snack foods (e.g. crisps), canned fish, bacon, ham, dried fish, soy sauce, salted butter, fast foods and many ready meals; baking powder (containing **sodium** bicarbonate) and any foods that contain it (e.g. cakes, biscuits, baked desserts); foods containing mono**sodium** glutamate, which is a flavour enhancer used in foods such as takeaway foods and ready meals to make them taste more savoury.

Effects of a deficiency or excess in the body

Deficiency:

This will lead to muscle cramps and can be caused by losing salt in sweat in hot climates or by sickness and diarrhoea.

Excess:

- Too much sodium can cause **high blood pressure**.
- This can put a strain on the heart and kidneys, which will affect how efficiently they work.

Why does this happen?

- Without sodium to help control the nerves, the muscles will not work properly.
- The excess sodium makes the body retain too much water instead of getting rid of it through the kidneys.
- The extra water increases the volume of blood and raises the blood pressure as the heart has to work harder to pump it round the body.

Fluoride

Function in the body

To strengthen the bones and the enamel in the teeth and help prevent tooth decay.

Main food sources

Fish and seafood, some water supplies, tea.

Effects of a deficiency or excess in the body

Deficiency:

May lead to weak enamel on the teeth and therefore more chance of tooth decay.

Excess:

This may lead to permanently discoloured teeth.

Why does this happen?

- The enamel will not be so strong so acid from bacteria in the mouth will be able to dissolve it more easily.
- Too much fluoride, e.g. from drops given to babies to strengthen their teeth when they are are developing will affect the normal mineralisation of the teeth.

Iodine

Function in the body	Main food sources
• To produce the hormone **thyroxin**, in the thyroid gland in the neck, which controls the metabolic rate of the body (the rate at which chemical reactions happen).	Seafood, vegetables (depending on the amount in the soil they are grown in), milk and dairy foods. 

Effects of a deficiency or excess in the body	Why does this happen?
Deficiency: • This will lead to a swelling in the neck called a **goitre** (this is how you say it: goy-ter). • If a mother is deficient in iodine when she is pregnant, her baby may develop cretinism, which means it will be born with permanent brain damage.	The thyroid gland will swell up so that it has more chance of picking up any iodine that might pass through it in the blood stream.

Phosphorus

Function in the body	Main food sources
• Along with calcium, phosphorus mineralises the bones and teeth to make them strong. • It is essential for energy release and other chemical reactions in the body in the body. • It makes up phospholipids, which are special fat molecules that are found in cell membranes throughout the body, but especially in the brain and nervous system.	Found in a wide range of foods. 

Effects of a deficiency or excess in the body
Deficiency: Rare in the UK

Activity

Using the information in the tables, produce a set of revision/flash cards to help you learn the information.

Amount of minerals needed every day for different life stages

Minerals are needed in small significant amounts. These are the measurements that are used for them:

Milligrams – mg (1mg = 1/1000 of a gram)

These are the amounts of calcium, iron and sodium needed by different groups of (healthy) people every day:

Age/gender		Calcium	Iron	Sodium†		Fluoride	Iodine	Phosphorus
Children	1–3 years	350mg	6.9mg	500mg	2g	–	–	–
	4–6 years	450mg	6.1mg	700mg	3g	–	–	–
	7–10 years	550mg	8.7mg	1200mg	5g	–	–	–
Teenagers (male)	11–14 years	1000mg	11.3mg	1600mg	6g*	–	–	–
Teenagers (female)	11–14 years	800mg	14.8mg	1600mg	6g	–	–	–
Teenagers (male)	15–18 years	1000mg	11.3mg	1600mg	6g	–	–	–
Teenagers (female)	15–18 years	800mg	14.8mg	1600mg	6g	–	–	–
Adults (male)	19–50 years	700mg	8.7mg	1600mg	6g	–	0.14 mg	–
(female)	19–50 years	700mg	14.8mg	1600mg	6g	–	0.14 mg	–
(male)	50+ years	700mg	8.7mg	1600mg	6g	–	0.14 mg	–
(female)	50+ years	700mg	8.7mg	1600mg	6g	–	0.14 mg	–
Pregnant women		700mg	14.8mg	1600mg	6g	–	0.14 mg	–
Women lactating (breastfeeding) for up to 4 months		1250mg	14.8mg	1600mg	6g	–	0.14 mg	–
Women lactating (breastfeeding) for over 4 months		1250mg	14.8mg	1600mg	6g	–	0.14 mg	–

Key to table:

– No figure available intake per day)

* 6g of salt is a level teaspoon

† Salt (maximum recommended

Practice questions

1. a) It is recommended that from 11 years onwards, people should eat no more than 6g of salt each day. Explain why there is concern about the amount of salt people eat. *(5 marks)*

   b) Salt has been used for centuries to preserve and flavour foods. State three ways in which people can flavour their foods instead of using salt in cooking and at the table. *(3 marks)*

   c) State one reason why salt (sodium) is needed in the body. *(1 mark)*

2. a) Explain, giving reasons and examples, how some minerals and vitamins work together in the body. *(6 marks)*

   b) Using the examples in the first part of your answer, plan a menu for a main meal (2 courses) for a family of 2 adults and 2 children (a boy of 10 years and a girl of 14 years) giving reasons for your choices. *(8 marks)*

3. Laura is 16 years old. Lately she has been feeling very tired and has little energy. She tends to eat a lot of ready-made processed and fast foods (mainly based on chicken and white fish) and very few fresh vegetables and fruit.

   a) Suggest reasons for Laura's symptoms. *(6 marks)*

   b) Discuss ways in which Laura could improve her diet to help her feel better. *(6 marks)*

1.1.6 Water

What will I learn?

In this section you will learn about:

- the **functions** of water in the body
- the main **sources** of water in the diet
- the effects of a **deficiency** or an **excess** of water in the diet
- the **amount** of water needed every day for different life stages.

Functions of water in the body

Water is vital for life – we can only survive a few days without it. Water has many functions in the body:

1. All cells and body tissues contain water.
2. All body fluids contain water (e.g. saliva, sweat, blood, urine, digestive juices).
3. Many chemical reactions in the body use water.
4. Body temperature is controlled by removing heat from the body during sweating.
5. It is needed for the digestion of food and the absorption of nutrients from the small intestine into the body.
6. It removes waste products from the body in the urine (made in the kidneys) and faeces (made in the large intestine).
7. It keeps the linings of the digestive system, mucous membranes and the lungs healthy and moist.
8. It controls the concentration of substances, such as minerals, in the blood.
9. It helps keep the skin moist and healthy.

Main sources of water in the diet

Drinking plain water regularly throughout the day is an essential part of a healthy lifestyle. Tap water in the UK is very safe to drink, inexpensive and easily available. Bottled water costs 500–1,000 times more than tap water and the disposal of the used plastic bottles causes significant environmental problems because of the energy used to make them and their disposal after use.

Water is found naturally in many foods (e.g. fruits, vegetables, milk and milk products, meat, fish, and eggs). Water is also added to many foods during preparation, cooking and processing (e.g. soft drinks, fruit juices, pastries, breads, soups, sauces, meats such as ham and bacon, boiled rice and pasta).

Effects of a **deficiency** of water in the diet

Water is lost from the body during sweating, from the lungs in breath, and in the urine and faeces. It needs to be regularly replaced, so that the body stays **hydrated**, especially if the climate is hot or someone has been doing a lot of physical activity, otherwise the body will start to **dehydrate** and suffer.

Key terms

Hydrated: the body has enough water

Dehydrated: the body does not have enough water

Effects of a deficiency of water	Why does this happen?
Feeling thirsty	In the brain, there is an area that detects when the body is becoming dehydrated. It sends a message to our mouth that we are thirsty.
Getting a headache	The blood becomes more concentrated when we are dehydrated and as it goes through the brain it can give us a headache.
The urine becomes very dark in colour	If the body is hydrated, the urine should be a very pale yellow colour. If the body is dehydrated, the kidneys try to conserve water and the colour of the urine will darken because it is concentrated, as shown in the chart below:

1		Good
2		Good
3		Fair
4		Dehydrated
5		Dehydrated
6		Very dehydrated
7		Severe dehydration

Feeling weak and sick	If it is dehydrated, the body's normal chemical reactions will be affected and this may give these symptoms.
The body becomes overheated	The body cannot cool itself down properly if it is dehydrated and will rise above the normal temperature of 37°C, which is dangerous.
Wrinkled skin	The skin contains water and, if dehydrated, the moisture will be taken away from the skin for more urgent uses in the body.
Feeling confused	Dehydration starts to affect how the brain works.
Changes in blood pressure and heart rate	Dehydration reduces the volume of blood in the body which will affect blood pressure and the rate at which the heart pumps blood around the body.

Effects of an **excess** of water in the diet

Drinking too much water in a short period of time (e.g. after physical exercise or in a competition) can cause the concentration of substances in the blood, such as minerals, to become dangerously over-diluted. This can quickly affect the function of vital organs in the body, such as the heart and kidneys, and can be fatal.

Amount of water needed every day for different life stages

In temperate climates such as the UK, it is recommended that people drink 1–2 litres of water or other fluids a day, which is approximately 6–8 medium-sized glasses of water. This would need to be increased if the temperature was high or a lot of physical activity has taken place.

Practice questions

1. State three ways in which you could encourage young children to drink more water. *(3 marks)*

2. Discuss the reasons why it is better for people to drink water rather than sweetened, fizzy drinks. *(4 marks)*

3. Explain why an athlete who is taking part in a sports competition in a hot country needs to control their water intake very carefully. *(4 marks)*

Chapter 2 Nutritional needs and health

1.2.1 Making informed food choices for a varied and balanced diet

What will I learn?

In the previous section, you have learned about the **nutrients** in food. In this section, you will learn about:

- what is meant by a healthy, balanced diet
- how eating a variety of foods can give us a healthy diet
- how to choose an interesting and varied diet
- how to provide the right diet for different people at different life stages (e.g. young children, teenagers, adults, the elderly) and special dietary groups (e.g. vegetarian, vegan, coeliac).

Dietary guidelines

Health experts and the Government have worked together and produced a set of **Dietary Guidelines and an Eatwell Guide** to help people make informed choices when they are deciding what to eat. These are shown below. You will see that there are also guidelines about your **lifestyle** choices as well as what you eat.

1. Base your meals on **starchy** foods.
2. Eat lots of **fruit and vegetables**.
3. Eat more **fish** – including a portion of **oily fish** each week.
4. Cut down on saturated fat and sugar.
5. Eat less **salt** – no more than **6g a day** (1 level teaspoon) for adults.
6. Get active and be a healthy weight.
7. Don't get thirsty – drink plenty of water.
8. Don't skip breakfast.

Key terms

Healthy, balanced diet: a **diet** that contains the **correct** proportions of carbohydrates, fats, proteins, vitamins, minerals and water necessary for good health, to grow properly, be active and maintain a healthy body

Diet: the food that you eat every day. There are also special diets (e.g. a low-fat diet, a calorie-controlled diet, a vegetarian diet)

Lacto-vegetarian: someone who does not eat meat or fish but will eat milk and milk products

The Eatwell Guide is based on the five food groups. The size of the segments for each of the food groups shown in the Eatwell Guide matches the Government's recommendations for a **diet** that would provide all the nutrients needed by a healthy adult or child (over the age of 5 years). From the age of 2–5 years, children should gradually start eating a greater variety of foods as shown in the Eatwell Guide (Ref: Public Health England '8 tips for eating well', 2016).

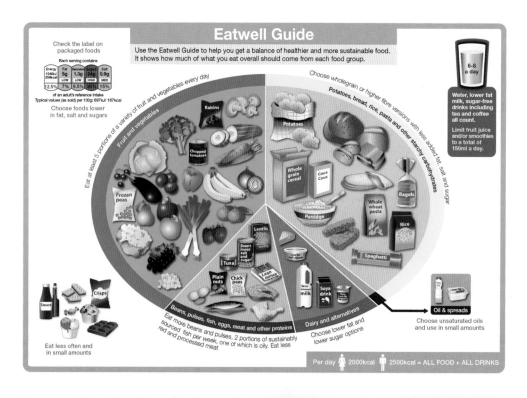

The **Eatwell Guide** helps people to understand the variety of the main food groups that are needed for a healthy, balanced diet. It is not meant to show the balance required in any one specific meal or over a particular period of time; it represents the *overall balance* of a healthy diet.

Food group	Segment of Eatwell Guide	How much should we eat?
Potatoes, bread, rice, pasta and other starchy carbohydrates		• About ⅓ of all the food we eat should be from this group. • If possible, choose wholegrain or higher fibre versions with less added fat, salt and sugar foods because they contain more dietary fibre and nutrients and make us feel full for longer. • Include at least one starchy food in each main meal.
Fruit and vegetables		• About ⅓ of all the food we eat should be from this group. • *Eat at least* 5 portions of a variety of fruit and vegetables every day (fresh, canned, frozen). • 1 portion = 80g (e.g. one apple, banana, orange or similar sized fruit). • 3 heaped tablespoons of vegetables. • A dessert sized bowl of salad. • A glass (150ml) of fruit juice (counts as a maximum of one portion a day). • 30g dried fruit (counts as a maximum of one portion a day). • Does not include potatoes.
Dairy and alternatives		• Eat 2–3 foods a day from this group. • For example, a glass of milk (150ml), a small pot of yogurt, a piece of cheese about 25g, a small pot of fromage frais. • Choose lower fat and lower sugar options (e.g. 1% fat milk, reduced fat cheese, natural or low sugar yogurts). • Alternatives include 'milks' and related products such as yogurts made from soya beans, nuts, oats and rice. • Try to choose unsweetened alternative milks that have been fortified with calcium.
Beans, pulses, fish, eggs, meat and other proteins		• Eat more beans and pulses (peas and lentils). • Vegetable protein foods include tofu, tempeh, textured vegetable protein and mycoprotein. • Eat 2 portions of sustainably sourced fish per week – one of which is oily. • Eat less (no more than 70g a day) red and processed meat products (e.g. sausages, meat pies, cold meat, smoked and cured products such as bacon and salami) which can be high in fat, salt and food additives.
Oils and spreads		• Eat only small amounts of foods in this group. • Choose unsaturated oils (e.g. olive oil, rapeseed oil, vegetable oil) and unsaturated vegetable fat spreads.

The Eatwell Guide also recommends:

• Sweet, salty and fatty foods such as crisps, chips, cakes, biscuits, chocolate, ice cream and sauces should be eaten less often and in smaller amounts.

• People should drink 6–8 cups or glasses of fluid a day (water, lower fat milk, sugar-free drinks, and unsweetened tea and coffee). Fruit juice and/or smoothies should be limited to 150ml a day.

• People should check the nutritional labels on packaged foods and choose foods lower in fat, salt and sugars.

• The total daily intake of energy from all food and drinks should be 2000kcals for adult females and 2500kcals for adult males.

Planning balanced meals: introduction and recipes

Throughout the book there are recipes that you may want to use in your practical lessons. The recipes have been set out to help you understand how they link to the different parts of the course specification to show which nutrients they contain (their *nutritional profile*), which cooking methods and food preparation skills they use, and the science behind the recipe.

An example recipe for a *Roasted vegetable and pasta medley*, which is suitable for a lacto-vegetarian, is given on page 40.

Roasted vegetable and pasta medley

Ingredients:
(serves 3–4 people)

Suggested vegetables (you can use others; see below):
1 red or green pepper – remove the seeds and chop into strips
1 medium courgette – cut into batons (sticks)
1 onion – cut into wedges
1 small sweet potato or parsnip – peeled and cut into cubes
seasoning (salt and pepper)
2 tbsp oil

Pasta
100g penne or other pasta

Mornay sauce (Béchamel sauce flavoured with cheese):
50g unsalted butter or vegetable fat spread
50g plain flour
500ml milk
½ tsp dried mustard (optional)
100g mature cheddar cheese

You need a medium-to-large ovenproof casserole or lasagne dish.

Storage instructions:
Refrigerator: allow to cool then cover and store in the refrigerator (0°C to below 5°C) for up to 3 days. Reheat only once until at least 75°C ('piping hot').
Freezer: allow to cool then chill in refrigerator. Cover in aluminium foil or freezer grade plastic and freeze for up to 3 months.

Variations:
Other vegetables you could use include butternut squash, carrot, raw beetroot, leek, garlic.
To lower the fat content, you could use reduced fat Cheddar cheese, and semi-skimmed, skimmed or 1% milk.

Method:

1. Heat the oven: Gas 6/200°C (190°C if you are using a fan oven).

2. Roasted vegetables:
- Spread the vegetables on a roasting tray and drizzle the oil over them.
- Add the seasoning and roast the vegetables in the oven for 25–30 minutes, turning them occasionally until browned (caramelised) and tender.

3. Pasta:
- Boil the pasta in a large pan of water until it is tender. Drain it using a sieve or colander.

4. Cheese sauce:
- Grate the cheese onto a plate.

All-in-one microwave method:
- Put the flour and the mustard powder in a mixing bowl.
- Gradually add the milk, mixing it to make it smooth with a wooden spoon or balloon whisk.
- Add the butter.
- Place the bowl into the microwave and set the timer to 1 minute.
- When it stops, stir the sauce thoroughly and microwave again for 1 minute – stir the sauce again.
- Repeat this 4–5 times until the sauce has thickened and is smooth and glossy.
- Take it out of the microwave and add ¾ of the grated cheese. Stir until the cheese has melted.

Béchamel (roux) method:
- In a small saucepan, melt the butter on the hob – do not let it burn.
- Add the flour and mustard and continue heating it, stirring it all the time with a wooden spoon, for 1 minute (roux).
- Remove the pan from the heat.
- Gradually add the milk to the roux, stirring well each time to avoid any lumps forming, until all the milk has been added.
- Put the pan back on the heat and, stirring all the time, heat the sauce until it boils and thickens – the sauce should coat the back of the wooden spoon and be smooth and glossy in appearance.
- Remove the pan from the heat and add ¾ of the grated cheese. Stir until the cheese has melted.

5. Assemble the dish
- Put the roasted vegetables and the cooked pasta into the dish, then pour the sauce over.

Topping
- Sprinkle the rest of the cheese on top.
- Place the dish under a hot grill and heat until golden brown on top.
- Serve with a crisp salad and warm crusty bread.

Stretch and challenge activity

How could this recipe be modified ...	... for a vegan?
	... for a non-vegetarian?
	... for a coeliac?
	... for someone who is lactose intolerant?
	... to increase the fibre content?
	... to lower the fat content?

What variations could you make to ...	... the roasted vegetables?
	... the pasta?
	... the sauce?
	... the topping?

What is the nutritional profile of this recipe?

Macronutrients

Which ingredient(s)?

Protein

Milk, cheese	HBV
Pasta	LBV

Fat

Oil, milk, cheese, butter

Carbohydrate

Pasta, flour, root vegetables	Starch
Some vegetables (e.g. onions, parsnips)	Sugars (intrinsic)
Vegetables, wholegrain pasta	Dietary fibre

Eatwell Guide

Micronutrients

Which ingredient(s)?

Vitamins

	Vitamin A:
Vegetables: pepper, sweet potato	Beta carotene
Cheese, milk, butter	Retinol
	Vitamin B group:
Milk, cheese, vegetables, wholegrain pasta, flour	Thiamine B1
Milk, cheese	Riboflavin B2
Milk, flour	Niacin B3
Milk, cheese	Folic acid B9
Milk, cheese	B12
Pepper (some lost in cooking)	Vitamin C
Milk, cheese, butter	Vitamin D
Oil, vegetables, milk	Vitamin E
Cheese	Vitamin K

Minerals

Milk, cheese	Calcium
–	Fluoride
Vegetables, milk, cheese	Iodine
Flour, pasta	Iron
All ingredients	Phosphorus
Cheese	Sodium

Which cooking methods and practical skills does this recipe use?

Cooking methods

Boiling
Roasting
Microwaving
Grilling

Practical skills

Knife skills – vegetables

Cooking pasta

Sauce making:
    All-in-one microwave method
    OR
    Béchamel (roux) method

What is the science behind this recipe?

Gelatinisation of starch in the pasta when it is boiled and the sauce (flour) when it is heated and thickens.

Caramelisation of natural (intrinsic) sugars in the onions, parsnip, sweet potato when they are roasted.

Coagulation of the protein in the cheese when it is grilled.

Heat transfer

Conduction	Heating the water to cook the pasta
	Roasting the vegetables in the oven
Convection	Boiling the water to cook the pasta
	Heating the air in the oven when roasting the vegetables
Radiation	Grilling the completed dish
Microwaves	All-in-one sauce: the microwaves cause the water molecules in the milk to vibrate and give off heat

How do you match up to the Eatwell Guide?

Record all the food and drinks you consume (eat and drink) over a 24-hour period.

Analyse how well the food you have consumed matches the Eatwell Guide.

Which group did you consume too little of?

Which group did you consume too much of?

How could you adapt what you consumed to match the Eatwell Guide?

Food group	Segment of Eatwell Guide	What did you consume (eat and drink)?
Potatoes, bread, rice, pasta and other starchy carbohydrates		
Fruit and vegetables		
Dairy and alternatives		
Beans, pulses, fish, eggs, meat and other proteins		
Oils and spreads		

Planning balanced meals: general considerations

Whenever you are planning meals for people, there are a few general considerations that apply to everyone that you should take into account.

- Their likes and dislikes for different foods.

- Is the meal for everyday or a special occasion?

- Do they have any food allergies or intolerances (see pages 216–219)?

- Are there any religious or cultural dietary rules that they follow (see pages 211–215)?

- The nutritional profile of the meal – how does it fit in with current dietary guidelines?

- Do they have a particular health condition which means they should either eat less or eat more of certain foods?

- Do they need help in buying, preparing and cooking their food?

- What types of meals will suit their lifestyle – are they physically active or less active?
- How much time do they have available to prepare and cook food?
- The cost of ingredients – how much can they afford to spend on food?
- Which foods are available for them to buy?
- Which foods are in season?

Portion size and costing

When planning meals, especially for a large number of people (e.g. for school or hospital meals), it is helpful to have guidelines about how much of each different food type is enough for an average portion per person.

There are various guidelines available (e.g. in books such as the *Food Portion Sizes* guide by the Food Standards Agency (2002)), as well as visual guides, such as the examples shown here, which compare portion sizes to familiar everyday items to help people choose the amount of food they should eat.

Stretch and challenge activity

Investigate how portion sizes have increased in recent years for fast food restaurant products such as fried chicken, burgers, fries, soft drinks and popcorn. Discuss the effects on and the implications of these portion size increases for the health of individuals, food sustainability and the environment.

Activity

Using the weblink http://www.healthyfood.co.uk/portions-guide, consider and comment on the information that is given in the food portion chart, as follows:

a) Who would benefit from using a portion guide like this?

b) How do the pictures of familiar everyday objects help people to portion their food? Give some specific examples.

Here are some examples of portion sizes, shown by weight in grams, for a variety of foods.

Food	Description of portion size	Weight of portion size (g)
Cheddar cheese	3 tbsp if finely grated or a small cube	25g
Minced beef	Medium, cooked portion	70g
Pork chop	With bone – grilled or fried	120g
White fish (e.g. haddock)	Medium-sized fillet	150g
Tuna	Sandwich portion	45g
Baked beans	Medium portion	135g
Butter or vegetable fat spread	For 1 slice of bread	7–10g
Oil	1 tbsp	11g
Mayonnaise	1 heaped dessertspoon	20g
Peanut butter	Spread on 1 slice of bread	20g
Peas	Medium portion	70g
Carrots	Large portion	85g
Apple	Medium	100g
Grapes	Small bunch	100g
Dried fruit (e.g. raisins)	1 tbsp	30g
Fruit juice	Medium glass	160g (ml)
Potatoes, boiled	Medium portion	160g
Potatoes, mashed	1 scoopful	60g
Bread, wholemeal	1 medium slice	36g
Breakfast cereal	Medium portion	30g
Rice, boiled	Medium portion	180g

Key term

Life stages: phases of development that people go through during their life, such as infancy (babyhood), childhood, adolescence (teenagers), adulthood and the elderly

Study tip

Because prices vary in different shops and at different times, you can only work out average prices when you are costing foods. Some computer nutritional analysis software enables you to work out costing of recipes and meals.

Costing

Once you have looked at the portion sizes for meals, you need to work out the price. It is usually possible to find out the price of a food per kg/100g/litre or 100ml. Most supermarkets and food suppliers give this information on their shelves and on their websites. Once this information is known, it is easy to work out the price of a portion of food, as the following examples show. (NB: The prices listed are **averages** only.)

Food/portion size	Price per kg	Price per 100g	Price per litre	Price per 100ml	Price of portion
Cheese (25g)	£6.50p	65p			65p ÷ 100 = 0.65p per g × 25g = **16p** per portion
Dried fruit (30g)	£2.75p	27.5p			27.5p ÷ 100 = 0.275p per g × 30g = **8.25p** per portion
Milk (150ml)			66p	6.6p	6.6p ÷ 100 = 0.066p per ml × 150ml = **9.9p** per portion

The following charts show specific meal planning considerations for different people at various life stages.

Planning balanced meals for young children – 1–12 years

Pre-school children (1-4 years old)

What happens at this life stage?	Which nutrients are particularly important?	
Body growth and development are rapid. A lot of energy is used in activity.	Protein	Vitamins – all
	Carbohydrate (limit free sugars)	Fibre
	Fat	Water
	Minerals – all	

What would be their best eating habits and lifestyle choices?

Encourage young children to:

- eat small regular meals and drinks
- try new foods, but do not force them to eat them if they refuse at first – try again another time
- eat fresh and raw foods
- drink unsweetened drinks, especially water and whole milk
- eat until they are full, rather than expecting them to finish what is on their plate, so that they recognise the messages their body will give them – this will help to prevent them from over-eating
- sit at a table to eat to help develop their social habits and make eating a happy, fun time
- share and enjoy food with other children.

Discourage young children from:

- eating snacks between meals
- eating snacks that have high sugar, fat and salt contents (e.g. crisps, biscuits and sweets).

Advice for parents/carers:

- Serve small portions as children's appetites are much smaller than adults.
- Be aware of foods that may cause choking – encourage children to bite and chew food carefully.
- Involve children in all aspects of eating such as shopping, meal preparation and cooking. Talk to children about where their food comes from.
- The Eatwell Guide does not apply fully to this age group, but in their food choices, they should be moving towards it.
- Encourage them to care for their teeth.

Children aged 5-12 years

What happens at this life stage?	Which nutrients are particularly important?	
- Growth continues in 'spurts'. - Children should be physically active most of the time, but increasing numbers become sedentary (inactive) if they use computers, social media or watch TV, which can lead to them becoming overweight or obese.	Protein	Vitamins – all
	Carbohydrate (limit free sugars)	Fibre
	Fat	Water
	Minerals – all	

What would be their best eating habits and lifestyle choices?

Encourage children to:

- follow the Eatwell Guide and dietary guidelines
- continue to try new foods and to eat fresh and raw foods regularly
- eat regular meals, especially breakfast
- find out about how food is produced, how it is prepared and cooked, and what it contains
- take part in shopping, preparing and cooking family meals.

- have enough sleep
- take part in physical activities.

Discourage children from:

- 'grazing' and snacking between meals
- frequent consumption of sweet, fizzy drinks, fatty and salty snack foods and sweets.

On page 46 is a main meal recipe that children would enjoy.

Section 1: Food, Nutrition and Health

Fishcakes

Ingredients:

(serves 4 people as a main meal)
350g potatoes
200g canned tuna or cooked fish
    (e.g. haddock)
25g butter or vegetable fat spread
1 egg
small bunch of parsley
200g dried breadcrumbs or stale
    bread (grate or turn into crumbs
    in a food processor)
seasoning
flour for shaping the fish cakes

Storage instructions:

Refrigerator: allow to cool
    then cover and store in the
    refrigerator (0°C to below 5°C)
    for up to 3 days. Reheat only
    once until at least 75°C ('piping
    hot').
Freezer: allow to cool then chill in
    refrigerator. Cover in aluminium
    foil or freezer grade plastic and
    freeze for up to 3 months.

Method:

1. Peel the potatoes and cut into 1cm dice.

2. Place the potatoes in a large pan, cover with cold water and bring to the boil. Simmer for 20 minutes until the potatoes are soft.

3. Open can, place tuna or cooked fish on a plate and flake with a knife and fork.

4. Wash the parsley, remove stalks and chop finely.

5. When the potatoes are cooked, drain and mash them with a potato masher until smooth.

6. Add the butter or vegetable fat spread, fish and parsley; season with black pepper and mix well with a spoon.

7. Crack the egg into a small bowl and beat with a fork.

8. Place the breadcrumbs on a plate (or a piece of greaseproof paper).

9. Sprinkle some flour on your chopping board and hands. Shape the fish mixture into a sausage shape and then cut and shape into eight even-sized pieces.

10. Dip each fishcake into the egg mixture, brushing with a pastry brush.

11. Remove with a palette knife, place into the breadcrumbs and coat each side evenly.

12. Bake the fish cakes on a greased baking tray for 15–20 minutes at Gas 6/200°C (190°C if you are using a fan oven) until golden and crispy on the outside.

13. As an alternative cooking method, the fishcakes can be shallow fried in a little hot oil until they are golden and crispy on both sides. Turn them over a few times when frying to ensure that they are evenly cooked.

Stretch and challenge activity

1. What could you serve this recipe with to turn it into a complete meal (e.g. add a starter or dessert, or other vegetables)?

2. Think of some interesting ways to serve the meal to encourage young children to eat it.

3. There are concerns that some types of fish that we eat regularly have been over-fished, so that the stocks that are left in the sea are in danger of being made extinct. Find out what 'fish from sustainable sources' means, and which types of sustainable fish could be used as alternatives to tuna and haddock in the recipe.

4. Think of some other ingredients for the fishcake coating that you could either add to or use instead of breadcrumbs, to give a crispy coating.

What is the nutritional profile of this recipe?

Which ingredient(s)?

Macronutrients

Protein

Fish, egg	HBV
Bread	LBV

Fat

Butter/vegetable fat spread, tuna fish	

Carbohydrate

Bread, potatoes	Starch
–	Sugars (intrinsic)
Bread – if wholemeal used, parsley	Dietary fibre

Which ingredient(s)?

Micronutrients

Vitamins

	Vitamin A:
Parsley	Beta carotene
Egg, butter/vegetable fat spread	Retinol
	Vitamin B group:
Eggs	Thiamine B1
Eggs	Riboflavin B2
–	Niacin B3
Parsley	Folic acid B9
Fish	B12
Parsley	Vitamin C
Butter/vegetable fat spread, egg yolk, tuna	Vitamin D
Vegetable fat spread	Vitamin E
	Vitamin K

Minerals

Canned tuna	Calcium
–	Fluoride
–	Iodine
Egg yolk, parsley	Iron
All ingredients	Phosphorus
Fish	Sodium

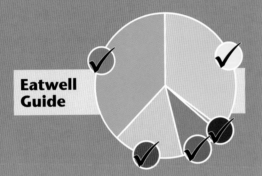

Eatwell Guide

Which cooking methods and practical skills does this recipe use?

Cooking methods	Practical skills
Boiling	Vegetable preparation/knife skills
Simmering	Fish preparation/knife skills
Baking	Coating and shaping

What is the science behind this recipe?

Gelatinisation of starch in the potatoes when they are simmered in the water.

Coagulation of the protein in the egg in the coating when it is baked.

Heat transfer
Conduction   Heating the water in the pan to cook the potatoes
Convection   Boiling the water to cook the potatoes
                       Heating the air in the oven when baking the fish cakes

Planning balanced meals for adolescents (teenagers)

What happens at this life stage?	Which nutrients are particularly important?	What would be their best eating habits and lifestyle choices?
The body grows rapidly at certain times and develops from a child into an adult.	Protein Vitamins A, B group, C, D, E Carbohydrate (starch and fibre; limit free sugars) Fats – especially unsaturated and omega 3 fatty acids Minerals – all	**Encourage teenagers to:** • follow the Eatwell Guide • eat regular, balanced meals, especially breakfast • eat plenty of fresh foods • regularly eat oily fish and/or seeds (e.g. pumpkin seeds) • drink plenty of water • take regular exercise to strengthen muscles, maintain a healthy weight and oxygenate the body • always eat breakfast. **Discourage teenagers from:** • eating lots of energy dense ready meals, snacks and fast foods • eating lots of sugar and salt • skipping meals.
This is an important stage when minerals are taken into the bones and teeth so that the skeleton reaches peak bone mass when they are adults.	Calcium and vitamin D	**Encourage teenagers to:** • include plenty of calcium-rich foods in the diet (see page 31) • spend time outdoors in the sunshine and take regular, load-bearing exercise to stimulate the bones to take up minerals. **Discourage teenagers from:** • drinking lots of sugary, fizzy (carbonated) drinks which may affect how many minerals are taken into the bones.
Girls start to menstruate (have periods) which may mean they do not have enough iron and become anaemic.	Iron and vitamin C	**Encourage teenage girls to:** • eat plenty of fresh fruit and vegetables and iron-rich foods (see page 32) • eat regular, well-balanced meals.
Staying up late and pressures of school may lead to lack of energy, poor concentration and tiredness.	Vitamin B group Iron and vitamin C	**Encourage teenagers to:** • eat a balanced breakfast every day including wholegrain cereals to release energy (glucose) slowly into the bloodstream and help concentration • eat regular, well-balanced meals • allow enough time for the body to rest and sleep.

On page 49 is a main meal recipe that teenagers would enjoy.

Study tip

Here are some useful website addresses for information about feeding children:
www.schoolfoodplan.com
www.childrensfoodtrust.org.uk

Jambalaya

Ingredients:
(serves 4 people as a main meal)

1 or 2 chicken breasts OR 200g
mycoprotein chunks (e.g. Quorn®)
50g chorizo sausage (optional)
2 cloves garlic
150g long grain rice
1 pepper
1 large onion
1 stick of celery
1 tbsp oil
1 tsp dried thyme
1 tsp paprika
1 tsp tabasco sauce
300ml chicken stock (you can use
a stock cube made up to 300ml
with boiling water)
400g can chopped tomatoes

Storage instructions:
Refrigerator: allow to cool then
cover and store in the refrigerator
(0°C to below 5°C) for up to
3 days. Reheat only once until at
least 75°C ('piping hot').
Freezer: allow to cool then chill in
refrigerator. Cover in aluminium
foil or freezer grade plastic and
freeze for up to 3 months.

Stretch and challenge activity

How could this recipe be modified ...

... for a vegetarian?
... to increase the fibre content?

What variations could you make to ...

... the vegetables?
... the carbohydrate?
... the flavouring?

Method:

1. Cut the chicken and chorizo sausage into small, bite-sized pieces.

2. Finely dice the onion and celery.

3. Peel and crush the garlic.

4. De-seed and slice the peppers thinly.

5. Heat oil in a large saucepan or frying pan.

6. Fry the chicken or mycoprotein for 5–8 minutes, until it is starting to go brown. Remove it and put it in a clean bowl.

7. In the same pan, fry the onion, celery, garlic and pepper for 5 minutes.

8. Stir in the rice and fry for 1 minute.

9. Stir in the thyme, paprika and tabasco sauce.

10. Add the chicken or mycoprotein, chorizo sausage, chicken stock and canned tomatoes and bring to the boil.

11. Reduce the heat and simmer the mixture for 20 minutes, stirring frequently, until all the liquid has been absorbed and the rice is cooked. Be careful not to let the rice stick and burn on the base of the pan.

12. Serve with a crisp salad.

Stretch and challenge activity

What is the nutritional profile of this recipe?

Using the information you have learnt about nutrients earlier in this chapter, complete the nutritional profile for the jambalaya recipe in the chart below (the Eatwell Guide has been completed for you).

Which cooking methods and practical skills does this recipe use?

Which ingredient(s)?	Macronutrients	
	Protein	
		HBV
		LBV
	Fat	
	Carbohydrate	
		Starch
		Sugars *(intrinsic)*
		Free sugars
		Dietary fibre

Which ingredient(s)?	Micronutrients	
	Vitamins	
		Vitamin A:
		Beta carotene
		Retinol
		Vitamin B group:
		Thiamine B1
		Riboflavin B2
		Niacin B3
		Folic acid B9
		B12
		Vitamin C
		Vitamin D
		Vitamin E
		Vitamin K
	Minerals	
		Calcium
		Fluoride
		Iodine
		Iron
		Phosphorus
		Sodium

Cooking methods
Shallow frying
Simmering

Practical skills
Vegetable preparation/knife skills
Chicken preparation/knife skills
Cooking rice

What is the science behind this recipe?

Gelatinisation of starch in the rice when it is simmered in the stock.

Caramelisation of natural *(intrinsic)* sugars in the onions when they are fried.

Coagulation of the protein in the chicken when it is fried.

Heat transfer
Conduction Heating the oil in the frying pan to cook the chicken and vegetables

Eatwell Guide

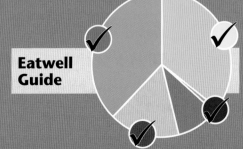

Planning balanced meals for adults

What happens at this life stage?	Which nutrients are particularly important?	What would be their best eating habits and lifestyle choices?
The body does not grow anymore in height after approximately 21 years of age. The body needs to be maintained to keep it free from disease, strong and active. The metabolic rate gradually slows down. Weight gain can occur if the energy intake of the diet is unbalanced and insufficient physical activity is taken. 	Protein Vitamins A, B group, C, D, E Carbohydrate (starch and fibre) Fats – especially unsaturated and omega 3 fatty acids Minerals – all	**Encourage adults to:** • follow the Eatwell Guide • eat regular, balanced meals, especially breakfast • eat plenty of fresh foods • regularly eat oily fish and/or seeds (e.g. pumpkin seeds) • drink plenty of water • take regular exercise to strengthen the skeleton and muscles, and oxygenate the body. **Discourage adults from:** • eating lots of energy dense snacks and fast foods • adding lots of sugar and salt to their food • eating lots of foods with hidden sugar, fat and salt.
The skeleton continues to take up minerals until peak bone mass is reached around 30 years of age. 	Calcium and vitamin D	**Encourage adults to:** • include plenty of calcium-rich foods in the diet (see page 31) • spend time outdoors in the sunshine and take regular, load-bearing exercise to stimulate the bones to take up minerals. **Discourage adults from:** • drinking lots of sugary, fizzy (carbonated) drinks which may affect how many minerals are taken into the bones.
Women continue to menstruate (have periods) until the menopause (approximately late 40s/early 50s) which may mean they do not have enough iron and become anaemic.	Iron and vitamin C	**Encourage female adults to:** • eat plenty of fresh fruit, vegetables and iron-rich foods (see page 32) • eat regular, well-balanced meals.

On page 52 is a recipe that demonstrates your knife skills and could be used as a main meal for adults or for the whole family.

Planning balanced meals for elderly adults

What happens at this life stage?	Which nutrients are particularly important?	What would be their best eating habits and lifestyle choices?
• Body systems such as digestion and blood circulation start to slow down. • Blood pressure may increase. • The body needs to be maintained to keep it free from disease, strong and active. • The metabolic rate gradually slows down. • The appetite usually gets smaller. • The sense of smell and taste may be lost. • Weight gain can occur if the energy intake of the diet is unbalanced and insufficient physical activity is taken.	Protein Vitamins A, B group, C, D, E Carbohydrate (starch and fibre) Fats – especially unsaturated and omega 3 fatty acids Minerals – all	**Encourage elderly adults to:** • follow the Eatwell Guide • eat small, regular, balanced meals, especially breakfast • enjoy their food by making meals look appetising and tempting to eat • eat plenty of fresh foods • regularly eat oily fish and/or seeds (e.g. pumpkin seeds) • drink plenty of water • take regular exercise to strengthen muscles and oxygenate the body. **Discourage elderly adults from:** • eating lots of energy dense snacks and fast foods • adding lots of sugar and salt to their food.
• The skeleton naturally starts to lose minerals and the bones can become fragile (osteoporosis). • Staying indoors may prevent exposure to sunshine and vitamin D. • Joints and muscles become stiff and weaker.	Calcium and vitamin D	**Encourage elderly adults to:** • include plenty of calcium-rich foods in the diet (see page 31) • spend time outdoors in the sunshine and take regular, load-bearing exercise to stimulate the bones to continue to take up minerals.
• It may be difficult for the body to absorb certain nutrients, which could lead to deficiency diseases such as scurvy or anaemia.	Iron and vitamin C	**Encourage elderly adults to:** • eat plenty of fresh fruit, vegetables and iron-rich foods (see page 32) • eat regular, well-balanced meals.
• The eyesight may weaken.	Vitamins A, C, E	**Encourage elderly adults to:** • eat plenty of fresh fruit and vegetables to help prevent age-related eye conditions.
• Short- and long-term memory may become poor.	Vitamin B group, especially vitamin B12	**Encourage elderly adults to:** • eat foods containing B group vitamins (see pages 24–25).

On page 54 is a main meal recipe that elderly people might enjoy.

Lemon, garlic and thyme roasted chicken with mustard and onion mash

Ingredients:
(serves 4 people as a main meal)
1 whole chicken or 4 large
  chicken joints
4 cloves garlic, peeled and
  crushed
1 lemon, washed and sliced into
  wedges (remove the seeds)
handful of fresh thyme or 1 tbsp
  dried thyme
1 large onion, peeled and sliced
  into wedges
seasoning, black pepper
2 tbsp oil

Mash
500g old potatoes suitable for
  mashing
1 tbsp wholegrain mustard
  (optional)
1 large onion, finely chopped
1 tbsp olive oil
20g butter
Approx. 4 tbsp milk

Storage instructions:
Refrigerator: allow to cool
  then cover and store in the
  refrigerator (0°C to below 5°C)
  for up to 3 days. Reheat only
  once until at least 75°C ('piping
  hot').
Freezer: Cooked chicken: allow
  to cool then chill in refrigerator.
  Cover in aluminium foil or freezer
  grade plastic and freeze for up
  to 3 months.

Method:

1. Joint the chicken into eight pieces, cutting off any excess fat. Leave the skin on.

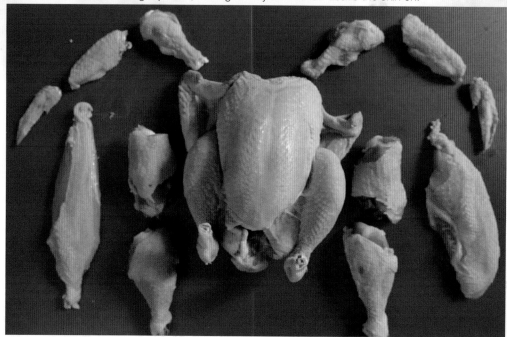

2. Heat the oven to Gas 6/200°C (190°C if you are using a fan oven) and place the chicken joints, onion wedges, garlic, lemon wedges, thyme and black pepper in a roasting tin. Drizzle with the 2 tbsp of oil.

3. Place the chicken in the oven and roast for 25–30 minutes, turning the ingredients over about half way through the cooking time to even out the cooking.

4. Meanwhile, peel and chop the potatoes into small pieces and boil the potatoes in a medium or large pan until they are soft.

5. Fry the onion in the olive oil in a frying pan, until it has caramelised.

6. Drain the water from the pan of potatoes and mash the potatoes with the butter, milk and mustard. Stir in the cooked onions.

7. Serve the potatoes with the roasted chicken and the vegetables (you can remove the wedges of lemon as they will have given their flavour to the chicken).

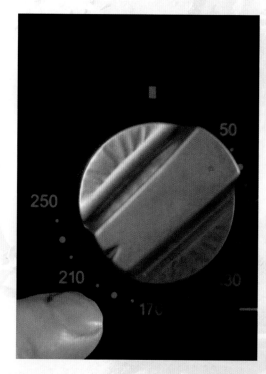

What is the nutritional profile of this recipe?

Which ingredient(s)?

Macronutrients

Protein

Chicken	*HBV*
Milk	*LBV*

Fat

Oil, butter, chicken

Carbohydrate

Potatoes	Starch
Onion, Milk	Sugars *(intrinsic)*
Onion	Dietary fibre

Which ingredient(s)?

Micronutrients

Vitamins

	Vitamin A:
–	*Beta carotene*
Milk, butter	*Retinol*
	Vitamin B group:
Chicken, milk	*Thiamine B1*
Milk	*Riboflavin B2*
Milk	Niacin B3
–	*Folic acid B9*
Chicken	*B12*
Potatoes (a little), lemon	Vitamin C
Butter	Vitamin D
Oil	Vitamin E
–	Vitamin K

Minerals

Milk	Calcium
–	Fluoride
–	Iodine
–	Iron
All ingredients	Phosphorus
–	Sodium

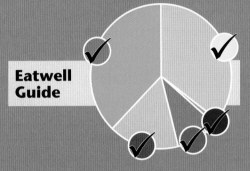

Eatwell Guide

Which cooking methods and practical skills does this recipe use?

Cooking methods

Boiling

Roasting

Practical skills

Vegetable preparation/knife skills

Jointing a whole chicken/knife skills

What is the science behind this recipe?

Gelatinisation of starch in the potatoes when they are boiled.

Caramelisation of natural (intrinsic) sugars in the onions when they are roasted and fried.

Coagulation of the protein in the chicken when it is roasted.

Heat transfer

Conduction	Roasting the chicken and vegetables in the oven
Convection	Boiling the water to cook the potatoes
	Heating the air in the oven when roasting the vegetables

Stretch and challenge activity

How could this recipe be modified ...	... to add iron?
	... for someone who is lactose intolerant?
	... to increase the fibre content?
	... to lower the fat content?

What variations could you make to ...	... the roasted vegetables?
	... the mashed potato?
	What could you serve this recipe with to turn it into a complete meal (e.g. add a starter or dessert, or other vegetables)?

Section 1: Food, Nutrition and Health

Cottage pie with cheddar and sautéed leek mash

Ingredients:
(serves 2 people as a main meal)
250g minced lamb or beef
1 onion, finely diced
1 carrot, finely diced
1 clove of garlic, finely chopped
1 stick of celery, finely diced
200g can chopped tomatoes
1 tbsp tomato purée
1 tsp dried mixed herbs
ground black pepper
¼ tsp freshly grated nutmeg

Mashed potato:
300g old potatoes suitable for
  mashing
1 medium sized leek, washed
  carefully and finely chopped
1 tbsp olive oil
10g butter
Approx. 2 tbsp milk
50g grated cheddar cheese

**You will need an oven
proof dish.**

Storage instructions:
Refrigerator: allow to cool then
cover and store in the refrigerator
(0°C to below 5°C) for up to
3 days. Reheat only once until at
least 75°C ('piping hot').
Freezer: allow to cool then chill in
refrigerator. Cover in aluminium
foil or freezer grade plastic and
freeze for up to 3 months.

Method:

1. Dry fry (no oil) the meat in a large saucepan, until browned all over.

2. Add the onion, garlic, carrot and celery and fry for about 5 minutes.

3. Add the chopped tomatoes, tomato purée and mixed herbs.

4. Add the black pepper and freshly grated nutmeg to taste.

5. Put the lid on the pan (tilted slightly) and simmer the mixture gently for 25–30 minutes, stirring occasionally, until the vegetables are tender.

6. Meanwhile, peel and chop the potatoes into small pieces and boil the potatoes in a medium or large pan until they are soft.

7. Sauté the chopped leek in the olive oil in a frying pan, until it has softened.

8. Drain the water from the pan of potatoes and mash them with the butter, milk and half of the grated cheese. Stir in the cooked leeks.

9. Pour the meat sauce into an oven proof dish. Carefully place the potato mixture on top and level it off with a fork or knife.

10. Sprinkle the remaining cheese on top and place the dish under a hot grill until the cheese has turned a golden brown.

Stretch and challenge activity

How could this recipe/meal be modified ...	What could you serve this recipe with to turn it into a complete meal (e.g. add a starter or dessert, or other vegetables)?
... to add more vitamin C? ... for a vegetarian?	
What variations could you make to ... ... the vegetables? ... the mashed potato?	

What is the nutritional profile of this recipe?

Which ingredient(s)?

Macronutrients

Protein

Meat, milk, cheese	HBV
–	LBV

Fat

Oil, butter, meat, cheese	

Carbohydrate

Potatoes	Starch
Onion, leek, carrot, milk,	Sugars *(intrinsic)*
Onions, leek, carrot, celery, tomatoes	Dietary fibre

Micronutrients

Vitamins

	Vitamin A:
Carrot, leek, tomatoes, tomato puree	*Beta carotene*
Butter, milk, cheese	*Retinol*
	Vitamin B group:
Meat, milk	*Thiamine B1*
Milk	*Riboflavin B2*
Milk, meat	Niacin B3
Leek	*Folic acid B9*
Meat, cheese	B12
Potatoes (a little)	Vitamin C
Butter	Vitamin D
Oil	Vitamin E
–	Vitamin K

Minerals

Milk, cheese	Calcium
–	Fluoride
Milk, cheese	Iodine
Meat	Iron
All ingredients	Phosphorus
Cheese	Sodium

Which cooking methods and practical skills does this recipe use?

Cooking methods

Dry frying
Simmering
Boiling
Sautéing
Grilling

Practical skills

Vegetable preparation/knife skills
Meat cookery

What is the science behind this recipe?

Gelatinisation of starch in the potatoes when they are boiled.

Caramelisation of natural *(intrinsic)* sugars in the onions when they are fried.

Coagulation of the protein in the meat when it is dry fried; and in the cheese when it is grilled.

Heat transfer

Conduction Dry frying the meat and simmering the mixture in the pan

Convection Boiling the water to cook the potatoes

Radiation Grilling the cheese and potato topping

Eatwell Guide

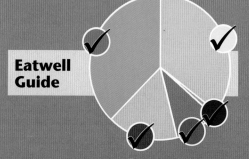

Practice questions

1. Plan and make a savoury recipe for one of the following people and, using the Eatwell Guide, explain what you would serve with it to make it a complete meal:

    *   A child. *(5 marks)*

    *   A teenager's packed lunch (male or female). *(5 marks)*

    *   An elderly adult (male or female). *(5 marks)*

2. Plan a balanced meal for the following people/situations, working out the portions required for each part of the meal. Each meal must be based upon the Eatwell Guide (except for the picnic lunch for the toddlers):

    *   A picnic lunch for four toddlers (1–2 years old).

    *   A packed lunch for a 10-year-old child.

    *   A birthday tea party for six children aged 5 years.

    *   An evening meal for a teenager who has played a hockey match.

    *   A breakfast for a teenage girl.

    *   A main evening meal for an adult who has a physically active job.

    *   A main meal for a single adult with limited cooking facilities (a hob and grill).

    *   A lunch for a family of two adults and two school-aged children who have a limited income.

    *   A main meal for two elderly adults. *(5 marks each)*

Activity

1. Cook one or two dishes from your chosen meal menu above.

2. Carry out a nutritional analysis of your chosen meal and, using the data, explain how it meets the needs of the person/people who would eat it.

3. Explain how your chosen meal could be improved or modified.

Planning meals for specific groups

When planning meals, it is important to remember that some people have specific dietary needs for a variety of reasons, such as:

*   they **choose** not to eat certain foods

*   they have a **dietary intolerance** or are **allergic** to certain foods

*   they have a **medical** or **health condition** that requires them to either avoid or eat more of certain foods.

The following chart lists some specific groups with special dietary needs, and shows which foods they should avoid and which ones they can eat.

Vegetarians

Specific group	Foods that can be eaten	Foods to avoid
Lacto-ovo vegetarians	• Dairy products (milk, cheese, yogurt, cream, butter); eggs; all plant foods; (e.g. fruits, vegetables, nuts, seeds).	• Any animal food where the animal was killed to produce it – this includes fish and shellfish.
Lacto vegetarians	• Dairy products (milk, cheese, yogurt, cream, butter); all plant foods (e.g. fruits, vegetables, nuts, seeds).	• Eggs, and any animal food where the animal was killed to produce it – this includes fish and shellfish.
Vegans	• Plant foods only, including some products made from plants (e.g. soya milk, tofu, TVP) (see page 4).	• All animal products, even if the animal was not killed to produce it, which includes fish and shellfish.

Coeliac

Dietary needs	Foods that can be eaten	Foods to avoid
• People with this condition cannot digest and absorb the protein **gluten** in their small intestine. • The gluten causes the lining of their small intestine to become damaged. • Until they are diagnosed, coeliacs will suffer from weight loss and nutrient deficiencies (anaemia, poor growth in children, lack of energy, weakened bones) because they cannot absorb other nutrients. • The only way to live with this condition is to avoid all foods that contain gluten.	• Foods that **do not contain** wheat, barley, oats and rye. • Rice and rice products, soya flour, maize (corn), millet, cassava (tapioca), linseeds, polenta, peas, beans, lentils, quinoa, sorghum, agar, nuts. 	• All wheat and wheat products including breads, cakes, biscuits, pastries, etc. • All foods containing barley, oats, rye. 

Lactose intolerance

Dietary needs	Foods that can be eaten	Foods to avoid
• People with this condition cannot digest the disaccharide sugar **lactose**. • Instead, **bacteria** in the intestines break down the lactose and this causes a lot of **abdominal pain, diarrhoea, flatulence** and **nausea**. 	• Any food that **does not contain lactose**. This means checking food labels carefully. • Specially produced lactose-free milk and dairy products can be bought. 	• Milk and milk products and any food that contains lactose. 

A high-fibre diet

Dietary needs	Foods that can be eaten	Foods to avoid
• Some people need to increase their dietary fibre (NSP) intake to avoid developing problems in their digestive system, including: • **constipation** • **diverticula disease** (a painful condition that affects the lining of the intestines) • **cancer** of the colon or rectum.	• Fresh, whole foods that have had little processing (e.g. fresh fruits and vegetables, wholemeal (wholegrain) cereals and cereal products such as breads, pasta, rice, breakfast cereals).	• Refined and processed foods that have had most of their fibre removed (e.g. white flour and products made from it; white rice; smooth fruit juices.

A low-sugar diet

Dietary needs	Foods that can be eaten	Foods to avoid
• Some people may need to reduce their sugar intake because they have Type 2 diabetes, or are trying to reduce their energy intake or prevent tooth decay.	• Sweet foods that contain mainly natural intrinsic sugars (e.g. fresh fruits and vegetables); extrinsic milk sugars in milk and milk products.	• Foods that have been sweetened with free sugars (e.g. breakfast cereals, soft drinks, desserts, cakes, biscuits, confectionery, sauces and ice creams).

A fat-reduced diet

Dietary needs	Foods that can be eaten	Foods to avoid
• Some people need a fat-reduced diet if they are trying to reduce the energy density of their diet or have CHD (see pages 71–72).	• Naturally low-fat foods such as fruits and vegetables, cereals (wheat, rice, barley etc.), white fish (e.g. cod, haddock, whiting); **fat reduced versions of foods** such as milk, cheeses.	• Full-fat versions of dairy foods; foods containing 'invisible' fats and oils such as pastries, meat products, fried snack foods, cakes, biscuits, desserts; fatty meats.

A low-sodium/salt diet

Dietary needs	Foods that can be eaten	Foods to avoid
• Some people need a low sodium/salt diet if they have high blood pressure or if there is a chance they may develop it.	• Naturally low sodium/salt foods such as fruits and vegetables, milk, eggs.	• Foods that have been preserved or flavoured with salt (e.g. yeast extract, cheese, dried fish, canned fish), some types of bread, sauces (e.g. soy sauce, ketchup), pickles and chutneys, ready meals, foods that contain monosodium glutamate (a flavour enhancer), fast foods, fried snack foods, foods that have baking powder added (e.g. cakes, biscuits, scones). Some bottled mineral waters contain high levels of sodium.

Practice questions

1. Breakfast is an important meal.

    a) Explain why it is important for teenagers to eat a balanced breakfast every day. *(5 marks)*

    b) Plan a balanced breakfast that would be suitable for teenagers to eat on a busy weekday when they don't have much time, and a breakfast that they could eat at the weekend when they have more time. *(5 marks)*

2. a) State two reasons why it is important to encourage young children to eat a variety of fresh foods. *(2 marks)*

    b) State two reasons why it is important to discourage young children from eating sugary snack foods between meals. Explain how the correct dietary habits can help keep children's teeth healthy. *(7 marks)*

1.2.2 Energy needs

What will I learn?

In this section you will learn about:

- the **functions** of energy in the body
- the main **sources** of energy in the diet
- the effects of a **deficiency** or an **excess** of energy in the diet
- the **amount** of energy needed every day for different life stages.

Functions of energy in the body

Energy is vital for life. We get our energy from the foods we eat and then use it all the time in the body for different jobs, for example to:

- allow the body to grow and develop
- move muscles and be physically active
- produce heat to keep the body warm
- produce sound when talking, singing, shouting
- send messages from the brain to make the nerves work
- make chemical reactions take place in cells, the digestive system, the brain, etc.

Main sources of energy in the diet

Energy is measured in either **kilocalories (kcal)** or **kilojoules (kJ)**.

1kcal = 4.2kJ

The main sources of energy are:

Key term

Kilocalorie (kcal)/kilojoule (kJ): units used to measure energy

Source of energy: Carbohydrate

Energy value
1g of pure carbohydrate gives 3.75kcal/16kJ of energy

Main sources
Foods containing sugars and starch (e.g. fruits and vegetables); cereals (e.g. rice, wheat, maize, barley etc.); cereal products (e.g. cakes, biscuits, breads, pasta, pastries); honey and syrups; sugar used in cooking.

Carbohydrate is the main source of energy for the body.

When foods containing carbohydrate are eaten, the body breaks them down and uses the **glucose** they contain for energy.

Some glucose is stored as **glycogen** in the liver and muscles and used as a quick source of energy.

The energy from excess carbohydrate that is eaten and not used is converted into fat and stored in the body. This happens very easily with sugars, particularly sugars in fizzy drinks.

Source of energy: Fat

Energy value

1g of pure fat gives 9kcal/37kJ of energy

Main sources

Foods containing **visible fats and oils** (e.g. butter, lard, vegetable fat spread, cooking oil, suet, ghee, fat on meat, oily fish, etc.).

Foods containing **invisible fats and oils** (e.g. cakes, pastries, fried foods and snacks, biscuits, chocolate), meat products (e.g. sausages and burgers), ice cream, cheesecakes, cheese, cream, avocados, coconut, seeds, nuts, some fast foods and ready meals.

Fats and oils have the same energy values.

Fat that is not used for energy is stored in special cells in adipose tissue under the skin or elsewhere in the body.

Fat is converted into glucose and used for energy. This is a relatively slow process, so is only used if the diet does not have enough carbohydrate.

Source of energy: Protein

Energy value

1g of pure protein gives 4kcal/16kJ

Main sources

Meat, poultry, fish, shellfish, eggs, milk, dairy foods (e.g. cheese, yogurt, quark, fromage frais), soya beans, quinoa, lentils, peas, beans, cereals (e.g. wheat, rice, oats, barley, rye, millet), nuts, seeds, gelatine.

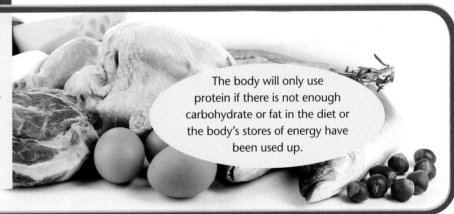

The body will only use protein if there is not enough carbohydrate or fat in the diet or the body's stores of energy have been used up.

Source of energy: Alcohol

Energy value

1g of pure alcohol gives 7kcal/29kJ

Main sources

Many people drink alcohol in drinks such as beers, wines and spirits (vodka, whisky etc.).

Drinking alcohol regularly can significantly contribute to energy intake and, if the energy it provides is not used up, it will be converted to fat and stored in the body.

Foods that contain a high proportion of fat and carbohydrate (especially sugars) are said to be **energy dense** (e.g. pastries, chocolate bars, cakes, biscuits, meat products such as sausages, pies, pizzas).

Effects of a **deficiency** of energy in the diet

The body needs a supply of energy every day.

Effects of a deficiency of energy	Why does this happen?
The body loses weight.	If there is not enough energy in the diet to meet the needs of the body, the energy stored in body fat will be used. This will gradually reduce fat stores.

Effects of an **excess** of energy in the diet

Energy from food that is not used up by the body each day will be stored in body fat cells in case it is needed in the future. If this happens on a regular basis, the weight of the body will gradually increase.

Amount of energy needed every day for different life stages

The amount of energy we need from food depends on the amount of energy we use every day. This is influenced by three things:

1. Our Basal Metabolic Rate (**BMR**).

2. Our Physical Activity Level (**PAL**).

3. Our life stage – e.g. children need extra energy for growth; extra energy is needed during pregnancy, or to breastfeed a baby.

Basal Metabolic Rate

This is the amount of energy needed by the body just to stay alive and keep working, i.e. to keep the heart beating, the lungs breathing, the brain working and the chemical reactions happening.

Depending on a person's age and lifestyle, 40–70% of the energy they require each day is for BMR. The BMR varies in different people, depending on:

- their **age** – children have lower rates than adults. BMR decreases in old age

- their **body size** – as the body grows, the BMR increases because more energy is needed by the larger body

- their **gender** – women usually have a lower BMR than men, because they tend to be smaller and they have less lean tissue and more body fat than men. Lean tissue uses more energy than fat

- their **PAL** – people who regularly exercise can raise their BMR level.

Physical Activity Level

Regular physical activity is an important part of a healthy lifestyle.

Key terms

Energy dense: a food that contains a lot of fat and/or carbohydrate and has a high energy value

BMR: Basal Metabolic Rate is the amount of energy we need to keep our body alive

PAL: this means Physical Activity Level, and is the amount of energy we use for movement and physical activity every day

Energy balance: the amount of energy we get from food each day is the same as the amount of energy we use each day

There is a lot of evidence that being physically active every day:

- reduces the risk of developing a number of diseases, such as heart disease, obesity and some cancers
- improves the health of the skeleton and muscles
- keeps the brain alert and working well
- makes people feel good about themselves.

Health experts are concerned that many people (children and adults) are not physically active enough because of their lifestyles, which tend to be **sedentary** (inactive). This is due to sitting down for long periods of time, for example at a desk, watching TV, using the Internet or playing computer games.

In the UK, the Chief Medical Officer has produced recommendations about how much physical activity people should do every day.

Age	Recommendation
Under 5 years old	A minimum of 3 hours of physical activity, spread throughout the day.
5–18 years	Physical activity for up to 60 minutes at a time, for several hours a day.
19–64 years	30 minutes of physical activity on at least 5 days a week, for a minimum of 10 minutes at a time.

Energy balance

In order for our bodies to maintain a healthy weight, we need to be in **energy balance**. This means that the amount of energy we take in from the food we eat each day must be used up by the Basal Metabolic Rate and Physical Activity Level.

If we take in **more energy** from food than we use every day, the energy we do not use will be stored as fat and the body will gradually **gain weight**.

If we take in **less energy** from food than we use every day, the energy stored in body fat will need to be used, and the body will gradually **lose weight**. This is the basis of weight reducing diets.

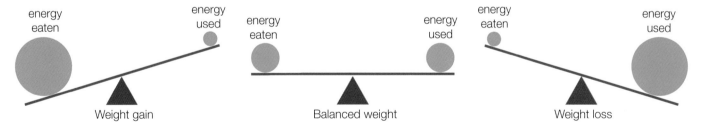

Amount of energy needed every day from different nutrients

Energy comes from foods that contain carbohydrate, fat and protein. Health experts recommend that these nutrients should give us the following amounts of energy each day.

Nutrient	% of food energy per day
Carbohydrate	50% ***Most of which*** should come from starch, intrinsic and milk sugars **No more than 5% should come from intrinsic sugars from fruits and vegetables, and free sugars**
Fat	35% or less
Protein	15%

Activity

Suggest some ways in which you could reduce the energy value of each of the following recipes/foods by changing some of the ingredients and/or the method of cooking.

Name of recipe	Energy dense ingredients	Change to the ingredient or method of cooking
Beef lasagne	Minced beef (20% fat)	
	Cheddar cheese in Béchamel sauce	
	Cream used in the Béchamel sauce	
Fried fish and chips	Deep fried batter on fish	
	Deep fried chips	
Cheesecake	Full fat cream cheese	
	Double cream	
	Crushed biscuit base made with butter	
Deep filled sandwich	Tuna in oil mixed with mayonnaise	
	Coleslaw made with mayonnaise	

Practice questions

1. The chart below gives the energy values (in kcal) of six groups of foods.

Food group	Food	Kcal per 100g
1	Apple	35
	Avocado	220
2	Cheese, cottage	100
	Cheese, Cheddar	400
3	Cod, steamed	80
	Cod, fried in batter	200
4	Mushrooms, raw	15
	Mushrooms, fried	210
5	Potatoes, boiled	80
	Potatoes, chips	250
	Potato crisps	530
6	Sausage roll	500
	Quiche	400
	Cornish pasty	330

a) For food groups 1–5 in the chart, explain why the energy values are different for the foods listed in each group. *(10 marks)*

b) For each of the foods in group 6, explain why it is an energy dense food. *(6 marks)*

2. Joe is 20 years old and works in an office, using a computer all day. He travels to work on the bus and likes to socialise with friends after work and go to local fast food restaurants for a meal with them 3–4 times a week. On other days after work, Joe goes home, eats a ready meal, drinks several sweetened fizzy drinks and watches TV for several hours in the evening. Joe eats very little fresh fruit or vegetables. He often eats potato crisps or chocolate bars in between meals.

a) If Joe continues to follow this lifestyle for several years, consider what might be the consequences for his long-term health. *(6 marks)*

b) Explain, in detail, the changes you think Joe could make to his lifestyle to benefit his long-term health. *(10 marks)*

[1.2.3] How to carry out nutritional analysis

What will I learn?

In this section you will learn about:

- where to find out nutritional information for different foods
- how to plan and **modify** recipes, meals and diets to reflect current guidelines for a healthy diet.

Nutritional information and data

The majority of foods that we eat contain more than one nutrient – they have a **nutrient profile**.

- Some foods, such as milk, contain many different nutrients; some, such as honey, contain only a few.
- We know the nutrient profile for many foods because scientists have tested lots of food samples and recorded the nutrients and energy value that average samples of each contain.
- Nutrient profiles for many foods are available in books as **food tables** and computer programs as **nutritional analysis software**.
- Nutritional analysis software in particular makes it fast and easy to work out the average amounts of nutrients and energy value of different foods, meals and recipes.

Carrying out a nutritional analysis

Task Tip:

As part of the NEA Food Preparation Task you will have to carry out nutritional analysis for the three final dishes. Being able to explain the nutritional data will be very important.

- If you are comparing similar foods, e.g. if you are comparing the protein and fat content and energy value of different cheeses, you would use the same unit of weight (e.g. 100g) for each cheese to achieve a direct comparison between them.
- If you are using nutritional analysis software to assess the nutrient content of a recipe that will serve six people, you would enter the total amounts of the different ingredients used in the recipe. Most software will allow you to enter the number of portions the recipe will serve and work out the nutrient profile per portion.
- If you want to find out how well your recipe or meal will suit a particular person or reflect the current guidelines for a healthy diet, most software will work out the proportion of different nutrients it provides compared to the Dietary Reference Values for different ages and the current guidelines.

Modifying recipes, meals and diets to reflect nutritional guidelines for a healthy diet

The chart on pages 64–67 lists five of the current **dietary guidelines** for a healthy diet (see page 38) and gives suggestions as to how these can be met when choosing and buying, preparing, cooking and serving foods, recipes and meals (you may be able to think of some more suggestions):

Key terms

Modify: change something in a recipe, e.g. an ingredient or cooking method to make it more suitable for current guidelines for a healthy diet

Nutrient profile: the different nutrients that a specific food contains

Section 1: Food, Nutrition and Health

Dietary guidelines

1. Base your meals on **starchy** foods

Choosing/buying foods, recipes and meals

- Choose wholegrain/wholemeal cereal foods and cereal products (e.g. pasta, breads, crisp breads, rice cakes, oatmeal).
- Choose a variety of starchy vegetables (e.g. potato, sweet potato, squash, yam, beans, carrot, parsnip, beetroot, pumpkin, plantain, lentils, peas).
- Choose a variety of seeds (e.g. pumpkin, sunflower, linseed, sesame).

Preparing foods, recipes and meals

- Use wholegrain/wholemeal flours from different cereals (e.g. wheat, rye, rice, maize) for baked products.
- Add seeds to desserts, breads, crumbles, porridge, stews and soups.

Cooking foods, recipes and meals

- Toast or bake breads with seasonings/olive oil/garlic/herbs to vary their texture and flavour.
- Add rice flour, semolina, toasted seeds to biscuits and cake recipes to add a crunchy texture.

- Roast starchy vegetables with oil and seasoning to concentrate their flavour and change their texture.
- Add a little oil to raw potato chips and bake them in a hot oven for about 30 minutes rather than deep fry them.
- Boil and mash together different combinations of starchy vegetables, such as carrot, parsnip and potato; butternut squash and potato; peas, mint and potato; swede/turnip and carrot; celeriac and potato.

Serving foods, recipes and meals

- Add bread (fresh/toasted/garlic/flatbread/nachos) as an accompaniment to different meals (e.g. soups, salads, cauliflower cheese/eggs au gratin, pâtés, curries, stews).
- Dry fry seeds (e.g. pumpkin, sesame) and sprinkle them on salads, soups, breakfast cereals, etc.
- Serve food (e.g. cooked meats and salad) in cereal-based wraps, such as tortillas, pittas, rolls.

2. Eat lots of fruit and vegetables

Choosing/buying foods, recipes and meals

- Choose vegetables and fruit that are as fresh as possible (they have the most nutrients) and not damaged or going mouldy.

- Try to find locally produced fruit and vegetables as they will have travelled fewer food miles and should be in the best condition.

- Try to eat fruit and vegetables in season as they should be the most economical and have the best flavour and nutritional profile.

- Add vegetables to main meals (e.g. meat sauces, stews, soups and fish sauces) to make the meal go further and add variety of flavour and texture.

- Frozen fruit and vegetables are convenient and usually have a good nutrient content because they are frozen shortly after they have been picked.

- Where possible, buy organically grown fruit and vegetables to avoid pesticide use.

Preparing foods, recipes and meals

- For people who are not keen to eat fruit and vegetables, cut them very finely or purée them when adding them to main meal recipes (e.g. soups and stews, smoothies) so that they are disguised by the other ingredients and may not be noticed.

- Make sure you remove tough parts of fruit and vegetables (e.g. apple cores, tough skins, outside leaves), which may not cook well and will spoil the texture of the meal.

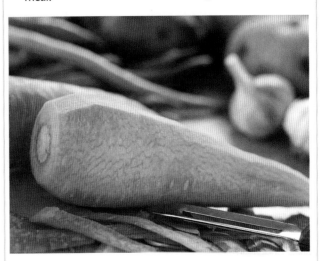

Cooking foods, recipes and meals

- Many fruits and vegetables are eaten raw and can be used to accompany main meals, such as fresh fruit with breakfast; a side salad with a main meal; vegetable sticks with dips as a starter or snack.

- Add finely diced vegetables (e.g. peppers, mushrooms, carrots, courgette, sweet potatoes, peas, sweetcorn) to boiled rice or cooked pasta to add colour, flavour and variety.

- Roast vegetables in a little oil until they are tender (e.g. sweet potato, butternut squash, raw beetroot, onion, peppers, aubergines, courgette, celeriac, turnip, parsnip) to concentrate their flavours. Dice or cut them into batons so they cook evenly.

- Add finely grated carrot to grated cheese, mix well with a little mayonnaise and use it as a sandwich filling.

- Cook vegetables and fruits for the minimum amount of time and serve them straight away in order to conserve water soluble vitamins (see page 27).

- Add peas (e.g. chickpeas), beans and lentils to soups, stews and pie fillings to make them go further and add extra protein and other nutrients.

Serving foods, recipes and meals

- Make use of fruit and vegetables to decorate and garnish finished meals.

- Use a variety of fruit and vegetables to make a meal look colourful, appetising and interesting.

3. Eat more fish – including a portion of oily fish each week

Choosing/buying foods, recipes and meals

- Use fresh, frozen, canned or dried fish – be aware of the salt content of canned and dried fish, which can be high.

- The bones of canned fish are softened in the canning process and add a useful source of calcium and other minerals to the diet.

- If you are unsure how to prepare whole, fresh fish, most shops will do this for you.

- Choose fresh fish that has bright eyes (not sunken), bright red gills, firmly attached scales, firm flesh, smells fresh and is not slimy.

- Choose varieties of fish that have been sustainably sourced from the sea or rivers (see pages 271–272), rather than those, such as cod, that have become endangered by over-fishing.

Preparing foods, recipes and meals

- Pay close attention to food hygiene when preparing fresh fish.

- Remove as many small, fine bones as possible, especially if serving the fish to children.

- The flavour of fish is quite delicate so season it lightly or add flavours such as lemon or lime juice, olive oil, fresh herbs, fresh ginger, spring onions, garlic.

- Recipes such as home-made fish cakes and fish fingers/nuggets are very easy to make and will encourage children to eat fish.

Cooking foods, recipes and meals

- Fish cooks quickly, so simple cooking methods can be used (e.g. poaching, pan frying, baking, grilling and steaming).

- Fish can be used in starters, main meals, breakfast dishes, soups and salads.

Serving foods, recipes and meals

- Fish is often served with a sauce to add more flavour and texture.

4. Cut down on **saturated fat** and **sugar**

Choosing/buying foods, recipes and meals

- Study food labels carefully to see how much (invisible) fat and (hidden) sugar different foods contain.
- Eat fewer energy dense foods such as fried snacks, chocolate bars and biscuits, pastries, cakes, sweet carbonated (fizzy) drinks, sauces and salad dressings (e.g. mayonnaise).
- Eat more low-energy foods such as fruit, salads and other vegetables, wholemeal cereals and cereal products.
- Choose lean meat and meat products.
- Choose low-fat or low-sugar versions of some foods.
- Choose to eat more foods with intrinsic sugars (see page 19) rather than a lot of free sugars (see page 19).

Preparing foods, recipes and meals

- Many cake, dessert and biscuit recipes can have the sugar content reduced without significantly affecting the finished result – try experimenting with different recipes.
- Remove visible fat from foods such as fresh meat before cooking it.

Cooking foods, recipes and meals

- Where possible, use vegetable oils instead of solid fats for cooking.
- Choose cooking methods that do not involve frying foods in oil (e.g. baking, steaming, grilling, microwaving, poaching).
- Grill meat and meat products (e.g. sausages) to allow some of the fat they contain to drain away.
- Make home-made versions of dressings and sauces, using low-fat ingredients such as quark, plain yogurt, herbs, fruit juice, puréed fruit, etc.
- Limit the consumption of ready-made pasta sauces which often contain high levels of sugar.

Serving foods, recipes and meals

Avoid serving meals with energy dense accompaniments such as rich creamy sauces, grated cheese, mayonnaise, ice cream, custard, chocolate/butterscotch sauce, whipped cream.

5. Eat less **salt** – no more than **6g a day** (1 level teaspoon) for adults

Choosing/buying foods, recipes and meals

- Study food labels carefully to see how much salt they contain.
- Eat fewer salty snacks (e.g. potato crisps), take away and ready-meals, and baked items (e.g. cakes and biscuits) that contain baking powder which contains sodium.
- Eat fewer foods that have salt added during processing to preserve or flavour them such as dried fish, cheese, yeast extract (e.g. Marmite), soy sauce, processed meat products (e.g. sausages, cooked meats).
- Choose low-salt versions of some foods.
- Choose to eat naturally low-salt foods (e.g. fresh fruit and vegetables).

Preparing foods, recipes and meals

- Avoid or reduce the amount of salt added to foods when preparing them.
- Limit the consumption of ready-made pasta sauces which often contain high levels of salt.
- Many recipes have salt in their ingredients – either reduce the amount or leave it out altogether and use an alternative flavour (e.g. lemon or lime juice, olive oil, fresh herbs, vinegar (except rice vinegar), fresh ginger, dried spices, spring onions, garlic, honey).

Cooking foods, recipes and meals

- Avoid or reduce the amount of salt added to foods when cooking them.
- Avoid or reduce the amount of salty ingredients (e.g. cheese, soy sauce, stock cubes (all types), ready prepared sauces and sauce mixes).

Serving foods, recipes and meals

- Serve food with alternative seasonings/accompaniments rather than salt (e.g. finely chopped chilli peppers, finely chopped herbs such as parsley and coriander, balsamic vinegar, paprika or cayenne pepper, lemon, lime or orange zest and/or juice).
- It is quite popular to serve food with rock salt crystals, but remember that these contain a lot of sodium and it is easy to eat too much.

Practical challenge

1. Plan a two-course main meal, which meets current dietary guidelines, for a 10-year-old child who is a fussy eater and does not eat many vegetables.

   Describe how you will make the meal interesting and appetising so that the child is encouraged to eat it.

   Carry out a nutritional analysis of your planned meal and explain how it meets the dietary needs of a 10-year-old child.

2. Adapting recipes – this could be carried out as a class activity

   Many recipes can be adapted to reduce the amount of certain ingredients in them, without significantly affecting the finished result. A typical example is home-made cakes. Many traditional cake recipes use a lot of sugar and it is possible to reduce the amount, which is recommended in current dietary guidelines for a healthy diet.

   Aim: to investigate the effects of changing the ratio of sugar in a cake recipe. In this activity, a standard cake recipe has been adapted by reducing the amount of sugar

   Standard cake recipe – makes six small cakes

   Ingredients for each batch of six cakes

   50g self-raising flour

   50g butter or vegetable fat spread

   50g caster sugar

   1 medium egg

   ½ tbsp milk

   Adaptations for each batch of six cakes:

   Reduce the sugar content by:

   25% (37g used in recipe)

   50% (25g used in recipe)

   75% (12g used in recipe)

   Controls

   All the other ingredients stay the same.

   The same cooking temperature and time is used, so the sugar content is the only variable.

   Task Tip:

   When carrying out the Food Investigation Task you will need to establish controls when experimenting to ensure a fair test (pages 251 and 254). Think about the controls for this investigation to ensure fair and accurate results.

   ## Method

   1. Set oven to Gas 5/190°C (180°C if you are using a fan oven).

   2. For each batch of cakes, place all the ingredients in a mixing bowl and either beat with a wooden spoon or use an electric whisk until the mixture is smooth and light.

   3. Divide the mixture between 12 cake cases in a bun tin.

   4. Bake each batch of cakes for 12–15 minutes until risen and set.

   5. Set out each batch of cakes with a label A, B, C and D (do not show which sugar content they contain).

   6. Ask a group of people to conduct a sensory analysis of the cakes as follows:

   Try a sample of each of the cakes and rate them out of 10 (1 = least preferred, 10 = most preferred) for the following criteria/qualities:

Results

Cake: Draw or photograph and annotate a cross-section of each cake	Appearance	Texture (lightness)	Texture (moistness)	Flavour	Comments	Actual sugar content
A						
B						
C						
D						

Discuss the results as a class, giving reasons:

- Which cake sample was the most popular?
- Which cake sample was the least popular?
- How was the appearance, texture and flavour of each cake sample affected by altering the sugar content?
- How easily do you think people would get used to reduced sugar recipes?

Stretch and challenge activity

Write a short report to conclude the practical investigation.

Activity

Changing the quantity of sugar in a cake is one way to reduce the sugar content.

Research other ways to reduce the sugar content of cakes. Think about replacing sugar and adding ingredients that contain natural sugars.

Find two cake or biscuit recipes with a low-sugar content.

1.2.4 Diet, nutrition and health

What will I learn?

In this section you will learn about:

- the relationship between diet, nutrition and health

- the major diet-related diseases: obesity, cardiovascular disease (coronary heart disease, high blood pressure), skeletal disease (rickets, osteoporosis, tooth decay), anaemia and Type 2 diabetes

- the **risk factors** for each disease.

Key terms

Risk factor: an action or a natural tendency that makes you more likely to develop a disease or health condition

Malnutrition: having a diet that is not balanced

Diet-related disease: a disease or health condition where one or more of the risk factors for developing it are what or how much of particular foods or beverages (drinks) you eat or drink over a period of time

Relationship between diet, nutrition and health

Being in 'good health' means feeling well, alert and energetic, growing and developing properly, and being able to fight disease. This is dependent on a number of things:

- Eating a healthy, balanced diet (see pages 38–39).
- Drinking plenty of water.
- Being physically active.
- Having enough sleep and relaxation.
- Avoiding too much stress.

Unfortunately there are many people who develop diseases and health conditions that spoil their quality of life and that are often caused by an unbalanced diet. They become **malnourished**, either because they have had too much or too little of particular nutrients or foods in their diet over a period of time.

In the following sections, you will learn about some of the most common, **diet-related diseases**.

Obesity

What is it?

- Obesity is a diet-related disease in which the body contains **too much stored fat**.

- It has become a very serious concern to health experts as more and more people are becoming obese all over the world.

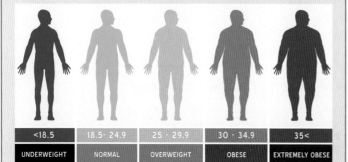

The categories of obesity showing the BMI ranges

What causes it (risk factors)?

- Obesity is caused by **not being in energy balance** (see page 61).

- If a person gets **more energy** from food than they use every day, the energy they do not use will be stored as fat and they will gradually become **overweight** and eventually **obese**.

- Many processed foods, ready-meals, snack foods, hot and cold drinks and fast foods are **energy dense** because they contain a lot of hidden fat and sugar.

- It is easy to take in more energy from food than the body needs every day without realising it and, over a period of weeks and months, the extra energy will gradually increase body weight as it is stored as fat.

- If the stored energy is not used for physical activity it will remain in the body.

What happens to the body?

- The stored fat will build up under the skin (**adipose fat**) and inside the body around the abdomen and intestines (**visceral fat**).

- Visceral fat eventually pushes up the diaphragm (at the bottom of the ribs), which squashes the lungs and makes it difficult to breathe.

- The extra weight being carried by the body puts stress and strain on the heart, blood vessels, liver, kidneys, skeleton and muscles.

- Obesity leads to other serious health conditions such as Type 2 diabetes, heart disease, breathing difficulties, high blood pressure, cancer and arthritis (where the joints in the knees and hips wear out and become very painful).

How can it be prevented and treated?

- To prevent weight gain, a person needs to be in **energy balance** (see page 61).

- In order to lose some of the stored body fat, an obese person needs to take in **less energy** from food than they use every day.

- If they do this over a period of time (often several months), the energy stored in the body fat will need to be used and their body will gradually **lose weight**.

- If they increase their physical activity at the same time, this will help to use up the stored energy more quickly and efficiently.

Cardiovascular disease

What is it?

- The cardiovascular system in the body is the **heart** and the **blood vessels** (veins, arteries and capillaries).

- Diseases can affect all parts of this system, e.g. coronary heart disease (CHD). The heart is a pump that is made of muscle.

- It continually pumps blood, which contains oxygen, nutrients and glucose (for energy), to all parts of the body.

- The heart has its own blood supply that is brought to it by the **coronary arteries**.

- To work properly, the coronary arteries need to be clear inside to allow the blood to pass through them, otherwise CHD develops.

High blood pressure (hypertension)

- The blood vessels carry blood all around the body, to and from the heart.

- The pressure of the blood can be measured as it passes through the blood vessels, and during the day it will go up and down, which is quite normal.

- If, over a period of time, the blood pressure measurement is consistently high, then this can be a cause for concern, because high blood pressure can lead to other conditions such as CHD (see pages 71–72), stroke (a blood clot in the brain) or damage to the eyes and kidneys.

What causes it (risk factors)?

Coronary heart disease (CHD)

- If people eat a lot of **salt** in their diet, this can change the volume and consistency of the blood, which means the heart has to work harder to pump it round the body, which can lead to a heart attack.

- If people are overweight or obese, the extra body weight may put a strain on the heart as it tries to pump blood around the body, which could lead to CHD.

- Smoking cigarettes can change the consistency of the blood, which may make it **clot** inside a blood vessel and block it, leading to a heart attack.

- Heart muscle needs to be exercised to keep it healthy and strong by doing regular physical activity. If people are **sedentary**, they are more at risk of CHD.

- People who are often **stressed** or drink a lot of **alcohol** are more at risk of CHD.

- Some people have a family history of CHD, which puts them at greater risk of developing it.

High blood pressure (hypertension)

- The risk factors and effects on the body of high blood pressure are the same as for CHD.

What happens to the body?

Coronary heart disease (CHD)

- In **coronary heart disease**, the coronary arteries become **blocked** by **fatty deposits (plaques)**, which prevent the blood flowing properly to the heart muscle.

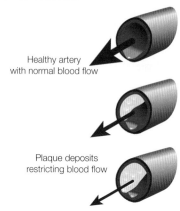

Healthy artery with normal blood flow

Plaque deposits restricting blood flow

- These fatty deposits develop in some people if their diet contains a lot of **saturated fat**.

- **Saturated fat** can increase the levels in the blood of a fatty substance called **cholesterol**, which is naturally produced in the body.

- If the blood cholesterol level is high, the cholesterol may be deposited in, build up and block the **coronary arteries** that supply the heart muscle with blood and oxygen.

- If the heart muscle does not receive enough oxygen from the blood because the arteries are blocked, the muscle will stop working.

- This can result in a **heart attack**, which can permanently damage the heart muscle and may cause death.

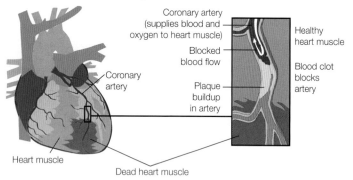

Coronary artery (supplies blood and oxygen to heart muscle)
Blocked blood flow
Coronary artery
Plaque buildup in artery
Healthy heart muscle
Blood clot blocks artery
Heart muscle
Dead heart muscle

High blood pressure (hypertension)

- The lining of blood vessels can also become less flexible, especially as people get older, which makes it harder for the heart to pump blood round them.

How can it be prevented and treated?

Coronary heart disease (CHD)

- By following the **dietary guidelines** (see pages 38–39).

- By eating foods that contain **antioxidant vitamins A, C and E** (see page 27).

- By **reducing salt intake** (see page 33).

- By **losing weight** if necessary.

- By taking **regular physical exercise**.

- By trying to **reduce stress levels**.

- By **limiting alcohol intake**.

- By **not smoking**.

High blood pressure (hypertension)

- The advice is the same as for CHD.

Skeletal disease

What is it?

- The skeleton includes the bones and the teeth.

- Diet-related diseases can affect the strength of the bones and teeth in children and adults, such as:

Rickets

- Rickets is the name given to a **deficiency of Vitamin D** in children (see page 23), which means that not enough calcium is absorbed into the body from food.

- In adults, a lack of vitamin D will lead to the bones becoming weakened (**osteomalacia**).

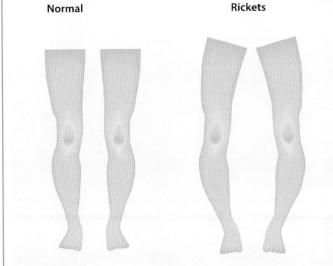

| Normal | Rickets |

Osteoporosis

- Osteoporosis is the name given to a **natural ageing process** that usually becomes apparent in old age but can happen earlier in life.

- Osteoporosis means '**porous bones**'.

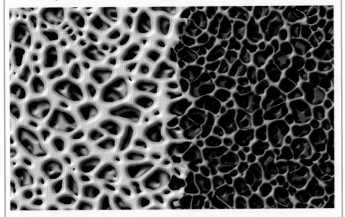

Tooth decay

- Teeth are an important part of the skeleton as they are involved in the **physical breakdown of food** to enable us to **digest and absorb** the nutrients from it.

- Teeth are vulnerable to becoming **decayed and diseased**, which makes them unable to carry out their job.

What causes it (risk factors)?

Rickets

- A lack of vitamin D is often caused by not having enough exposure to **sunlight** (see page 23), either through staying indoors too much or completely covering the body with clothing, so that the skin is not exposed to sunlight.

Osteoporosis

- The effects of osteoporosis are worse if the bones never reached peak bone mass when the person was younger.

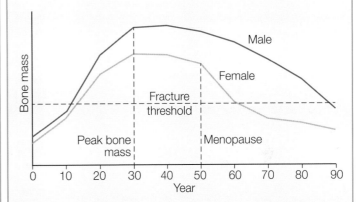

- Some people have a family history of osteoporosis so are more at risk of developing it.

Tooth decay

- Healthy teeth look like this inside:

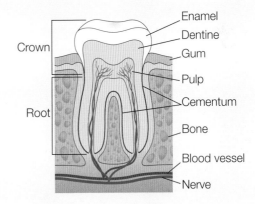

- In the mouth, there are millions of **microscopic bacteria** (see pages 171–175) that live on and around the teeth and gums.

- Every time we eat and drink, especially foods and drinks that contain starches and/or free sugars (see page 19), very quickly a sticky film called '**plaque**' builds up on the enamel of the teeth.

- The bacteria feed on the plaque and turn the sugars and starches it contains into **acids**.

- The acids stay on the teeth for around 45 minutes before the saliva produced in the mouth starts to neutralise them.

- Many children suffer from tooth decay due to poor diets and poor dental care.

What happens to the body?

Rickets

- In children and young people, having rickets means that the bones and teeth are unlikely to contain enough calcium to enable them to reach their maximum strength (**peak bone mass**).

- As the bones are not strong enough, the leg bones will bend under the weight of the body, and the skeleton will remain weak and more likely to break as the person gets older.

Osteoporosis

- Once bones reach peak bone mass at about 30 years old, very gradually over a number of years, minerals are removed from them and not replaced.

- Eventually, the bones become porous and therefore weak, and are more likely to break easily.

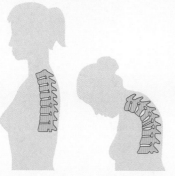

Normal   Osteoporosis

- In some people, osteoporosis is severe and they have a lot of pain and bone weakness and become bent over.

Tooth decay

- The acids gradually **erode** (dissolve) the protective white enamel surface of the teeth, leaving a hole into which more bacteria enter and cause an infection and eventual decay of the tooth.

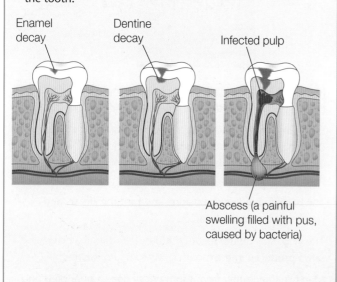

Enamel decay   Dentine decay   Infected pulp

Abscess (a painful swelling filled with pus, caused by bacteria)

How can it be prevented and treated?

Rickets

- By ensuring that the diet has enough calcium and other minerals.

- By ensuring that the skin is exposed to sunlight on a regular basis.

- By ensuring that the diet contains sources of vitamin D.

Osteoporosis

- The rate at which minerals are lost from the bones can sometimes be slowed down by making sure that there is enough calcium and vitamin D in the diet and staying physically active.

Tooth decay

- Avoid eating snack foods containing starch and sugars between meals on a regular basis.

- Avoid drinking sweetened soft drinks.

- Avoid drinking concentrated fruit juices that contain a lot of free sugars and natural acids that also cause the enamel to dissolve.

- Drink water after eating food to help cleanse the mouth.

- Clean the teeth thoroughly twice a day and use floss between the teeth to remove food debris from between the teeth.

- Visit the dentist regularly to have the health of the teeth and gums checked.

Iron deficiency anaemia

What is it?

- Anaemia is a diet-related health condition caused by a deficiency of iron in the blood.

- The body needs the mineral **iron** to make the substance called **haemoglobin** (see page 32) in **red blood cells**.

- Haemoglobin picks up the **oxygen** we breathe in from the lungs and carries it to all body cells where it is used, with **glucose**, to produce **energy** during **respiration**.

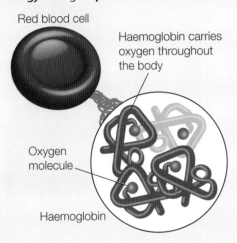

Red blood cell

Haemoglobin carries oxygen throughout the body

Oxygen molecule

Haemoglobin

- **Vitamin C** is needed to help the body **absorb iron** from food during digestion.

- **Vitamins B9** and **B12** are also needed to make haemoglobin.

What causes it (risk factors)?

- If there is not enough iron (or vitamin C) in the diet or absorbed from food, the body will develop a condition called **iron deficiency anaemia**.

- Anaemia can affect all age groups, but teenage girls and women who are **menstruating** are at more risk of developing it.

Study tip

Remember that nutrients do not work by themselves in the body – they work with other nutrients. Make sure that you understand how other nutrients work too.

What happens to the body?

- The symptoms of iron deficiency anaemia are:
  - lack of energy
  - tiredness
  - pale inner eyelids
  - pale complexion
  - weak, ridged finger nails
  - muscle weakness
  - feeling cold.

How can it be prevented and treated?

- Make sure the diet contains plenty of iron-rich foods (see page 32) and vitamin C-rich foods (see page 25), preferably eaten together to help absorption of the iron.

Sources of vitamin C:

Sources of iron:

Type 2 diabetes

What is it?

- In order for all our body cells to produce **energy** during respiration, they need a continual supply of **glucose**.

- Type 2 diabetes is on the increase in many countries world-wide, including the UK.

- Glucose enters the bloodstream after it has been absorbed from the food we eat.

- In order to get into the body cells, the glucose needs a hormone called **insulin**, which is produced by the **pancreas** (just behind the stomach).

- Imagine that each body cell has a 'door' that needs to be 'unlocked' to allow the glucose in. The 'key' that will unlock the door is insulin.

- If there are no 'keys' (i.e. **no insulin**) the 'doors' cannot be unlocked and the glucose cannot enter the cells and stays in the bloodstream.

- This is what happens in **Type 1 diabetes**, which can develop in young children and teenagers, and cannot be prevented.

- If there are plenty of 'keys' (i.e. **enough insulin**), but the 'locks' are damaged or will not work (often called **insulin resistance**), the glucose cannot enter the cells and stays in the bloodstream.

- This is what happens in **Type 2 diabetes**, which usually develops in older adults (and increasingly in younger adults) and **can** be prevented.

What happens to the body?

- Someone with diabetes will have a variety of symptoms, including:
  - **feeling thirsty** (because the glucose in the bloodstream makes it concentrated and the body needs to dilute it)

  - **feeling tired and weak** through lack of energy (because it cannot be produced in the blood cells)
  - **weight loss** (because the body's fat stores have to be used to get energy)
  - **frequent urination** (because the extra glucose goes into the urine and more water is drunk)
  - **blurred vision** (because the extra glucose in the blood affects the tiny blood vessels in the back of the eye [retina]).

- Diabetes can lead to permanent damage to parts of the body because of the excess glucose in the blood, including:
  - poor eyesight and maybe eventual blindness
  - damage to the tiny blood vessels (capillaries) in the fingers and toes and other areas of the body, leading to numbness
  - the skin may not heal properly if it gets infected or damaged because the blood vessels are damaged.

What causes it (risk factors)?

- Insulin resistance and eventually Type 2 diabetes may develop if the **diet is unbalanced**, and particularly if foods containing a lot of **free sugars and refined starch (e.g. white bread, white flour, white rice)** are frequently eaten every day.

- The pancreas has to keep producing insulin to deal with the large amounts of glucose that keep entering the bloodstream from these foods, and this leads to the 'locks' in the body cells becoming damaged or faulty.

- People who are overweight or obese, have high blood pressure, and/or are sedentary are more likely to develop Type 2 diabetes.

How can it be prevented and treated?

- By following the **dietary guidelines** (see pages 38–39).

- By **losing weight** if necessary.

- By taking **regular physical exercise**.

- By **limiting alcohol intake**.

Practice questions

1. Explain why eating a healthy, balanced diet and being physically active are both important in the prevention and treatment of obesity. Give reasons and examples in your answer. *(20 marks)*

2. a) Explain why it is important not to eat lots of sugary snacks and sweetened soft drinks in between meals. *(5 marks)*

   b) Outline the advice you would give to a child to encourage them to care for their teeth. *(5 marks)*

Stretch and challenge activity

Here are three pieces of information that appeared in news reports in March 2016.

'UK children are becoming obese at younger ages.'

'Children born in the UK since the 1980s are up to three times more likely than older generations to be overweight or obese by the age of 10 years.'

'The Chancellor of the Exchequer announced that a tax on sugary soft drinks will be introduced in the UK. The money raised from the tax will go towards sports in schools.'

Investigate the following:

1. Why is there so much concern about the numbers of children in the UK who are overweight or obese?

2. Why are children more likely to become overweight or obese compared to previous generations?

3. Why has the Chancellor of the Exchequer introduced a sugar tax? Why is the money that will be raised being targeted at sports in schools?

Chapter 3 Cooking of food and heat transfer

2.1.1 Why food is cooked and how heat is transferred to food

What will I learn?

In this section you will learn about:

- the reasons why food is cooked
- the different methods of **transferring heat** to food: conduction, convection and radiation.

Key terms

Heat transfer: the way in which heat energy is passed into food

Conduction: transferring heat through a solid object into food

Convection: transferring heat through a liquid or air into food

Radiation: transferring heat by infra-red waves that heat up what they come into contact with

High-risk foods: foods that are more likely to cause food poisoning than others

Reasons why food is cooked

Food is cooked for a variety of reasons. The table below tells you the reasons why:

To make food safe to eat

Explanation

Some foods must be thoroughly cooked to destroy the food poisoning bacteria they are likely to contain.

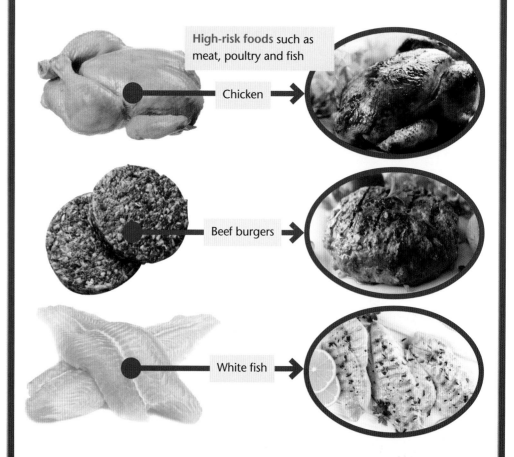

High-risk foods such as meat, poultry and fish

Chicken →

Beef burgers →

White fish →

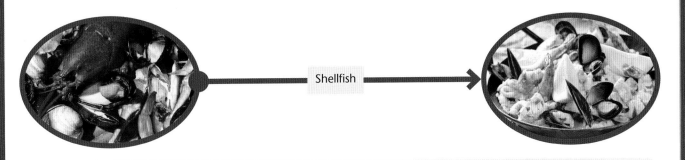

Shellfish

Explanation

Some foods contain natural toxins (poisons) that would be harmful if the food was eaten raw. Cooking destroys the toxins and makes the food safe to eat.

Raw red kidney beans must be boiled for at least 15 minutes. Canned red kidney beans are safe because they are cooked when they are canned.

To develop flavours in the food

Explanation

Cooking develops flavour by causing chemical reactions to take place in the food, for example:

Cakes: fat melts, proteins in eggs and flour coagulate, sugars caramelise, starch gelatinises.

Meat stew: vegetables soften and cook, meat protein coagulates, extractives (juices) in the meat muscle are squeezed out into the liquid, meat flavour develops as the proteins tenderise.

Quiche flan: flavours from each filling ingredient combine with the egg and milk, egg protein sets, cheese melts and develops a golden, well-flavoured layer on top.

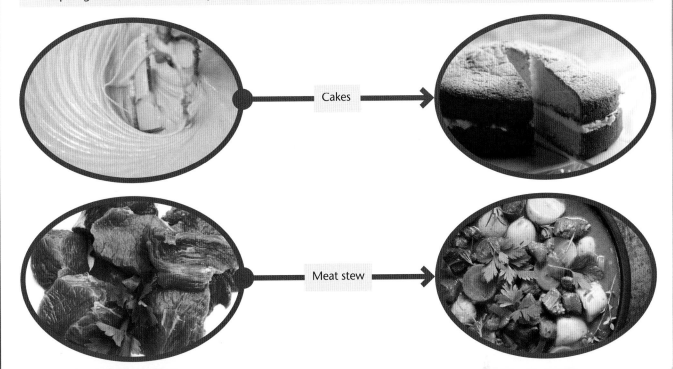

Cakes

Meat stew

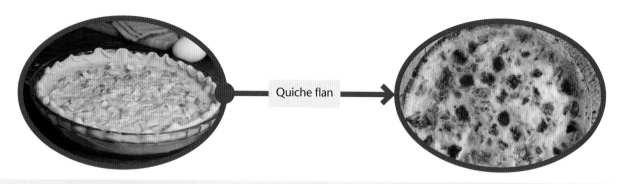

Quiche flan

Explanation

Cooking concentrates and intensifies flavour by causing water to evaporate, for example:

Roasted vegetables

Fruit sauce

Caramelised sugar

To improve the texture and appearance

To improve the texture and appearance of food, and make it easier to eat, swallow and digest.

Explanation

Cooking causes starch granules to swell, gelatinise and thicken or soften a food, for example:

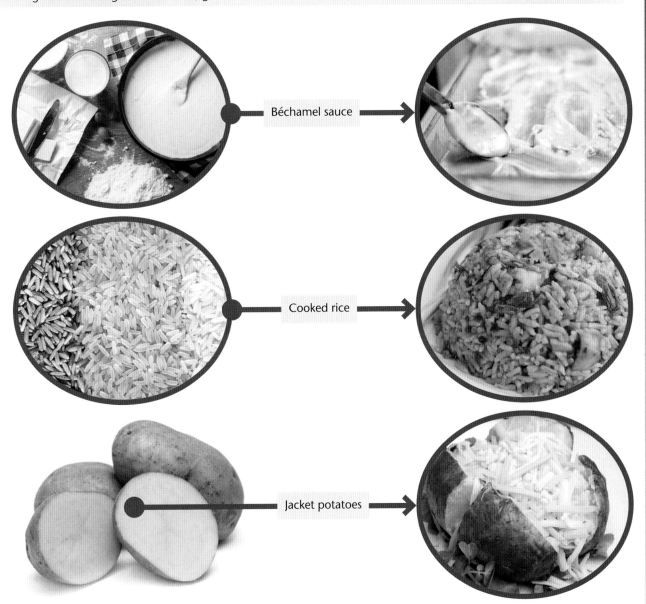

Béchamel sauce

Cooked rice

Jacket potatoes

Explanation

Cooking tenderises meat. This means the cooking process softens the meat so that it is easy to chew and digest.

Stewing or braising steak

Cooking melts fat and gives foods a smooth 'mouth-feel', for example:

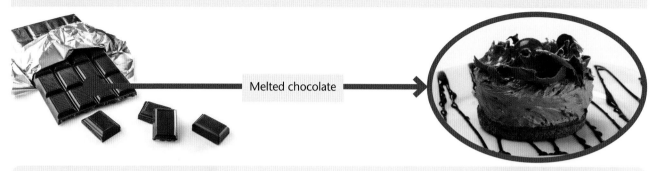

Melted chocolate

Explanation

Cooking softens the structure of the cells in vegetables to make them less bulky and easier to eat, for example:

Boiled carrots

Spinach

Mashed swede (turnip)

Explanation

Cooking turns raw doughs into risen, light-textured and crusty bread and bun products.

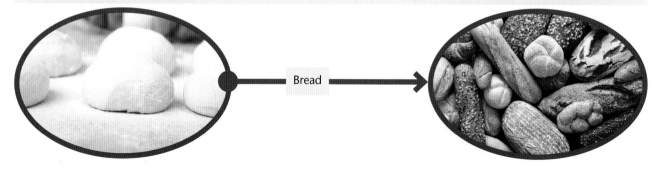

Bread

Explanation

Cooking develops a crisp texture on the outside of some foods, for example:

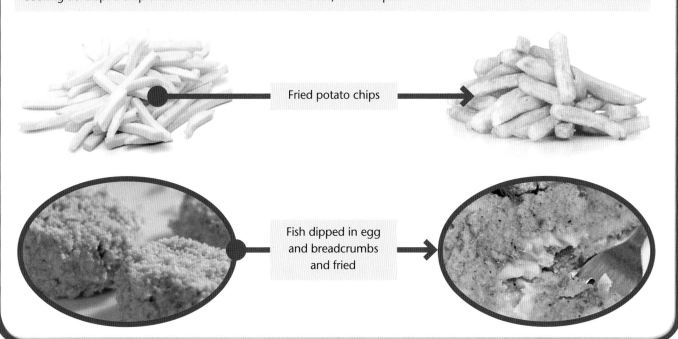

Fried potato chips

Fish dipped in egg and breadcrumbs and fried

To improve its shelf-life

Explanation

Cooking destroys harmful micro-organisms such as bacteria and moulds, which preserves the food (makes the food last longer), for example:

Ultra Heat Treated (long-life) milk

Canned foods

Cook-chilled ready meals

Jams and chutneys

To give people a variety of foods in their diet

Explanation

Foods can be cooked in different ways to give variety, for example, potatoes.

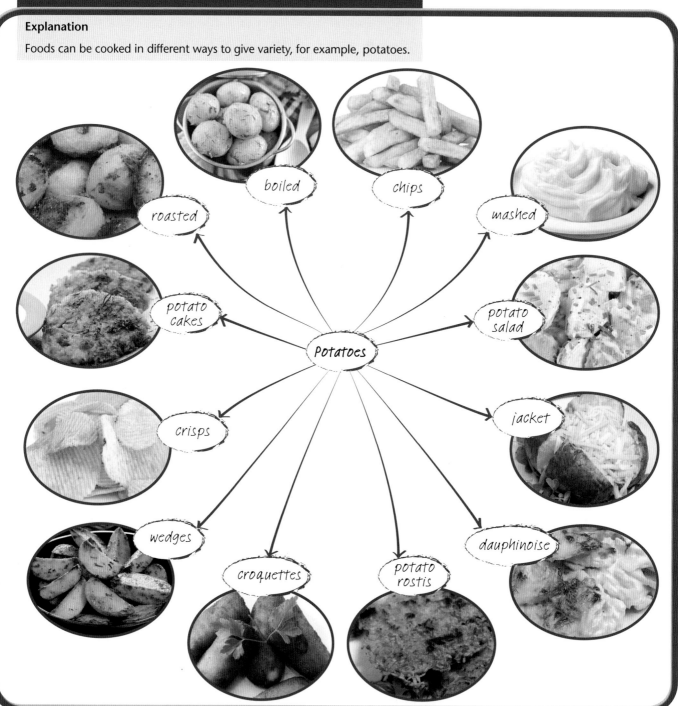

roasted

boiled

chips

mashed

potato cakes

Potatoes

potato salad

crisps

jacket

wedges

croquettes

potato rostis

dauphinoise

Activity

Choose one of the following foods and make a mind map to show the different ways in which it can be cooked and/or used in different recipes to give variety to the diet:

- Chicken

- Fish

- Eggs

- Tofu.

Extend your mind map to give reasons why the different ways of cooking your chosen food are used (e.g. for food safety, to develop flavour/texture etc.).

Different methods of transferring heat to food

In order to cook food, **heat energy** has to be transferred to it from a source of heat on the cooker hob or in the oven – either gas flames or an electric element or from fire (e.g. in a barbeque).

Heat energy is transferred to food in three ways, as shown in the table below:

- Conduction.
- Convection.
- Radiation.

Conduction

Method of heat transfer	What happens?
• Cooking pans and baking tins are usually made from any of these metals: iron, steel, stainless steel, copper or aluminium. • Metal is a very good conductor of heat. This is because of its **atomic structure**. • Some materials, such as wood, some plastics and thick materials such as cotton and wool are poor conductors of heat. They are called **heat insulators**.	• When we heat a metal pan on the hob, or a baking tin in the oven, it quickly heats up and transfers heat energy to the food inside. • It does this by the process of conduction. • The atoms that make up metals are tightly packed together in a **lattice**:  • As the heat energy from the cooker hob or oven is transferred into the pan, it makes the metal atoms start to **vibrate**. • As they vibrate, they knock against adjoining atoms and pass on the heat energy, then they pass it on to others, and so on. 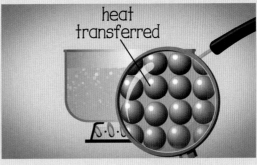

Section 2: Food Science

Why is it important in cooking?

- This is why if you put a metal spoon into a pan of boiling water, or use a metal spoon instead of a wooden spoon to stir a Béchamel sauce, it will gradually heat up until it is too hot for you to hold the spoon handle.

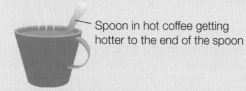

Spoon in hot coffee getting hotter to the end of the spoon

- This is why we use metal pans and baking tins to cook and bake food quickly and efficiently.

- It is important for a pan to have a well-made, flat and strong base so that it stays in close contact with the hob and allows the heat energy to conduct through it evenly.

flat, strong base

- Poor quality pans may warp (buckle and bend) because the base is too thin, which means it will not transfer the heat evenly.

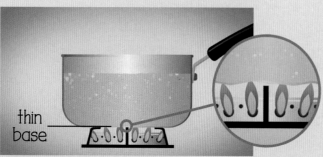

thin base

Heat insulators are used in a variety of ways to prevent us from burning ourselves when we are cooking, for example:

- Pan handles are often made of plastic or wood so they are comfortable to hold.

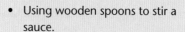

- Some pans have metal handles that are hollow inside, and the air they contain prevents the metal from becoming too hot, as air is a heat insulator.

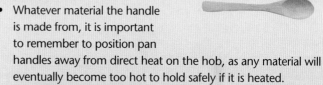

- Using wooden spoons to stir a sauce.

- Whatever material the handle is made from, it is important to remember to position pan handles away from direct heat on the hob, as any material will eventually become too hot to hold safely if it is heated.

- Insulated pan stands made from wood, ceramics or metal should be used to stand a hot pan or baking tin on, rather than the worktop, which might blister with intense heat.

A blistered worktop caused by a hot pan
©www.plastic-surgeon.co.uk

Convection

Method of heat transfer

- Convection is the name given to the transfer of heat energy by the movement of molecules in a liquid or in the air from a warm area to a colder area.

- Two examples of this are heating water in a pan and heating the air in an oven.

What happens?

- When you heat a pan of cold water on the hob, the heat energy passes through the metal pan by conduction and is then transferred to the water molecules in the pan.

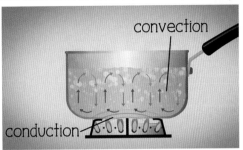

- As the amount of heat energy going into the water increases, the water molecules start to move upwards where the water is cooler, and collide with other molecules as they do so, thus passing on the heat energy into the food cooking in the water, such as vegetables, rice or pasta.

- The more heat energy that passes into the water, the faster the water molecules move and the more they collide with other molecules.

- When they reach the surface of the water, the molecules start to slow down and sink back down again.

- As they reach the bottom of the pan, they receive more heat energy and start to move upwards again.

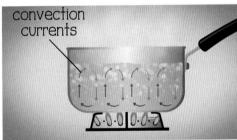

- This sets up **convection currents**, and eventually when there is enough heat energy in the water, it will boil, which means that the water molecules are moving at their fastest and you can see the water rapidly moving – this is sometimes called 'a rolling boil'.

Why is it important in cooking?

- Convection also happens when you heat an oven, only this time it is the molecules of air that move upwards as they receive heat energy, then fall back down as they cool.
- This sets up convection currents of hot air.

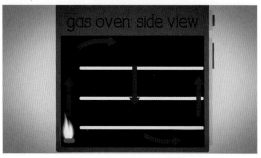

- In gas ovens, the temperature is hottest at the top of the oven, and coolest at the bottom of the oven.
- This results in 'zones of heat' in the oven so, for example, a cake that is put into a gas oven on the top shelf will cook faster than a cake put on the middle or lower shelf of the oven.
- There is also a risk that the outside of the cake may burn on the top shelf, and the middle might not be fully cooked.
- If put on the lowest shelf, the cake may not rise properly because it is too cool and may take quite a bit longer to set.
- The usual advice with a gas oven is to cook foods, such as cakes, on the middle shelf, where the temperature will be what you have set the oven to.

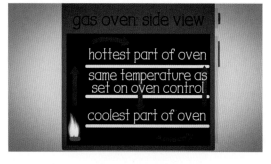

- Some electric ovens are **fan assisted.**

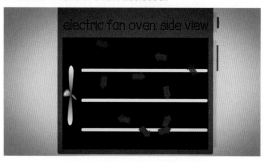

- This means that they have a fan positioned at the back that blows the hot air around the oven so that the temperature on each shelf is the same, and there are no zones of heat.
- Because of this, foods tend to cook quite quickly in fan ovens, so in recipes you will often see two separate temperatures given for electric ovens, with the fan oven temperature being between 10°C and 20°C lower than an ordinary electric oven, which will have zones of heat like a gas oven.
- If you are cooking a sauce in a pan on the hob, you need to stir it all the time.
- This is because the sauce liquid is thicker than water, so the convection currents move more slowly than they do in water.
- Stirring the sauce prevents the starch granules in the sauce from staying at the bottom of the pan for too long and makes sure that they are evenly spread throughout the sauce to thicken it evenly.

- It will also prevent the sauce from becoming lumpy and possibly burning on the base of the pan.

Activity

To help you to learn about heat transfer, produce a mind map or a set of revision cards to explain:

- Conduction
- Convection
- Radiation.

Give examples of foods cooked by these methods.

Radiation

Method of heat transfer

- When food is grilled, it is heated by **radiation.**

- The heat energy in radiation is in the form of **infrared heat rays.**

What happens?

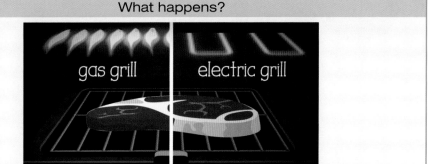

Infrared rays travel through the air and when they come into contact with a solid object, they are absorbed into the surface of the object and heat it up.

Why is it important in cooking?

- The temperature when grilling becomes very hot and intense (hotter than in an oven), so it is important not to place the food too close to the grill element, otherwise it may easily burn on the outside, but not be fully cooked on the inside.

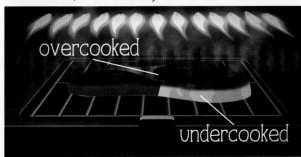

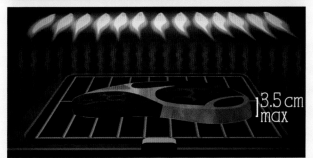

- It is also important that the food is not too thick (3.5cm maximum), otherwise it will not cook properly, which may cause a food safety risk.

- Radiant heat is also used when food is cooked on a barbeque.

- The radiant heat comes from the hot, glowing charcoal underneath the food.

- The same rules for grilling apply to barbequing food, and it is really important to make sure that the charcoal is hot enough to cook the food and that the food is placed far enough away from it so that it cooks all the way through and does not burn on the outside and remain raw in the middle, like the chicken in this picture.

Overcooked on the outside, but is it fully cooked inside?

Practice questions

1. a) Explain why it is good practice to wear oven gloves when using the oven. *(2 marks)*

   b) State how heat is transferred to food when it is roasted. *(1 mark)*

   c) Explain why roasted vegetables have a good, robust (strong) flavour. *(2 marks)*

   d) Explain why, in gas ovens, the top of the oven is the hottest part. *(2 marks)*

   e) State how heat is transferred to food when it is grilled. *(1 mark)*

   f) Explain why pieces of meat for grilling must be no more than 3.5cm thick. *(2 marks)*

2. Explain the reasons for the following:

   a) The base of a shortcrust pastry case for a flan takes longer to bake in a ceramic flan dish than it does in a metal flan tin. *(4 marks)*

   b) The outside of a grilled chicken leg is burnt, but the inside is undercooked. *(4 marks)*

   c) A cake cooked on the top shelf of a gas oven has overcooked on the outside, but the middle is still uncooked. *(4 marks)*

2.1.2 Selecting appropriate cooking methods

What will I learn?

In this section you will learn about:

- different methods of cooking
- how cooking methods affect the appeal, **sensory qualities**, **palatability** and nutritional value of foods
- how to prepare and cook fruits and vegetables to conserve their nutritional value.

Key terms

Sensory qualities: the characteristics of a food that give it a particular appearance, flavour, texture, 'mouthfeel' (what it feels like, not what it tastes like, when you put it in your mouth) aroma (smell) and sound (some foods are crunchy, crispy or crackly and make a sound when they are cooked or eaten)

Palatability: what makes a food acceptable and good to eat

Different methods of cooking

- There are different ways in which foods can be cooked.
- Choosing a suitable and appropriate method of cooking for specific foods and recipes is part of the skill and fun of cooking.
- Cooking methods can be categorised under three headings: moist methods (e.g. boiling), methods using oil (e.g. frying) and dry methods (e.g. grilling).
- The table starting on page 91 shows the different cooking methods, how they transfer heat to food and suitable foods that can be cooked by each method.

Method of cooking	Method of heat transfer	Examples of suitable foods
Methods using moisture to transfer heat		
Boiling – cooking food in water at 100°C	Conduction → Convection	Eggs, rice, pasta, vegetables (e.g. carrots, potatoes, swede), joints of meat, such as gammon (e.g. bacon/ham), beans, peas, lentils, vegetable or meat stock
Braising – sealing meat in hot fat, then cooking it slowly in a covered dish with a little liquid	Conduction → Convection	Meat, poultry, vegetables (e.g. carrots, fennel, red cabbage), tagines
Poaching – cooking food in a shallow pan of water or wine at just under boiling point	Conduction → Convection	Fish, eggs, fruit (e.g. pears, cherries, plums, apricots, peaches)
Simmering – cooking food in a liquid just below boiling point, so it bubbles gently	Conduction → Convection	Vegetables, soups, stews, fruit (e.g. apples), meat sauces (e.g. Bolognese sauce), curries, fish chowder (chunky soup)
Steaming – cooking food in the steam rising from a pan of boiling water beneath	Conduction → Convection	Green vegetables (e.g. broccoli, spinach, cabbage, Brussels sprouts), white fish, sponge puddings, dim sum dumplings, rice
Stewing – cooking food by simmering gently in a covered pot either in the oven, on the hob or in a slow cooker	Conduction → Convection	Meat, poultry, sausages, casseroles, fruit (e.g. apples, plums, rhubarb), tofu

Method of cooking	Method of heat transfer	Examples of suitable foods
Methods using oil to transfer heat		
Sautéing – frying food gently in a little oil in order to soften the food and develop the flavour	Conduction	Onions, leeks, peppers, meat/poultry and vegetables used as a base for soups and stews, celery, carrot, butternut squash, sweet potato, courgette
Shallow frying (pan frying) – frying food in a shallow frying pan in a little oil	Conduction	Eggs, fish (white or oily), bacon, burgers, sausages, meat cuts (e.g. chops, cutlets and steaks), pancakes, some flat breads, onions, potato slices, fishcakes, potato cakes, rissoles, bananas
Stir frying – frying food for a short time in a wok, using very little oil	Conduction	Finely cut vegetables and other foods (e.g. peppers, onion, mushrooms, courgettes, pak choi, spring onions, bean sprouts, mangetout, peas, bamboo shoots, root ginger, seafood, meat, poultry, nuts, tofu)
Roasting – cooking food in some oil or fat in a hot oven	Convection → Conduction	Meat and poultry joints, root vegetables (e.g. parsnips and potatoes), some fruits (e.g. plums), nuts
Deep fat frying – frying food in a deep pan of very hot oil, so that the food is fully immersed in the oil	Conduction → Convection	Fish, scotch eggs, chicken joints and pieces, battered vegetables (tempura), spring rolls, doughnuts, churros, seafood, fritters (e.g. apple, pineapple, corn), poppadums, onion bhajis, falafel, potato croquettes

Method of cooking	Method of heat transfer	Examples of suitable foods
Methods using dry heat to transfer heat energy		
Baking – cooking foods in a hot oven	Convection ➔ Conduction	Cakes, breads, biscuits, cookies, scones, pastries, potatoes, pizzas
Grilling – cooking foods by intense radiant heat on a metal grid or grill rack, underneath a heated grill element in a cooker **or** above the glowing charcoal/flames in a barbeque	Radiation	Meat and poultry joints, fish, sausages, burgers, toppings for au gratin dishes (e.g. cheese sauce), halloumi cheese, tomatoes
Toasting – cooking starch based foods with dry heat from a grill or flame	Radiation	Bread, buns, crumpets and other starch-based products, nuts, seeds
Dry frying – cooking food that naturally contains oil or fat in a frying pan without adding oil	Conduction	Minced meat (e.g. beef, lamb, pork), nuts, seeds, tacos, flat breads (e.g. naan breads)
Other methods of transferring heat energy		
Microwaving – cooking food by electromagnetic waves called microwaves in a microwave oven	Radiation	Sauces, cake and sponge pudding mixtures, scrambled eggs, vegetables, fruits, fish, soups, melting chocolate and butter

Method of cooking	Method of heat transfer	Examples of suitable foods
Induction cooking – a method of cooking where heat energy is transferred quickly to a pan through a specially designed ceramic cooking surface, over an induction coil that creates a magnetic current. Pans that are used on induction hobs must be made from metals that contain iron (e.g. cast iron, magnetic stainless steel or steel) 	Conduction	Any food that is cooked in a pan on the hob

How cooking methods affect the appeal, sensory qualities, palatability and nutritional value of foods

Different cooking methods affect the appeal, sensory qualities, palatability and nutritional value of foods, and it is important to know and understand how to select an appropriate method for different recipes you are going to make.

● Task Tip:

Choosing the appropriate cooking method will be an important element of the NEA Food Preparation task.

- Understanding what happens to different foods when they are cooked will help you to do this.

- The following table describes the ways in which each method of cooking affects different foods.

Methods of heat transfer using moisture

Boiling

Conduction → Convection

What happens to the ingredients?	What are the effects on the appearance of the food (colour, size, etc.)?	What are the effects on the palatability of the food (texture, aroma, flavour)?	What are the effects on the nutrients and digestibility of the food?
• Starch absorbs water and gelatinises between 60°C and 100°C • Protein denatures and coagulates, e.g. egg white protein coagulates at 60°C and egg yolk at 70°C • Fat will melt • Sauces and stocks reduce in volume as water evaporates	• Pasta, rice, peas, beans and lentils swell in size as their starch granules absorb the water • Green vegetables turn bright green for a few minutes, then gradually become a dark olive green if overcooked • Red/purple fruits and vegetables are affected by acids (makes them a brighter red/purple) and alkalis such as bicarbonate of soda, which makes them turn blue • Egg white becomes opaque and yolk becomes lighter in colour as protein denatures and coagulates • Meat/poultry shrink in size as protein denatures	• Pasta, rice, peas, beans and lentils soften in texture as they absorb the water • Vegetables soften and tenderise – may become mushy and disintegrate if boiled for too long • Meat will tenderise, but can dry out if boiled for too long because the protein coagulates too much and squeezes out the moisture it contains • Flavour of some vegetable intensifies, e.g. carrots become sweeter • Some flavour from meat will go into the water, but if the water is used to make gravy or stock, the flavour will be saved • Flavour of stock will intensify as the water evaporates	• Vitamin C, B1 (thiamine) and B2 (riboflavin) are destroyed by prolonged heating at boiling point • Water soluble vitamins (B group and C) dissolve into the cooking water • Overcooking meat will make the protein less digestible • Vitamin A remains stable when cooked • Starch granules are softened and some starch released which makes it easier to digest

Braising
Conduction → Convection

What happens to the ingredients?	What are the effects on the appearance of the food (colour, size, etc.)?	What are the effects on the palatability of the food (texture, aroma, flavour)?	What are the effects on the nutrients and digestibility of the food?
• Starch absorbs water and gelatinises • Protein denatures and coagulates • Meat: collagen in connective tissue is converted to gelatine • Vegetables tenderise • Fat will melt	• Colour of red meat becomes brown • Meat/poultry shrink in size as protein denatures and coagulates • Red cabbage becomes a deep red/purple colour • Glossy sauce develops	• Meat and poultry tenderise as food cooks slowly and absorbs flavours from stock, vegetables, herbs and spices	• Vitamin C, B1 (thiamine) and B2 (riboflavin) are affected by heat, but the damage may be less than in boiling • Water soluble vitamins (B group and C) dissolve into the cooking liquid, but this is served with the meal • Overcooking meat will make the protein less digestible • Starch granules are softened and some starch released, which makes it easier to digest

Poaching
Conduction → Convection

What happens to the ingredients?	What are the effects on the appearance of the food (colour, size, etc.)?	What are the effects on the palatability of the food (texture, aroma, flavour)?	What are the effects on the nutrients and digestibility of the food?
• Protein denatures and coagulates • Cell structure of fruit softens	• Egg white becomes opaque and yolk becomes lighter in colour as protein denatures and coagulates • Fish shrinks slightly, becomes opaque and separates into flakes of muscle as protein denatures and coagulates	• Fish and poultry tenderise • Fish is less likely to be overcooked because the temperature of the water is just under boiling point and it is easy to see when the protein has coagulated • Some flavour from poultry and fish will go into the water, but if the water is used to make gravy or stock, the flavour will be saved • The time needed to poach fruit (e.g. pears in wine and spices) enables the flavours from the poaching liquid to be absorbed into the fruit	• Vitamin C, B1 (thiamine) and B2 (riboflavin) are affected by heat, but the damage will be less than in boiling as the temperature is just below boiling point for poaching • Water soluble vitamins (B group and C) dissolve into the cooking liquid and will be lost when the liquid is poured away

Simmering
Conduction → Convection

What happens to the ingredients?	What are the effects on the appearance of the food (colour, size, etc.)?	What are the effects on the palatability of the food (texture, aroma, flavour)?	What are the effects on the nutrients and digestibility of the food?
• Starch absorbs water and gelatinises • Protein denatures and coagulates • Fat will melt • Stock reduces in volume as water evaporates • Cell structure of fruit softens	• Colours of ingredients intensify • Volume may reduce	• Meat and poultry tenderise • Vegetables tenderise • Food cooks slowly and absorbs flavours from stock, vegetables, herbs and spices	• Same as for braising

Steaming
Conduction ➜ Convection

What happens to the ingredients?	What are the effects on the appearance of the food (colour, size, etc.)?	What are the effects on the palatability of the food (texture, aroma, flavour)?	What are the effects on the nutrients and digestibility of the food?
• Starch absorbs water and gelatinises • Protein denatures and coagulates • Fat will melt • Cell structure of fruit and vegetables softens	• Green vegetables turn bright green for a few minutes, then gradually become a dark olive green if overcooked • Fish shrinks slightly, becomes opaque and separates into flakes of muscle as protein denatures and coagulates • Sponge puddings rise and set, but do not develop a golden crust because starch does not turn to dextrin in moist heat  • Rice grains swells as the starch gelatinises • Dim sums swell as the starch in the flour gelatinises, and the filling coagulates and sets	• Food cooks gently and is unlikely to be overcooked • Foods tenderise and develop a soft, moist, digestible texture 	• Loss of water soluble vitamins (B group and C) is reduced because the food does not come in direct contact with boiling water • Food can take a long time to cook, so more vitamin C may be destroyed as a result • Protein is unlikely to be overcooked by this method so is more digestible • Starch granules are softened and some starch released, which makes it easier to digest

Stewing
Conduction ➜ Convection

What happens to the ingredients?	What are the effects on the appearance of the food (colour, size, etc.)?	What are the effects on the palatability of the food (texture, aroma, flavour)?	What are the effects on the nutrients and digestibility of the food?
• Starch absorbs water and gelatinises • Protein denatures and coagulates • Meat: collagen in connective tissue is converted to gelatine • Fat will melt • Cell structure of fruit and vegetables softens	• Colours of ingredients intensify • Volume may reduce • Glossy sauce develops • Colour of red meat becomes brown • Fruit colours intensify • Red/purple fruits and vegetables are affected by acids (makes them a brighter red/purple) and alkalis such as bicarbonate of soda, which makes them turn blue  • Meat/poultry shrink in size as protein denatures and coagulates	• Same as for braising  	• Same as for braising 

Methods using oil to transfer heat

Sautéing

Conduction

What happens to the ingredients?	What are the effects on the appearance of the food (colour, size, etc.)?	What are the effects on the palatability of the food (texture, aroma, flavour)?	What are the effects on the nutrients and digestibility of the food?
• Intrinsic sugars caramelise • Starch absorbs oil and swells • Protein denatures and coagulates	• Onions, parsnips, carrots, potatoes become golden brown due to caramelisation • Red meat turns brown, poultry turns creamy/white colour • Meat/poultry shrink in size as protein denatures and coagulates	• Caramelised vegetables taste sweeter • Flavour intensifies as water evaporates • As meat and poultry protein coagulates and shrinks, juices are squeezed out and form flavour on the surface	• Vitamin C, B1 (thiamine) and B2 (riboflavin) are affected by the heat • Overcooking meat/poultry will make the protein less digestible • Fat/oil used for sautéing adds to the energy density of the food • Fat/oil will add some fat soluble vitamins (A, D, E, K) • Starch granules are softened and some starch released, which makes it easier to digest

Shallow frying (pan frying)

Conduction

What happens to the ingredients?	What are the effects on the appearance of the food (colour, size, etc.)?	What are the effects on the palatability of the food (texture, aroma, flavour)?	What are the effects on the nutrients and digestibility of the food?
• Starch absorbs oil and softens • Protein denatures and coagulates • Fat will melt • Cell structure of fruit and vegetables softens • Coatings such as egg and breadcrumbs (used for fish, chicken breast, fish cakes, potato cakes) will protect the food inside from drying out and overcooking as the egg protein coagulates and seals the food from the intense heat of frying	• Egg white becomes opaque and yolk becomes lighter in colour • Fish shrinks slightly, becomes opaque and separates into flakes of muscle  • Onions, parsnips, carrots, potatoes become golden brown due to caramelisation • Red meat turns brown, poultry turns creamy/white colour • Meat/poultry shrink in size as protein denatures and coagulates	• Foods develop a crispy texture on the outside, especially if the food is coated with egg and breadcrumbs  • Some vegetables will caramelise and become sweeter • Vegetables/fruits will soften as the starch and cell walls they contain soften • As meat and poultry protein coagulates and shrinks, juices are squeezed out and form flavour on the surface	• Vitamin C, B1 (thiamine) and B2 (riboflavin) are affected by the heat • Overcooking meat/poultry will make the protein less digestible • Fat/oil used for sautéing adds to the energy density of the food • Fat/oil will add some fat soluble vitamins (A, D, E, K)

Deep fat frying

Conduction → Convection

What happens to the ingredients?	What are the effects on the appearance of the food (colour, size, etc.)?	What are the effects on the palatability of the food (texture, aroma, flavour)?	What are the effects on the nutrients and digestibility of the food?
• Starch absorbs oil and softens • Protein denatures and coagulates • Cell structure of fruit and vegetables softens	• Meat/poultry shrink in size as protein denatures and coagulates • Fish shrinks slightly, becomes opaque and separates into flakes of muscle as protein denatures and coagulates • Fried foods containing starch and sugars develop a golden brown colour	• Foods develop a crispy texture on the outside, especially if the food is coated with egg and breadcrumbs or batter • Vegetables tenderise and develop a crisp coating, like these tempura vegetables 	• Oil used in deep frying adds significantly to the energy density of the food, especially if the oil is not hot enough when frying starts as it will be absorbed by the food • Vitamin C, B1 (thiamine) and B2 (riboflavin) are affected by the heat • Overcooking meat/poultry will make the protein less digestible

Roasting

Convection → Conduction

What happens to the ingredients?	What are the effects on the appearance of the food (colour, size, etc.)?	What are the effects on the palatability of the food (texture, aroma, flavour)?	What are the effects on the nutrients and digestibility of the food?
• Starch absorbs oil and softens • Intrinsic sugars caramelise • Protein denatures and coagulates • Cell structure of fruit and vegetables softens	• Red meat turns brown, poultry turns creamy/white colour • Onions, parsnips, carrots, potatoes become golden brown due to caramelisation • Colours of vegetables intensify • Vegetables shrink as water evaporates from them • Skin on poultry and fat on meat (e.g. pork) becomes golden brown  • Juices from meat and poultry are squeezed out and develop into a golden/brown glaze in the roasting pan  • Meat/poultry shrink in size as protein denatures and coagulates	• Vegetables/fruits tenderise inside and develop a crisp outer texture  • Juices from meat and poultry are squeezed out and develop flavour on the surface • Skin/fat on outside of joints of meat/poultry become crisp • Overcooking causes meat/poultry to dry out and become indigestible	• Fat used in roasting adds to energy density • Fat used adds fat soluble vitamins A, D, E, K • Vitamin C, B1 (thiamine) and B2 (riboflavin) are affected by the heat • Overcooking meat/poultry will make the protein less digestible

Stir frying

Conduction

What happens to the ingredients?	What are the effects on the appearance of the food (colour, size, etc.)?	What are the effects on the palatability of the food (texture, aroma, flavour)?	What are the effects on the nutrients and digestibility of the food?
• Starch absorbs oil and softens • Protein denatures and coagulates • Cell structure of fruit and vegetables softens	• Colours of vegetables intensify • Vegetables shrink as water evaporates from them • Meat/poultry/seafood shrink in size as protein denatures and coagulates	• Quickness of stir frying conserves the colour of vegetables • Vegetables tenderise a little but retain a degree of crispness • Meat/poultry/fish cook quickly so must be cut into small pieces in order to be tender and cooked right through	• Little oil used so energy density is low • Quick cooking minimises loss of vitamin B group and vitamin C

Methods using dry heat to transfer heat energy

Baking

Convection ➜ Conduction

What happens to the ingredients?	What are the effects on the appearance of the food (colour, size, etc.)?	What are the effects on the palatability of the food (texture, aroma, flavour)?	What are the effects on the nutrients and digestibility of the food?
• Gases from raising agents expand with heat • Protein denatures and coagulates • Free sugars melt and form a syrup that softens the gluten • Free sugars eventually caramelise • Fat will melt • Starch absorbs water and/or melted fat • Starch granules absorb moisture, swell and gelatinise • Alcohol produced by yeast evaporates in the heat of the oven • Yeast is killed by heat • Gluten, egg proteins and starch set and form a framework around gas bubbles inside baked product	• Baked foods containing raising agents rise and expand before setting in the heat of the oven  • Starch in the outside crust of baked goods becomes dextrinised and develops a golden brown colour	• Risen food sets and develops a tender, open/crumbly/spongy texture inside  • A crust develops on the outside • Caramelised sugars add flavour 	• Heat damages vitamin B group • Starch is more digestible through cooking process

Section 2: Food Science

Grilling/barbequing
Radiation

What happens to the ingredients?	What are the effects on the appearance of the food (colour, size, etc.)?	What are the effects on the palatability of the food (texture, aroma, flavour)?	What are the effects on the nutrients and digestibility of the food?
 • Protein denatures and coagulates rapidly • Fat melts and drains away from food • Starch turns to dextrin • Sugars caramelise	• Meat/poultry will shrink rapidly due to protein denaturing and coagulating • Fat melts and drains out • Surface of meat/poultry develops golden brown colour	• Juices from meat and poultry are squeezed out and develop flavour on the surface • If cooked too rapidly, meat and poultry can become dry and chewy due to protein denaturing, coagulating and squeezing out water • Flavour intensifies as water evaporates	• Vitamin C, B1 (thiamine) and B2 (riboflavin) are damaged by the intense heat • Fat melting out of meat, meat products and other foods reduces the energy density of the food • Overcooking meat/poultry will make the protein less digestible

Toasting
Radiation

What happens to the ingredients?	What are the effects on the appearance of the food (colour, size, etc.)?	What are the effects on the palatability of the food (texture, aroma, flavour)?	What are the effects on the nutrients and digestibility of the food?
• Starch turns to dextrin	• Food develops a golden brown crust	• Flavour intensifies • Crust adds texture to the food	• B vitamins damaged by the heat

Dry frying
Conduction

What happens to the ingredients?	What are the effects on the appearance of the food (colour, size, etc.)?	What are the effects on the palatability of the food (texture, aroma, flavour)?	What are the effects on the nutrients and digestibility of the food?
• Starch changes to dextrin • Fat will melt/natural oils will soften • Protein will denature and coagulate	• Food develops a golden brown colour • The oils in nuts and seeds melt and are released • Meat changes to a brown colour and fat and juices are released from it	• Flavour intensifies • Oils are released and add texture and flavour • Fat melts from meat • Proteins in meat denature and coagulate and squeeze out juices from the meat which develop flavour	• B vitamins damaged by the heat • Overcooking meat will make the protein less digestible • The fat from meat can be skimmed off to reduce the energy density 

Other methods of transferring heat energy

Induction cooking

Conduction

What happens to the ingredients?	What are the effects on the appearance of the food (colour, size, etc.)?	What are the effects on the palatability of the food (texture, aroma, flavour)?	What are the effects on the nutrients and digestibility of the food?
• Same as for other methods of cooking carried out on the hob	• Same as for other methods of cooking carried out on the hob	• Same as for other methods of cooking carried out on the hob	• Same as for other methods of cooking carried out on the hob

Microwaving

Radiation

What happens to the ingredients?	What are the effects on the appearance of the food (colour, size, etc.)?	What are the effects on the palatability of the food (texture, aroma, flavour)?	What are the effects on the nutrients and digestibility of the food?
• Water molecules will vibrate and transfer heat energy • Protein will denature and coagulate • Fat will melt • Sugar will caramelise and burn easily • Starch will gelatinise in presence of moisture	• Cakes, sponge puddings, meat and other foods do not develop much colour • Juices and water from meat will leak out as the protein denatures, coagulates and squeezes them out	• Meat will not develop flavours on the outside as it does in frying, roasting or grilling • Overcooking may result in sugars burning easily	• Less damage to B group vitamins and vitamin C due to rapid cooking time • Overcooking can make egg, meat and fish protein less digestible

How to prepare and cook fruits and vegetables (including fresh herbs) to conserve their nutritional value

Fruits and vegetables are important sources of **vitamins** and **antioxidants** (these are substances that help protect the body from developing heart disease and some types of cancer).

It is important to learn how to prepare and cook fruits and vegetables correctly to **conserve** as much of their nutritional value as possible.

Water soluble vitamins (B group and C) and antioxidants in these foods are especially vulnerable to being **damaged** and **lost** during preparation and cooking.

The table below explains the best ways to conserve the nutritional value of fruits and vegetables:

Preparation	Reason
Choose fruits and vegetables that are as fresh and undamaged as possible	The fresher the fruit or vegetables, the more nutrients they will contain Damage and bruising causes enzymes to be released which destroy vitamin C and antioxidants
Cut and tear fruits and vegetables just before cooking or serving	Cutting, grating and tearing causes enzymes to be released which destroy vitamin C and antioxidants
Prepare fruits and vegetables just before cooking or serving	Exposure to light and oxygen in the air destroys nutrients such as vitamin B1, vitamin C and antioxidants

Preparation	Reason
Cooking	
Cook in the minimum amount of water for the shortest time until the vegetables or fruit are just tender	Flavour, colour, texture, water soluble vitamins and antioxidants are increasingly damaged the longer the cooking time
Use the cooking water for gravy, soups or sauces	Vitamin C and vitamin B group are soluble in water and will be lost if the cooking water is thrown away
Serving	
Cook and serve straight away	Keeping cooked fruit and vegetables hot for a while before serving will destroy more water soluble vitamins and antioxidants

Practical challenge

Selecting an appropriate cooking method – this could be carried out as a group activity

Task Tip:

This is an example of how you could carry out an investigation and explains how to carry out sensory testing of the results in a controlled environment.

Many foods and recipes can be cooked by different methods (e.g. potatoes, carrots, rice, sausages, white fish, beef burgers, sponge puddings). Using different cooking methods varies the diet by giving the food or recipe a range of sensory qualities.

Aim: to investigate the effects of using different cooking methods on the sensory qualities of a food product.

Choose a food product (e.g. potatoes, home-made beef burgers or plain sponge puddings) and cook samples of the product using different cooking methods:

- For the potatoes you could use boiling, baking, make home-made oven chips, microwaving, roasting.
- For the burgers you could use shallow frying (pan frying), microwaving, baking and grilling.
- For the sponge puddings you could use steaming, microwaving, baking.

Task Tip:

When carrying out the Food Investigation Task you will need to establish controls when experimenting to ensure a fair test (page 251). Think about the controls for this investigation to ensure fair and accurate results.

Controls

If you are using a recipe, the ingredients should stay the same for each cooking method. If you are using a single food (e.g. rice), use the same type for each cooking method.

- Once you have cooked the samples, set them out with a label A, B, C, etc., or use random codes e.g. zxy, yxz , etc. (do not show which cooking method was used).

- Conduct a sensory analysis profiling test, by asking a group of people to test each of the samples as follows:

  1. Taste each of the samples (taking a sip of water between each to clear your palate).

  2. Give each sample a score out of 5 (1 = least preferred/worst, 5 = most preferred/best) for the sensory qualities you want to be assessed.

Example: RECIPE/PRODUCT: Home-made beef burgers

Sensory quality:	Tester ratings out of 5					Average score
						Add up each score out of 5 to get a total. Divide the total by the number of people who tasted the food
	1	2	3	4	5	
Sample A (pan fried)						
Appearance						
Flavour						
Texture – tenderness						
Texture – moisture						
Sample B (oven baked)						
Appearance						
Flavour						
Texture – tenderness						
Texture – moisture						
Sample C (grilled)						
Appearance						
Flavour						
Texture – tenderness						
Texture – moisture						
Sample D (microwaved)						
Appearance						
Flavour						
Texture – tenderness						
Texture – moisture						

Discuss the results as a class:

- Which cooking method was the most popular? Why was this?
- Which cooking method was the least popular? Why was this?
- How were the appearance, texture, flavour and nutritional profile of each sample affected by each cooking method?

Stretch and challenge activity

1. Write a short report to conclude the practical investigation.

2. Explain how you might use the information from the practical challenge when planning meals for different groups of people.

Practice questions

1. Explain why each of the following happens when cooking food:

   a) Pasta swells and softens when it is boiled.

   b) Eggs become solid and opaque white and yellow when they are boiled, poached or fried.

   c) Bread becomes golden brown and crisp on the outside when it is placed under a hot grill. *(6 marks)*

2. Explain how you would ensure that the maximum amount of vitamins and antioxidants are conserved when you are preparing and cooking the following meal:

   • Watercress soup and bread rolls.

   • Cheese and vegetable quiche, home-made coleslaw and pepper salad with boiled new potatoes. *(6 marks)*

3. Using your knowledge of cooking methods describe how you could reduce the energy density (how much energy [kcals] is provided by the different ingredients in the meal) of the following lunch menu:

   • Fried beef burger with potato chips and deep fried onion rings. Give reasons for your answers. *(6 marks)*

Chapter 4 Functional and chemical properties of food

2.2.1 Proteins

What will I learn?

In this section you will learn about:

- how proteins react to food preparation processes and cooking methods
- what denaturation means
- what coagulation means
- how gluten is formed
- how foams are formed.

In Section 1.1.1 you learned about protein as a nutrient and why it is needed by the body.

In this section, you will learn about how and why proteins react in particular ways when we prepare and cook foods that contain them, and how we use these reactions to make different recipes. This is called understanding the functional and chemical properties of food.

Structure of proteins

- Proteins are large molecules, made up of individual units called **amino acids.**
- As they are so large, protein molecules are often folded into compact 'bundles' so that they take up less space.
- Proteins are complex molecules which contain the elements: Oxygen, Carbon, Hydrogen, Nitrogen and sometimes Sulphur and Phosphorus.
- **Chemical bonds** in the protein molecule bundle hold it together and stop it unfolding, like this:

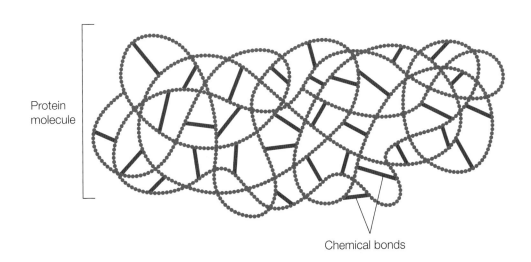

Protein molecule

Chemical bonds

Key terms

Chemical bonds: bonds that hold large protein molecules together in compact, folded bundles

Denaturation: the chemical bonds have broken and the protein molecule has unfolded and changed shape

Coagulation: the joining together of lots of denatured protein molecules, which changes the appearance and texture of the food

Denaturation

- Protein molecules can easily be **denatured**.

- This means that the chemical bonds that hold the protein molecule bundle together can be broken, which makes the protein molecule bundle unfold and change shape, like this:

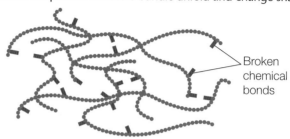

Broken chemical bonds

- Denaturation of protein molecules can be caused by:
  - heat (e.g. frying or boiling an egg)
  - acids (e.g. when adding lemon juice to cream [see chilled lemon flan recipe pages 108–109] or marinating meat in lime, tomato or lemon juice)
  - air bubbles (e.g. in a whisked sponge mixture [see recipe page 142])
  - mechanical agitation (e.g. when whisking egg whites for meringue).

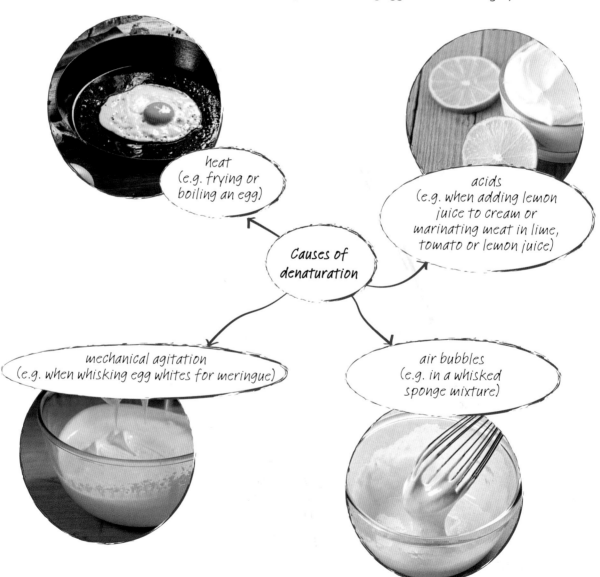

heat
(e.g. frying or boiling an egg)

acids
(e.g. when adding lemon juice to cream or marinating meat in lime, tomato or lemon juice)

Causes of denaturation

mechanical agitation
(e.g. when whisking egg whites for meringue)

air bubbles
(e.g. in a whisked sponge mixture)

Coagulation

- Denatured protein molecules are larger and take up more space than they used to.

- Because of this, they knock into other denatured protein molecules and start to join together in large groups – this is called **coagulation**.

- As they coagulate, the protein molecules trap and hold water from the food in pockets between them.

- As coagulation continues, the appearance and texture of the food changes, as you can see in this picture of an egg being fried:

  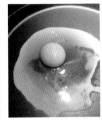 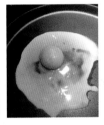 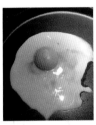 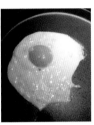 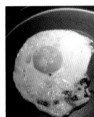

- and in eggs boiled for different lengths of time:

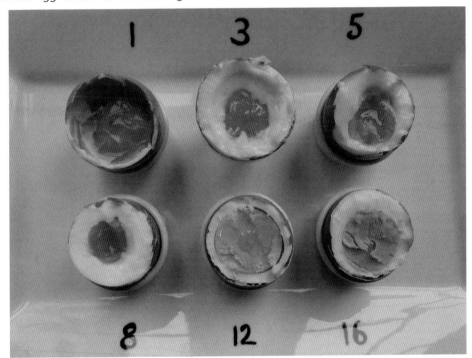

Eggs boiled for different lengths of time, as shown in minutes in the picture

- You can see that the egg white has changed from transparent to opaque white and the whole egg has changed from a liquid food to a solid food.

- Due to their ability to coagulate, the proteins in eggs are used in some recipes to hold other ingredients together (e.g. vegetables in a quiche flan, a breadcrumb or batter coating on the outside of some fried fish, the combining of ingredients of a fish cake or beef burger).

- If a food containing protein is overcooked, the coagulated protein molecules tighten up and squeeze out the water they were holding. This is why overcooked meat or fish is dry and chewy, and why overcooked scrambled egg becomes rubbery and watery.

On page 108 is a recipe to demonstrate protein denaturation and coagulation.

Ingredients:
(serves 12 people)
300ml double cream
1 large can (~397g) of
condensed milk – **NOT
evaporated milk**
3 medium sized or 2 large lemons
  – washed
250g plain digestive biscuits
  (1 small packet)
110g butter (preferably unsalted)
  or vegetable fat spread
Fresh fruit to decorate
**A flan dish – approx. 25cm
diameter (glass, china or
metal)**
The recipe can be halved and put
  into a smaller flan dish, approx.
  16cm diameter.

Storage instructions:
Refrigerator: cover and store in
  the refrigerator (0°C to below
  5°C) for up to 3 days.
Freezer: Can be frozen – best if it
  is not decorated with fruit. Cover
  the flan carefully with suitably
  strong foil or plastic and freeze
  for up to 3 months. Defrost
  thoroughly and then decorate.

N.B. This recipe demonstrates
  very well how proteins are
  denatured and coagulated by
  acids, which is why it has been
  included here. However, it is an
  energy dense and filling recipe
  because of its high fat and sugar
  content. Therefore, only small
  portions should be served. This
  flan will serve at least 12 people.

Chilled lemon flan

Method:

1. Melt the butter or vegetable fat spread in a small pan on a low heat or in the microwave oven. Do not let it boil or burn.

2. Crush the digestive biscuits **(this can be done in a food processor)** and mix them in a bowl with the melted butter.

3. Press the biscuit mixture into the flan dish base and up the sides of the dish using the back of a metal spoon.

4. In a large bowl, whip the cream carefully, until it forms soft peaks.

Soft peak stage

5. Add the condensed milk and mix thoroughly.

6. Finely grate the zest (rind) of one of the lemons and squeeze out the juice of both.

7. Add the lemon juice and some of the zest to the cream and condensed milk mixture.

8. Mix together thoroughly – the mixture will thicken as you do this.

9. Put the mixture into the flan base and spread it out evenly.

10. Put the flan into the refrigerator to chill.

11. Decorate and serve.

NB This recipe does not work well with oranges as they are not acidic enough.
You can use cream cheese instead of the double cream to make a cheesecake.

Stretch and challenge activity

| How could this recipe be modified ... | ... to make it less energy dense?
... for a coeliac?
... to lower the fat content? |
| What variations could you make to ... | ... the biscuit base?
... the filling?
... the decoration? |

Study tip

Whenever you are asked to explain the science behind a recipe, preparation or cooking method, always use the correct words/terms and give examples and reasons to show your understanding of what you have written.

What is a nutritional profile of this recipe?

Macronutrients

Protein

Condensed milk, cream	HBV
Flour in biscuits	LBV

Fat

Butter, cream, milk

Carbohydrate

Biscuits	Starch
Condensed milk (lactose), fruit in decoration	Sugars (intrinsic)
Condensed milk (sucrose), biscuits	Free sugars
Biscuits, fruit in decoration	Dietary fibre

Eatwell Guide

Micronutrients

Vitamins

	Vitamin A:
–	Beta carotene
Condensed milk, cream, butter/ vegetable fat spread	Retinol
	Vitamin B group:
Biscuits	Thiamine B1
Condensed milk, cream	Riboflavin B2
Condensed milk	Niacin B3
–	Folic acid B9
–	B12
Lemons/limes	Vitamin C
Condensed milk, cream, butter/ vegetable fat spread	Vitamin D
Vegetable	Vitamin E
Condensed milk	Vitamin K

Minerals

Cream, condensed milk	Calcium
–	Fluoride
–	Iodine
Biscuits	Iron
All ingredients	Phosphorus
Biscuits	Sodium

Which ingredient(s)?
Which ingredient(s)?

Which cooking methods and practical skills does this recipe use?

Cooking methods

Melting

Practical skills

Knife skills – preparation of fruit to decorate

Making a biscuit base

Whipping cream

Decorating a dessert

What is the science behind this recipe?

In the box below is an example of a student's answer to a question about the food science behind the chilled lemon flan recipe. How well do you think the student has explained the science?

Explain, giving reasons, what happens when you add the lemon juice to the cream/condensed milk mixture:

When you add the lemon juice to the cream and condensed milk mixture, almost straight away it thickens and you can spread it into the biscuit base. The reason it thickens is because of the acids in the lemon juice and the proteins in the condensed milk and cream.

Proteins are made of lots of units called amino acids and because they are big molecules, they are folded up in 'bundles', which are held together by chemical bonds.

Lemons are very acidic, and when you add the lemon juice to the mixture, the acids break the chemical bonds in the protein molecules and they start to denature. This means that they unfold and change shape.

The denatured protein molecules spread out and join up with other ones to form large groups. This is called coagulation, and this is what changes the texture of the chilled lemon flan filling and makes it go thick. The coagulated protein molecules hold the water from the lemon juice in between them, so even though you have added juice to the mixture, it is quite solid.

Gluten

- Consumers expect baked products such as bread and cakes to have a light and open texture.

- To create the desired texture, a raising agent is added to the uncooked mixture to introduce lots of gas bubbles, which will expand when the mixture is baked in the oven.

- The mixture itself must have the ability to stretch and rise as the bubbles expand.

- Baked mixtures are able to stretch and rise because of a protein called **gluten**.

- Wheat flour contains **gluten.**

- Strong plain flour contains a high proportion of **gluten** and is suitable for bread making.

- Gluten is a protein that is formed from two separate proteins called **glutenin** and **gliadin**, which combine when **liquid** is added to flour to make a **dough.**

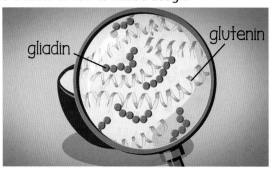

- When liquid is added to the flour, these proteins mix together to form a **gluten network**. This is usually just called gluten.

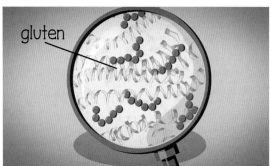

- The dough is kneaded to make it smooth and stretchy.

- Gluten gives the dough **plasticity**. This means that the dough can be **stretched** and **shaped** during **kneading**.

- Gluten also makes the dough **elastic**. This means it will shrink back when you stop stretching and shaping it.

- This is because the long gluten molecules are **coiled**, like the wires on some electrical appliances, and **bend** in different places along their length.

- As you knead and stretch the dough, the coils and bends straighten out then, when you stop, they relax and gradually go back to their original shape and size, as shown in the diagrams on page 111).

Coils of gluten stretched out

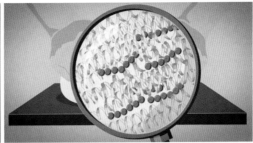
Coils of gluten relaxed

- Being able to be stretched and shaped is ideal for **bread making** because the bread dough needs to be able to stretch when the CO_2 **bubbles** produced by the **yeast** make the dough expand and **rise**.

CO_2 gas bubbles expanding

- The gluten network traps the bubbles and then sets when it is baked, thus forming the soft, light texture that you expect inside the bread.

Gluten and pastry making

- Some **pastry** recipes (e.g. shortcrust pastry) tell you to leave the dough to **rest** before you bake it.

- Resting allows the stretched gluten molecules to relax, which is important if you are using the dough to line a flan case (e.g. when using a shortcrust pastry case for a quiche flan).

- As the pastry rests, the stretched coils of gluten molecules gradually return to their original size and shape.

- If the dough has not been rested, the gluten molecules remain stretched and the **heat** of the oven will cause the stretched gluten molecules (and hence the pastry case) to **shrink rapidly,** which may cause the filling to leak out of the flan.

chilled and rested

unrested

unrested

On page 112 is a recipe to demonstrate the use of gluten.

Ingredients:
(serves 8 people)
450g strong plain white bread
 flour
½ level teaspoon salt
275ml warm water
10g fresh yeast OR 5g (1 level
 teaspoon) dried yeast
1 tsp sugar
(if you are using fast action dried
 yeast, you will need 5g or one
 sachet from a box of fast acting
 dried yeast, and should add the
 yeast directly to the flour – no
 need to activate it first)

Storage instructions:
Home-made bread rolls are best
 eaten on the day they are made.
Cover and store them in a cool,
 dry place.
When they cool down after
 baking, the water they contain
 is absorbed back into the starch
 in the flour. If they have dried out
 the next day, put them in a warm
 oven for a few minutes, and the
 water will be released as steam
 and will soften the rolls.
Freezer: Allow to cool. Place the
 rolls in a suitable container or
 cover carefully with suitably
 strong foil or plastic and freeze
 for up to 3 months.

Variations:
You can use 450g strong plain
 wholemeal flour instead of white,
 but you will need an extra 10ml
 of warm water because the
 dietary fibre in the flour absorbs
 more of it.
OR
You can use a mixture of 225g
 strong plain white flour and 225g
 strong plain wholemeal flour but
 you will need an extra 5ml of
 warm water because the dietary
 fibre in the wholemeal flour
 absorbs more of it.

Bread rolls

Method:

1. Set the oven: Gas 7/220°C (200°C if you are using a fan oven).

2. If you are using ordinary dried or fresh yeast: Dissolve yeast in the warm water.

3. Add the sugar and stir well.

4. Leave the yeast liquid to **activate** (start producing bubbles of gas) in a warm place for approx. 5 minutes.

5. If you are using fast action dried yeast: stir the yeast directly into the flour.

6. Add salt to the flour in a large bowl and mix it in well.

7. Add the yeast liquid/warm water to the flour and stir well **with a wooden spoon** until it is mixed to a dough.

8. Put a little flour on to the work surface and knead the dough for at least 5 minutes. It should be stretchy and smooth.

9. Cut the dough into eight pieces and shape them into bread rolls. The rolls can be covered in greased cling film to prevent a skin forming, which might prevent them from rising.

10. Put the rolls on a greased/lined baking tray and leave them to rise in a warm place for at least 15 minutes.

11. Glaze with beaten egg and sprinkle with poppy or sesame seeds.

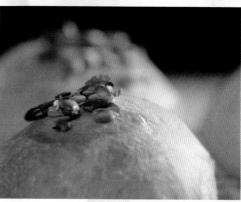

12. Bake the rolls for 15 minutes until they are well risen and golden brown. The cooked rolls should sound hollow when you tap them underneath with your finger.

What is the nutritional profile of this recipe?

Which ingredient(s)?

Macronutrients

Protein

–	*HBV*
Flour	*LBV*

Fat

	–

Carbohydrate

Flour	Starch
–	Sugars *(intrinsic)*
Flour, especially wholemeal	Dietary fibre

Eatwell Guide

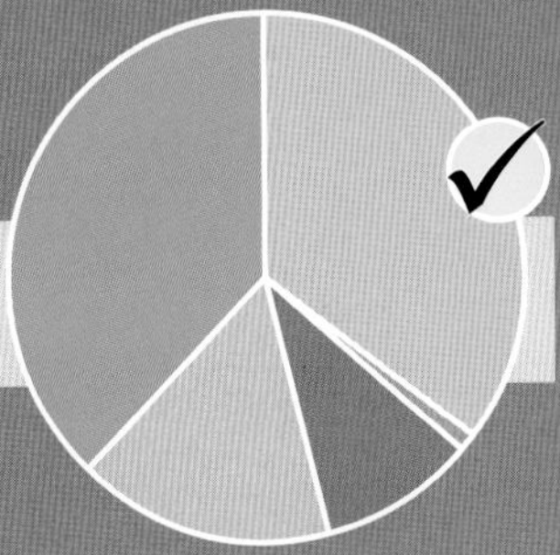

Micronutrients

Which ingredient(s)?

Vitamins

	Vitamin A:
–	*Beta carotene*
–	*Retinol*
	Vitamin B group:
Flour	*Thiamine B1*
–	*Riboflavin B2*
Flour	Niacin B3
–	*Folic acid B9*
Yeast	*B12*
–	Vitamin C
–	Vitamin D
–	Vitamin E
–	Vitamin K

Minerals

Flour	Calcium
–	Fluoride
–	Iodine
Flour	Iron
All ingredients	Phosphorus
Salt	Sodium

Which cooking methods and practical skills does this recipe use?

Cooking methods

Baking

Practical skills

Kneading and shaping dough

Explain the science behind this recipe

Complete the box below to show your understanding of the science of proteins and raising agents (see page 149):

Explain the role of the yeast and the gluten in this recipe.
Explain why the dough has to be kneaded and given time to rise.

Heat transfer

Convection   Heating oven to bake the bread rolls
Conduction   Heat passing through the baking tin into the bread dough

Stretch and challenge activity

How could this recipe be modified ...	... to increase the fibre content?
What variations/additions could you make to ...	... the dough/finished rolls?

How foams are formed

- The light texture of some foods such as mousses and meringue is produced by creating a **foam**. The chart below explains how this happens.

- Foams are formed when gases (often air) are trapped inside a liquid to form a **gas-in-liquid foam**.

- Gas (air)-in-liquid foams are produced when making recipes such as meringue and whisked sponges, as the chart below explains.

What happens when meringue is made:

Egg white is a liquid made of a mixture of proteins and water.

Egg white is capable of holding up to **seven times** its own volume of air, due to the ability of **egg white protein** to **stretch**.

When egg whites are whisked to make meringue, the action of the whisk rotating very fast traps lots of air bubbles to make a **gas (air)-in-liquid foam**.

The action of the whisk also makes some of the compact egg white protein molecules **denature** by breaking the bonds that hold them together and causing them to unfold, see page 106.

The denatured protein molecules start joining up and bonding with lots of other denatured protein molecules – this is called **coagulation**.

They then surround the air bubbles and make a 'wall' around them, which holds the air bubbles and water in place so that the foam is **stabilised**.

The foam will not form properly if there is any egg yolk or traces of fat in the mixing bowl.

If you over-whisk the egg whites, the foam will start to collapse and become watery and loose.

This is because over-whisking makes the coagulated protein molecules bond together too tightly so that they squeeze out the water they were holding. This is less likely to happen with very fresh eggs. Older eggs take up water through tiny pores in the shell, which makes the protein watery and weaker.

Making meringue: Gas-in-liquid foams

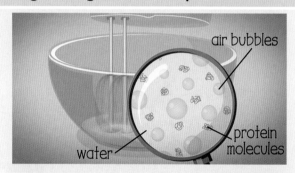

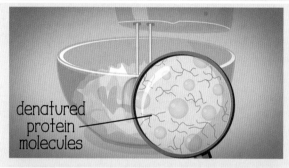

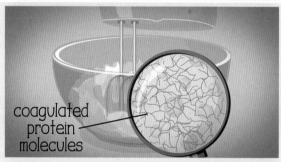

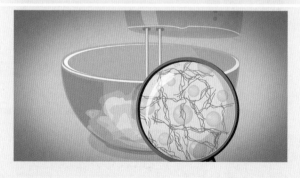

What happens when meringue is made:

Heating the meringue in the oven coagulates some of the other protein molecules in the egg white and drives some of the water out, so that the foam sets and becomes more solid. The meringue is now called a **solid foam**.

Making meringue: Gas-in-liquid foams

water driven out

What happens when a whisked sponge is made:

Whole eggs and sugar are whisked together to make a **whisked sponge mixture** that is used for Swiss rolls, sponge fingers, sponge flans and gateaux.

The eggs and sugar are whisked until a **thick gas (air)-in-liquid foam** is produced, into which the sieved flour is very carefully folded.

The air bubbles produce a light, spongy texture, which sets in the oven.

Practice questions

1. Explain, with reasons, why the following has happened:
   a) Some scrambled egg you have made has become rubbery and watery. *(3 marks)*
   b) A piece of meat you have grilled is hard and dry. *(3 marks)*
   c) Explain, with reasons, what you should do to avoid each of these from happening in the future. *(4 marks)*

2. Explain, with reasons, why the following ingredients are used in each of the following recipes:
   a) Eggs in a quiche flan. *(2 marks)*
   b) Lemons in a chilled lemon flan. *(2 marks)*
   c) Strong plain flour in bread rolls. *(2 marks)*
   d) Egg whites in a pavlova meringue. *(2 marks)*

3. State, giving examples to show your understanding, the meanings of the following words:
   a) Protein denaturation. *(4 marks)*
   b) Coagulation. *(4 marks)*

2.2.2 Carbohydrates

What will I learn?

In this section you will learn about:

- how carbohydrates react to food preparation processes and cooking methods
- what gelatinisation means
- what dextrinisation means
- what caramelisation means.

Key terms

Gelatinisation: the swelling of starch granules when they are cooked with a liquid to the point where they burst and release starch molecules

Dextrinisation: the breaking up of starch molecules into smaller groups of glucose molecules when they are exposed to dry heat

Caramelisation: the breaking up of sucrose (sugar) molecules when they are heated, which changes the colour, flavour and texture of the sugar as it turns into caramel

In Section 1.1.3 you learnt about carbohydrate as a nutrient and why it is needed by the body. You learnt that there are two groups of carbohydrates:

1. **Sugars,** including **sucrose** (the sugar used in cooking such as caster sugar, granulated sugar, brown sugar).

2. **Complex carbohydrates,** including **starch** (found in foods such as flour, rice, pasta, bread, root vegetables, cornflour).

Examples foods rich in carbohydrates

In this section, you will learn about how and why carbohydrates react in particular ways when we prepare and cook foods that contain them, and how we use these reactions to make different recipes.

There are three specific reactions involving carbohydrates that you need to know about to help you understand what happens when you make different recipes.

They are **gelatinisation, dextrinisation** and **caramelisation.** The chart on page 117 explains what happens in each reaction and how it is used in cooking.

Gelatinisation – what happens

Gelatinisation

- When starch is heated in a liquid, it **gelatinises**. The following text and diagrams explain how this happens when we use **starch** to make a **sauce**.

Examples of starchy foods

- Starch molecules are made of thousands of **glucose** (sugar) molecules joined together, either in **long straight chains** or **short chains with branches**.

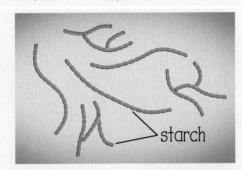

- The starch is stored in plants in tiny 'packets' called **starch granules.** The size and shape of the starch granules vary in different plants.

Potato starch magnified approximately 3,600 times

- When starch granules are in put into **cold water**, they sink to the bottom of the pan.

Section 2: Food Science

Gelatinisation

- When starch granules are put into water and then **heated**, at about **60°C** they start to **absorb** the water, which causes them to **swell up** and get bigger.

- In sauce making, this makes the sauce start to **thicken**, because there is less room for the swollen granules to move around.
- It is important to **stir the sauce regularly** as it is heating up, to prevent the starch granules from staying at the bottom of the liquid, where they would swell up, stick together and cause the sauce to have a **lumpy texture**.

- At about **80°C**, the starch granules are so swollen that they start to **burst** and **release starch molecules** into the surrounding liquid.

- These released starch molecules form a **3-dimensional (3D) network** that traps **water molecules** and stops them moving around so much.
  - At **boiling point** (100°C), the sauce completely **thickens.**
  - The sauce should be heated for a few minutes to make sure all the starch is cooked.
  - The sauce is now ready to pour out and serve.
  - This whole process is known as **gelatinisation.**

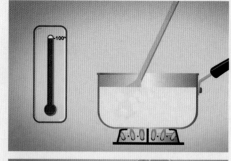

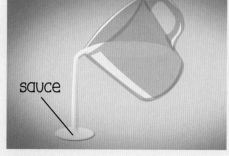

Gelatinisation

- As the cooked sauce **cools down**, the starch molecules start to form **longer chains** and the water molecules stay trapped inside them, so the sauce gradually becomes a **solid gel**.

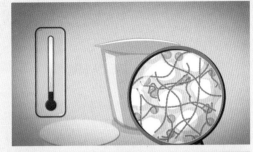

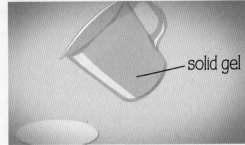

solid gel

- Gelatinisation also takes place when foods containing starch are cooked (e.g. when boiling rice, and pasta or when using potatoes to thicken a soup due to the release of starch).

- If these are boiled for too long, a lot of the starch granules they contain will burst and the starch that comes out will cause the grains of rice or pieces of pasta to stick together, which can make them difficult to serve and eat.

- Some types of rice used in recipes from Southeast and East Asia are naturally sticky because of the particular composition and amount of starch they contain (e.g. Thai sticky rice, sushi rice).

Thai egg custard and sticky rice served on a banana leaf

On page 120 is a recipe to demonstrate starch gelatinisation in a Béchamel sauce.

Study tip

Whenever you are asked to explain the science behind a recipe, preparation or cooking method, always use the correct words/terms and give examples and reasons to show your understanding of what you have written.

Ricotta and spinach lasagne

Method:

1. Pre-heat the oven to Gas 4/180°C (170°C if you are using a fan oven).

2. Heat the oil in a pan; add the chopped onion and garlic and sauté until softened.

3. Add the diced aubergine, pepper, courgette, tomatoes and dried herbs.

4. Season with salt and pepper and simmer for 20 minutes.

5. In a large saucepan, simmer the spinach in 100ml water for a few minutes until it has softened and wilted, then drain it and squeeze out any water.

6. Place the spinach in a food processor with the ricotta and egg and blend until smooth (or put these into a bowl and beat well with a wooden spoon). Season with black pepper and some grated nutmeg.

7. Make the Béchamel sauce by melting the butter in a small pan – do not let it burn.

8. Add the flour and cook for 1 minute. Remove the pan from the heat and gradually add the milk to make a smooth liquid.

9. Re-heat the sauce, stirring all the time until it has thickened. Simmer it for 3–4 minutes.

13. Cook in the oven for 45–50 minutes until golden and the lasagne sheets are tender.

14. Serve with a green salad or vegetables.

Ingredients:
(serves 4–6 people)

Tomato mixture
1 tbsp oil
1 medium onion – chopped finely
1 clove garlic – crushed
1 aubergine (egg plant) – diced
1 pepper – diced
1 courgette – diced
1 400g can of chopped tomatoes
1 tsp dried mixed herbs

Spinach mixture
150g spinach – washed well
1 egg
200g ricotta cheese
Black pepper and nutmeg

Béchamel sauce:
25g butter or vegetable fat spread
25g plain flour
300ml milk
70g cheddar cheese – grated
8–10 sheets of dried lasagna pasta (depending on the size of your dish) (fresh pasta could be made)
You need a medium shallow oven proof dish or baking tin.

Storage instructions:
Refrigerator: Allow to cool then cover and store in the refrigerator (0°C to below 5°C) for up to 3 days.
Freezer: Can be frozen. Allow to cool completely then cover the dish with suitably strong foil or plastic and freeze for up to 3 months.

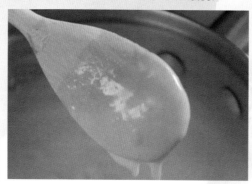

10. Remove the sauce from the heat and add half of the grated Cheddar cheese and stir well.

11. Lightly grease the ovenproof dish. Place half of the tomato mixture in the dish and add a layer of lasagne sheets. Add the spinach mixture, then some lasagne pasta sheets, then the rest of the tomato mixture. Finish with more lasagne pasta sheets.

12. Pour the cheese sauce over the top and sprinkle with the remaining cheese.

What is the nutritional profile of this recipe?

Which ingredient(s)?

Macronutrients

Protein

Cheese, milk, egg	*HBV*
Pasta	*LBV*

Fat

Oil, butter/vegetable fat spread, cheese

Carbohydrate

Pasta, flour	Starch
Onion, milk	Sugars *(intrinsic)*
Vegetables	Dietary fibre

Which ingredient(s)?

Micronutrients

Vitamins

	Vitamin A:
Vegetables	*Beta carotene*
Milk, cheese, butter/vegetable fat spread, egg	*Retinol*
	Vitamin B group:
Milk, cheese, egg	*Thiamine B1*
Milk, egg	*Riboflavin B2*
Milk, egg, flour	Niacin B3
Spinach	*Folic acid B9*
Cheese	*B12*
Spinach	Vitamin C
Eggs, butter/vegetable fat spread	Vitamin D
Vegetable fat spread	Vitamin E
Cheese, spinach	Vitamin K

Minerals

Milk, cheese, flour, spinach	Calcium
–	Fluoride
Vegetables, milk, cheese	Iodine
Spinach, egg yolk	Iron
All ingredients	Phosphorus
Cheese	Sodium

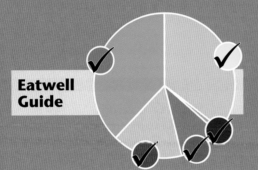

Eatwell Guide

Which cooking methods and practical skills does this recipe use?

Cooking methods

Sautéing

Baking

Practical skills

Knife skills – preparation of vegetables

Sauce making

Explain the science behind this recipe

Complete the box below to show your understanding of the science of carbohydrates and heat transfer:

Explain, giving reasons, what happens to the carbohydrate in the flour when you make the Béchamel sauce.

Explain, giving reasons, what happens to the carbohydrate in the lasagne pasta when it is baked in the oven.

Explain, giving details, how heat is transferred in this recipe.

Section 2: Food Science

Dextrinisation

- When foods containing starch such as bread, cakes, scones, biscuits and pastries are cooked by **dry heat** (grilling, baking, toasting), they develop a brown colour on the outside.
- This is partly due to the effect of the heat on the starch molecules, which break into smaller groups of glucose molecules called **dextrin**.
- The formation of the dextrin contributes to the flavour of the crust/toast.
- **Dextrinisation** is the name given to this process.
- You can see in this picture the effects of toasting some bread for different lengths of time.
- Carbohydrates are made from carbon, hydrogen and oxygen. When you toast the bread until it is very dark in colour, it means that it has gone past the dextrinisation stage and the oxygen and hydrogen have been driven off by the heat as water, and what is left behind is the carbon.

Activity

When you are next making toast at home try to remember why the bread is turning golden brown and explain this to a parent or friend.

Caramelisation

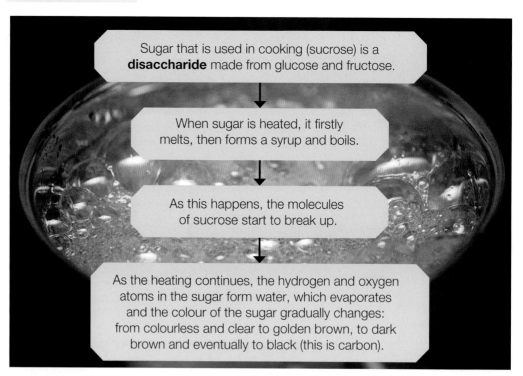

Sugar that is used in cooking (sucrose) is a **disaccharide** made from glucose and fructose.

↓

When sugar is heated, it firstly melts, then forms a syrup and boils.

↓

As this happens, the molecules of sucrose start to break up.

↓

As the heating continues, the hydrogen and oxygen atoms in the sugar form water, which evaporates and the colour of the sugar gradually changes: from colourless and clear to golden brown, to dark brown and eventually to black (this is carbon).

- The **flavour** gradually changes too – from very sweet, to a toffee/caramel flavour, to bitter and burnt.
- This whole process is called **caramelisation**.
- When you make caramel, it is usual to add water to the sugar in a pan and heat it gently on the hob until the water evaporates and the caramel forms.
- This avoids the risk of burning the sugar at the beginning of the process and helps the flavour to develop well.
- The **texture** of the sugar also changes, from crystals of sugar, to a syrup which, when it cools down, becomes a brittle toffee.

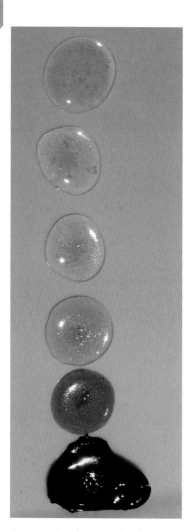

Stages in the gradual caramelisation and final burning of sugar

- It is important **not to stir** the syrup with a spoon as it caramelises – if you do, it will **crystallise** into large, hard lumps.
- You will notice when you make caramel, that when you pour it out, it forms long 'strings' of sugar that go brittle as they cool.
- You may have seen on TV food programmes a chef spinning sugar to create different finishing techniques like these:

- The temperature of caramelising sugar is at least **160°C to 170°C**, so you have to be very careful when making it.
- Some recipes use caramelised sugar as part of their ingredients, such as:

Crème caramel   Crème brûlée   Banoffee pie

- Some foods, such as onions, naturally contain sugar in their cells.
- This sugar will come out of the cells and caramelise if the food is sautéed or roasted for a period of time with some oil or fat, as shown in this picture:

On page 124 is a recipe to demonstrate the caramelisation of sugar in onions.

Ingredients:
(serves 6 people)
1 tbsp oil
2 onions, peeled and finely sliced
225g filo pastry sheets
50g butter, melted gently
75g goat's cheese or feta cheese
1 tsp dried thyme or mixed herbs

Storage instructions:
Refrigerator: Allow to cool, then
  cover and refrigerate for up to
  3 days.
Freezer: Allow to cool. Place in
  a suitable container or cover
  carefully with suitably strong foil
  or plastic and freeze for up to
  3 months. Defrost thoroughly
  then warm the tart in the oven to
  crisp up the filo pastry.

Caramelised onion and cheese tart

Method:

1. Heat the oil and add the onions. Sauté on a gentle heat, stirring regularly until the onions are soft and starting to caramelise.

2. In another small pan, melt the butter gently – do not boil or it may burn easily.

3. Heat the oven to Gas 5/190°C (180°C if you are using a fan oven).

4. Unwrap the filo pastry and, to prevent it from drying out, cover it with cling film or a tea towel.

5. On a baking tray, add one piece of filo pastry at a time, brushing the surface of each with some of the melted butter, until all the pastry is used.

6. Spread the pastry with the onions, leaving a small border around the edge so that each slice can be picked up without getting messy.

7. Break up the cheese into small pieces or slice it and scatter on top of the onions.

8. Sprinkle the thyme on top.

9. Bake in the oven for 10–15 minutes, until the filo pastry is golden and crisp.

10. Serve warm, cut into pieces.

Stretch and challenge activity

How could this recipe be modified ...	... to increase the fibre content?
What variations/ additions could you make to ...	... the topping ingredients?

Plan an interesting and well-balanced 3 course main meal (starter, main course and dessert), to include the caramelised onion and goat's cheese tart, and show your understanding of gelatinisation and dextrinisation by including these processes somewhere in your menu.

Which ingredient(s)?

Macronutrients

Protein

Cheese	HBV
Flour in pastry	LBV

Fat

Butter, oil, cheese

Carbohydrate

Flour	Starch
Onions	Sugars (intrinsic)
Onions	Dietary fibre

Which ingredient(s)?

Micronutrients

Vitamins

	Vitamin A:
–	Beta carotene
Butter, cheese	Retinol
	Vitamin B group:
Flour, cheese	Thiamine B1
Cheese	Riboflavin B2
Flour	Niacin B3
–	Folic acid B9
Cheese	B12
–	Vitamin C
Butter, cheese	Vitamin D
–	Vitamin E
Cheese	Vitamin K

Minerals

Cheese	Calcium
–	Fluoride
Cheese	Iodine
–	Iron
All ingredients	Phosphorus
Cheese	Sodium

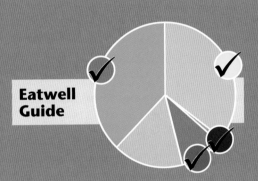

Eatwell Guide

Which cooking methods and practical skills does this recipe use?

Cooking methods

Baking

Practical skills

Knife skills – onions

Handling delicate filo pastry

Explain the science behind this recipe

Complete the box below to show your understanding of the science of carbohydrates:

Explain the role of the carbohydrates (in the flour and the onions) in this recipe.

Heat transfer

Convection Heating oven to bake the tart

Conduction Heat passing through the pan to the onions and the baking tin into the pastry

Study tip

Read through this section and produce a revision card to explain:
- gelatinisation
- dextrinisation
- caramelisation.

Make a list of recipes that use these three processes, so that you could use them as examples if required.

Practice questions

1. Describe what happens to the starch in a Béchamel sauce at 60°C, 80°C and 100°C. *(5 marks)*

2. Explain the reasons for and the science behind the following recipe instructions:

    a) 'Stir the Béchamel sauce all the time whilst it is being heated on the hob.' *(3 marks)*

    b) 'Sauté the onions gently until they turn a golden brown colour.' *(3 marks)*

    c) 'Bake the loaf in the oven for 25 minutes until it is well risen and golden brown.' *(3 marks)*

3. Show your understanding of food science by explaining the reasons for the following problems:

    a) In a crème caramel dessert:

    –   the texture of the egg mixture is rubbery and watery. *(2 marks)*

    –   the caramel is very dark and bitter. *(2 marks)*

    b) In a macaroni cheese:

    –   the sauce is lumpy. *(2 marks)*

    –   the sauce tastes a bit like raw flour. *(2 marks)*

    –   the pieces of macaroni are stuck together and hard to separate. *(2 marks)*

2.2.3 Fats and oils

What will I learn?

In this section you will learn about:

- the functional and chemical properties of fats and oils
- how fats and oils react to food preparation processes and cooking methods
- what plasticity means
- what shortening means
- what emulsification means
- what aeration means
- what happens when you heat fats and oils.

In Section 1.1.2 you learned about fat as a **nutrient** and why it is needed by the body.

You also learned about the **chemical structure** of fats, which is shown again for you below.

It is important that you understand this, because the chemical structure is the reason why fats and oils have different uses in cooking methods and recipes.

In this section, you will learn about how and why fats and oils react in particular ways when we prepare and cook foods that contain them, and how we use these reactions to make different recipes.

Study tip

Remember
Fats and oils have the **same basic chemical structure** and the same energy value. The main difference between them is that:
- fats are **solid** at room temperature
- oils are **liquid** at room temperature.

Chemical structure of fats

This is the **basic chemical structure** of a fat/oil:

Fats are composed of the chemical elements: carbon, hydrogen and oxygen.

Fat **molecules** are made of one unit of **glycerol** and three **fatty acids**, like this:

glycerol — Fatty acid 1
Fatty acid 2
Fatty acid 3

This molecule is called a **triglyceride**.

There are four specific reactions involving fats/oils that you need to know about to help you understand what happens when you make different recipes.

They are plasticity, shortening, aeration and emulsification – you may have already made recipes in your food lessons using these processes/reactions, such as cakes, sauces, pastries and biscuits.

Plasticity

Look at this picture of some vegetable fat being spread onto a piece of bread:

- The reason that this can be done is due to the **plasticity** of the fat – i.e. its ability to be shaped and spread with light pressure.

- The plasticity of fats enables us to carry out processes such as spreading raw cake mixtures into a cake tin, piping buttercream onto cakes, spreading cream cheese onto crackers, etc.

- The plasticity of fats is due to their **chemical structure**.

- All fats are a mixture of **triglycerides**, containing different **fatty acids.**

- The triglycerides all have different **melting temperatures.**

This is why a fat will soften and melt over a **range of temperatures**, for example, butter:

- Chilled butter is very hard and therefore difficult to spread – at this temperature, it has little **plasticity**.

- As the room temperature rises, the butter **softens**, becomes more **plastic** and able to be spread.

- With more heat, the butter eventually melts to become an oil.

Vegetable fat being spread onto a piece of bread

Plasticity: the ability of a fat to soften over a range of temperatures and be shaped and spread with light pressure

Shortening: the ability of fats to shorten the length of gluten molecules in pastry

Aeration: the ability of some fats to trap lots of air bubbles when beaten together with sugar

Emulsification: either keeping drops of oil or fat suspended in a liquid and preventing them from separating out; or keeping drops of water suspended in an oil or fat and preventing them from separating out

Chilled butter

Butter at room temperature

Butter melts to become an oil

Fats that contain a lot of **saturated fatty acids** (e.g. butter, lard, suet, solid coconut oil and ghee) tend to be **more solid** at room temperature and therefore have **less plasticity**.

- The more **unsaturated fatty acids** a fat contains, the **less solid** it is and the **more plasticity** it has.

- Some vegetable fat spreads are especially made using triglycerides with **low melting temperatures**, which means that they are easy to spread when they have just come out of the refrigerator – i.e. they have **good plasticity**.

On page 128 is a recipe to demonstrate plasticity.

Vegetable fat spreads have low melting temperatures which means that they are easy to spread

Ingredients

Basic cake mix:
225g self-raising flour
50g cocoa powder (not drinking chocolate)
1 tsp baking powder
225g softened butter or vegetable fat spread
175g caster sugar
3 large eggs
2 tbsp milk
Grated zest of an orange (optional)

Frosting:
175g icing sugar
25g cocoa
70g butter or vegetable fat spread (softened)
Juice of the orange

Decorations, e.g. grated chocolate, chocolate leaves, orange glacé slices, finely chopped pistachio nuts or almonds

Storage instructions:
Store the cake in an airtight tin or box at room temperature for up to 5 days.
Freezer: Can be frozen for up to 6 months, but must be well wrapped and protected from drying out and being damaged in the freezer.

Variations:
Instead of using cocoa powder and orange zest in the cake and frosting, the following flavourings could be used:
For the cake:
Vanilla – add 1tsp vanilla extract
Lemon drizzle – add the finely grated zest of 2 lemons to the mixture. To make the drizzle, squeeze the juice of the lemons and stir it into 2tbsp icing or caster sugar, and pour over the top of the cakes as soon as they come out of the oven (make a few holes in the top of the cakes with a skewer first).

All-in-one chocolate and orange cake

Method:

1. Basic cake mix – place all the ingredients for the basic cake mix into a mixing bowl and whisk at medium speed with an electric whisk, or beat well with a wooden spoon until well mixed and light in texture and colour.

2. Divide the mixture evenly between two 20cm sandwich cake tins, which have been greased or lined with non-stick paper.

3. Spread the mixture out evenly using a palette knife or the back of a spoon.

4. Bake at 190°C/Gas 4 (180°C if you are using a fan oven) for 20–25 minutes until the cakes are well risen and spongy to the touch.

5. Turn the cakes out onto a cooling rack and allow them to cool.

6. Frosting: whisk or beat together the sieved icing sugar, cocoa and softened butter or vegetable fat spread until well mixed – it may be a bit dry at this stage but that is quite normal. Add the orange juice, a teaspoonful at a time, until the mixture is smooth, creamy and easy to spread.

7. Spread some of the frosting onto one of the cooled cakes and sandwich both of the cakes together.

8. Spread more frosting on the top of the cake and, if you have enough left, you can then pipe it onto the top of the cake with a star nozzle and piping bag to decorate.

9. Add your other decorations to finish the cake.

This cake can also be coated and decorated with chocolate ganache.

Chocolate ganache

For a cake filling or for a thick glaze to go on the top of a cake, equal quantities of chocolate and double cream are needed, e.g. 300g of double cream and 300g of dark chocolate (70–75% cocoa solids is best).

1. Chop the chocolate into small pieces.

2. Pour the cream into a pan and heat it gently on a low heat on the hob for a few minutes.

It is important not to overheat the cream – it only needs to be warm enough to melt the chocolate. Carefully test – it should feel comfortably warm.

3. Remove the cream from the hob. Add the chocolate to the cream. Stir it gently then leave it for several minutes to give the chocolate time to melt.

4. Stir the ganache with a balloon whisk or wooden spoon, until it all looks the same colour and consistency.

5. The longer it is allowed to cool, the thicker the ganache will get.

6. For piping decorations on to a cake, the ganache needs to be completely cold. Give it a thorough stir before you use it for piping.

Stretch and challenge activity

To help you learn the food science behind this recipe:

- Go through the method and make notes of how and why each ingredient reacts during mixing, baking and finishing the cake.

- Explain this clearly to a family member or friend.

- Let them ask you questions afterwards about the food science to see if there are any parts of it you do not fully remember or understand.

What is the nutritional profile of this recipe?

Which ingredient(s)?

Macronutrients

Protein

Eggs, milk	HBV
Flour	LBV

Fat

Butter or vegetable fat spread, chocolate (if used for decoration)

Carbohydrate

Flour	Starch
Orange juice, milk	Sugars (intrinsic)
Sugar, icing sugar	Free sugars
Orange	Dietary fibre

Eatwell Guide

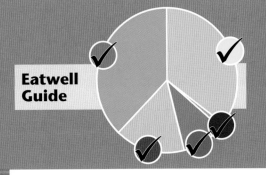

Which ingredient(s)?

Micronutrients

Vitamins

	Vitamin A:
–	Beta carotene
Butter or vegetable fat spread, eggs	Retinol
	Vitamin B group:
Milk	Thiamine B1
Milk, eggs	Riboflavin B2
Milk, eggs, flour	Niacin B3
–	Folic acid B9
–	B12
Orange	Vitamin C
Butter or vegetable fat spread, eggs	Vitamin D
Vegetable fat spread	Vitamin E
–	Vitamin K

Minerals

Milk, flour	Calcium
–	Fluoride
Milk	Iodine
Cocoa, flour, eggs	Iron
All ingredients	Phosphorus
Baking powder	Sodium

Which cooking methods and practical skills does this recipe use?

Cooking methods

Baking

Practical skills

All-in-one cake making method

Making frosting

Decorating cake

What is the science behind this recipe?

Trapping of air as a raising agent/baking powder as a raising agent.
Plasticity of fats to enable mixture to trap air and be spread.
Coagulation of protein molecules in egg to set mixture.
Softening of gluten in the flour by the sugar during baking.

Heat transfer

Convection

Conduction

Study tip

To help you learn the food science, make a revision chart where you list each of the reactions that occur when using proteins, fats and carbohydrates. Next to each, write brief bullet points to explain what happens and list examples of recipes where these occur.

Shortening

- 'Short' dough mixtures, such as shortcrust pastry and shortbread, have a very tender, crumbly, 'melt-in-the-mouth' texture when they are baked.

- This is because they have a relatively high fat content, which is mixed in with the flour and prevents the gluten in the flour from forming long molecules.
- The fat that is used for this is often called a '**shortening**'.

To explain this process, **shortcrust pastry** is going to be used as the example.

- When shortcrust pastry is made, the first stage involves cutting up the butter or solid vegetable fat spread and rubbing it into the flour with the fingertips.
- The fingertips are used because they are the coolest part of the hand and the aim is not to allow the fat to melt at this stage.
- The fat needs to have plasticity to allow you to rub it in easily.

- As the fat is rubbed in, the mixture gradually becomes crumbly to look at – a bit like breadcrumbs.

- Under the magnifying glass you can see that the particles of flour have been coated with a waterproof layer of fat.

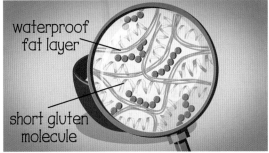

- When cold water is added to the mixture to bind it together and form the pastry dough, the waterproof layers of fat prevent the formation of long gluten molecules – only short ones are able to form.

- The **short gluten molecules** prevent the pastry dough from being stretchy so, when it is rolled out, it doesn't spring back like bread dough does.

On page 132 is a recipe to demonstrate shortening.

Cheese and vegetable pasties

Method:

1. Heat oven to Gas 6/200°C (190°C if you are using a fan oven).

2. Filling: sauté the onion and celery in the butter or oil until softened in a saucepan.

3. In another pan, boil the potato and carrot in water until just tender (about 10 minutes) – drain and mix with the onion/celery. Remove the pan from the heat.

4. Add the cheese and mix well – season with the pepper. Allow the filling to cool while you make the pastry.

5. Pastry – rub the vegetable fat spread or butter into the flour until it looks like breadcrumbs. Add the dried herbs, then the cold water and mix to a smooth dough. (The pastry can be made in a food processor to save time.)

6. Roll the pastry out carefully and cut it into 5–6 circles, each about the size of a saucer.

7. Place some of the filling mixture in the centre of each of the circles of pastry – dampen the edges with water and fold and seal the edges together. Neaten the edges by pressing them with a fork or using your fingers to 'flute' them into a wavy line.

8. Glaze the pastry with beaten egg.

9. Bake in the oven for 12–15 minutes until crisp and golden.

10. Serve warm or cold with salad and a tomato salsa.

Variations

Meat version: instead of cheese, use 75g lean minced beef – dry fry in a pan until browned all the way through and add to the cooked vegetables.

Empanadas: these are a different version of pasties, traditional in countries such as Spain, Portugal and Argentina. The fillings are usually meat-based and made using spices. The pastry ingredients can vary slightly but you can use the recipe below.

Spiced chicken empanadas

Ingredients:
2 chicken thighs
½ tbsp olive oil
1 small onion – finely diced
1 garlic clove – crushed
50g chorizo sausage – finely diced
¼ tsp cumin seeds
¼ tsp paprika
25g raisins, sultanas or finely diced dried
   apricots
salt and pepper

Method:

1. Roast the chicken in a pre-heated oven Gas 6/200°C (190°C if you are using a fan oven) for 20–25 minutes until cooked right through (minimum core temperature 70°C).

2. In a medium pan, sauté the onion in the oil until softened (about 8–10 minutes).

3. Add the other filling ingredients and heat through for 5 minutes.

4. Remove any bone and skin from the chicken and chop it into small pieces. Mix with the rest of the filling ingredients and turn into empanadas.

5. Bake for the same time as the pasties.

Ingredients:
(serves 6 people)

Pastry:
200g soft plain flour (white or
   wholemeal)
100g block vegetable fat or butter
1 tsp mixed dried herbs
10 tsp (50 ml) cold water
1 egg, beaten (for glazing the
   pastry)

Filling:
1 small onion – finely chopped
1 stalk celery – finely diced
1 small potato – peeled or
   unpeeled and finely diced
1 small carrot – peeled and finely
   diced
25g butter or 1½ tbsp vegetable
   oil
50g strong cheddar cheese –
   grated
black pepper

Storage instructions:
Refrigerator: cover and store in
   the refrigerator (0°C to below
   5°C) for up to 3 days.
Freezer: Can be frozen. Cover
   with suitably strong foil or plastic
   and freeze for up to 3 months,
   then defrost and warm before
   serving.

What is the nutritional profile of this recipe?

Which ingredient(s)?

Macronutrients

Protein

Egg, cheese	HBV
Flour	LBV

Fat

Butter/vegetable fat spread, cheese

Carbohydrate

Flour, potatoes	Starch
–	Sugars (intrinsic)
Vegetables, wholemeal flour	Dietary fibre

Eatwell Guide

Which ingredient(s)?

Micronutrients

Vitamins

–	Vitamin A:
Carrots	Beta carotene
Butter/vegetable fat spread, eggs	Retinol
	Vitamin B group:
Cheese	Thiamine B1
Cheese	Riboflavin B2
Cheese	Niacin B3
–	Folic acid B9
Butter/vegetable fat spread	B12
–	Vitamin C
Vegetable fat spread	Vitamin D
Vegetable fat spread	Vitamin E
Cheese	Vitamin K

Minerals

Cheese	Calcium
–	Fluoride
Cheese	Iodine
Flour	Iron
All ingredients	Phosphorus
Cheese	Sodium

Which cooking methods and practical skills does this recipe use?

Cooking methods

Sautéing

Boiling

Baking

Practical skills

Pastry making

Knife skills for vegetables

What is the science behind this recipe?

Complete the box below to show your understanding of the science of fats and heat transfer:

Explain how shortening occurs in this recipe.
Explain how heat is transferred in this recipe.

Argentinian fried empanadas

Aeration

- Fats such as butter and vegetable fat spreads are able to trap air bubbles when they are beaten together with sugar for a cake mixture.

- Butter and vegetable fat spreads can do this because they have plasticity, which means they can be beaten, spread and mixed easily with a wooden spoon or whisk.

- Cooking oils do not trap air as effectively as fats with plasticity.

- Mixing fat and sugar together is called **creaming** because, as the air bubbles are trapped, the mixture becomes lighter in colour and texture and its volume increases.

- The ability of the fats to **aerate** the mixture in this way is really important for producing a light, spongy texture in the baked cake.

- The raw cake mixture consists of a mixture of flour, fat, protein, sugar crystals and water (from the eggs) that is interspersed with trapped air bubbles, egg protein molecules which are tightly coiled and starch granules from the flour.

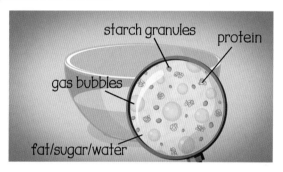

As the mixture bakes, several things happen:

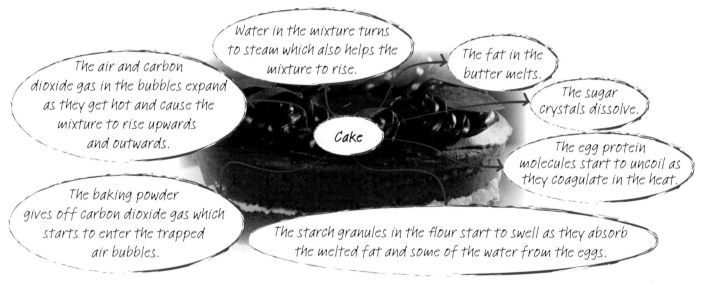

Water in the mixture turns to steam which also helps the mixture to rise.

The fat in the butter melts.

The air and carbon dioxide gas in the bubbles expand as they get hot and cause the mixture to rise upwards and outwards.

The sugar crystals dissolve.

Cake

The egg protein molecules start to uncoil as they coagulate in the heat.

The baking powder gives off carbon dioxide gas which starts to enter the trapped air bubbles.

The starch granules in the flour start to swell as they absorb the melted fat and some of the water from the eggs.

The mixture sets as the egg proteins become solid and the starch granules completely expand and, as it sets, the gases escape from the mixture.

Emulsification

Food products such as mayonnaise, milk, butter and Hollandaise sauce are **emulsions** of either oil-in-water or water-in-oil.

The chart below explains what emulsification means.

What happens when you mix oil and water

- If you put some oil and water into a jar and shake it up, the oil and water will mix together and form a cloudy looking liquid.

- If you leave the jar to stand for a few minutes, the oil and water will begin to separate – the oil will go to the top and form a layer on top of the water.

- This is because oil and water will not mix together permanently.

- Oil and water can be made to mix together by adding an **emulsifier.**

- This is what is done in sauce recipes such as Hollandaise sauce and mayonnaise.

- The emulsifier that is used in these recipes is called **lecithin**, which is found in egg yolk.

- This is how an emulsifier works.

- Emulsifiers are molecules with two ends.

- One end is attracted to water (it is **hydrophilic**) and the other end is attracted to oil (it is **hydrophobic** – it doesn't 'like' water).

- When an emulsifier is added to a mixture of oil and water, its molecules arrange themselves so that they prevent the oil and water from separating.

- The mixture is now an **emulsion.**

Emulsification

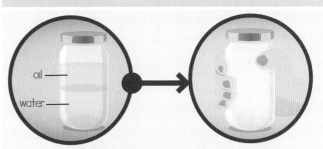

oil

water

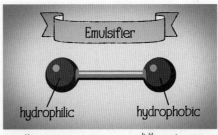

Emulsifier

hydrophilic

hydrophobic

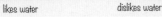

likes water

dislikes water

water suspended in oil

Section 2: Food Science

What happens when you mix oil and water

- Emulsions are either **oil-in-water** or **water-in-oil**, depending on how much oil and how much water is present.

- Milk, single and double cream, Hollandaise sauce and mayonnaise are all examples of **oil-in-water** emulsions, where the fat droplets stay suspended in the water and do not separate from it.

- Butter, vegetable fat spreads and vinaigrette salad dressing are all examples of **water-in-oil** emulsions, where the water droplets stay suspended in the fat/oil and do not separate from it.

- Vegetable fat spreads have emulsifiers such as **soy lecithin** and **monoglycerides** added to them to help them remain stable – you can see these written in the ingredients list on the label of a vegetable fat spread.

Emulsification

oil suspended in water

water-in-oil

BUTTERY-ISH SPREAD

INGREDIENTS: PURIFIED WATER, SOYBEAN OIL, PALM KERNEL AND PALM OIL, SALT, LECITHIN (SOY) VEGETABLE MONOGLYCERIDES, NATURAL FLAVOURS, VINEGAR, VITAMIN A PALMITATE, BETA CAROTENE (COLOUR).

From milk to butter

Oil-in-water emulsion

Milk

Water-in-oil emulsion

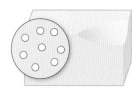
Butter

○ Water   ○ Oil

How butter is made

- Butter contains a natural emulsifier called lecithin, which keeps the emulsion stable.

- The diagram on the left shows what this means for butter, which is made from milk.

- In milk, the tiny fat droplets it contains are suspended in a white liquid containing protein, water, carbohydrate, minerals and vitamins.

- When the milk is left to stand in a cooled tank, the fat droplets rise to the top of the milk as a layer of cream.

- The cream is skimmed (taken) off the milk (which is why you get skimmed and semi-skimmed milk left behind, depending on how much cream is skimmed off).

- The cream is **churned**, which means it is continuously stirred until the droplets of fat start to stick to each other.

- As more and more of the fat droplets stick together, gradually the cream thickens and then turns into butter and most of the liquid (which is called buttermilk) is drained away.

- The small amount of liquid that is left forms tiny droplets within the fat and a natural emulsifier in the milk keeps them suspended in it.

Task Tip:

The information about emulsification in butter is an example of how you can present background research for the Food Investigation task on the working characteristics, functions and chemical properties of ingredients you are investigating.

What happens when you heat fats and oils?

- It is important to understand what happens when you heat fats and oils to know how to use them safely.

- When heated, solid fats melt and become oils.

- As heating increases, the **viscosity** of oils (how 'runny'/fluid they are) becomes thinner.

- The **triglyceride** molecules in the oil start to split up and **fatty acids** start to break away.

- Between 160°C and 250°C (depending on which oil is used), a bluish coloured haze appears above the heated oil, which can make you cough and your eyes sting.

- This stage is rapidly followed by smoke being given off – this is called the **smoke point** of the oil (look at the picture on the right).

- Oil that has reached smoke point will have poor quality and will rapidly reach **flash point** where it bursts into flames.

- You should never leave a pan of oil unattended when it is being heated.

- Every year in the UK, many house fires start because of a pan of cooking oil catching fire.

Oil heating up to smoke point

A serious kitchen fire caused by over-heated oil reaching flash point

If a pan of oil does catch fire, there are some very important safety rules you need to know and follow.

1. DO NOT attempt to move the pan of burning oil.

2. **Turn off** the heat under the pan of burning oil.

3. If you can, smother the flames, to exclude the oxygen, by using a metal pan lid, a specially designed fire blanket if you have one or a metal baking tray big enough to cover the pan.

4. Get everyone in the building outside and call the fire brigade.

5. NEVER pour water onto burning oil – it will make the flames far worse and cause the burning oil to float on the top and spill over.

Practice challenge

Selecting an appropriate fat for making cakes

There are many different types of vegetable fat spreads, butter and oil spreads available to buy.

Aim: to investigate the effects of using different types of fat/oil to make a basic sponge cake mixture, especially on the ability of the fat/oil to aerate the mixture.

Using the following recipe, make several samples using different types of fat:

Sample A: a block vegetable fat spread

Sample B: a vegetable fat spread in a tub

Sample C: a low-fat spread

Sample D: a blended butter and oil product

Sample E: butter

Sample F: vegetable, sunflower or corn oil (same weight as for the fats)

Recipe:

Standard cake recipe – makes six small cakes

Ingredients for each batch of six cakes

50g self-raising flour

50g fat

50g caster sugar

1 medium egg

Method

1. Set oven to Gas 5/190°C (180°C if you are using a fan oven).
2. For each batch of cakes, place sugar and fat/oil in a mixing bowl and cream (beat) together with a wooden spoon until the mixture is light and fluffy.
3. Whisk the egg with a fork in a small dish and gradually beat it into the fat and sugar mixture.
4. Sieve the flour and fold it into the mixture with a metal spoon until well mixed.
5. Divide the mixture between six cake cases in a bun tin.
6. Bake each batch of cakes for 12–15 minutes until risen and set.

Task Tip:

When carrying out the Food Investigation task you will need to establish controls when experimenting to ensure a fair test (page 254). Think about the controls for this investigation to ensure fair and accurate results.

Controls

The only variable in the recipe is the type of fat used. All the other ingredients stay the same. Once you have cooked the samples, set them out with a label A, B, C, etc. (do not show which sample contains which fat).

Ask a group of people to conduct a sensory analysis profiling test of each of the samples:

Look at the outside and the inside of each cake and then taste each of the samples (taking a sip of water between each to clear your palate).

Give each sample a score out of 5 (1 = least preferred/worst, 5 = most preferred/best) for the sensory qualities you want to be assessed, as shown in the table on page 139.

In the last column of the table, put the cakes in the order in which you preferred them (1 = most preferred, 6 = least preferred).

Results

Cake: Draw or photograph and annotate a cross-section of each cake	Appearance	Texture (lightness)	Texture (moistness)	Flavour	Comments	Order of preference (1 = most preferred, 6 = least preferred)
A						
B						
C						
D						
E						
F						

Discuss the results as a class, giving reasons for each of the following questions:

- Which cake sample was the most popular?
- Which cake sample was the least popular?
- Which cake had the best aeration?
- How were the appearance, texture and flavour of each cake sample affected by using different fats/oils?

Stretch and challenge activity

Using your knowledge and understanding of the functional and chemical properties of fats, write a short report to conclude the practical investigation, explaining how the different fats/oils performed.

Task Tip:

The activity on page 140 will give you an opportunity to practise gathering background research information for the Food Investigation task on the working characteristics, functions and chemical properties of ingredients.

Activity

Investigate why:

a. Opening the oven during cooking can affect how a cake rises.

b. Adding too much sugar can cause a cake to sink in the middle.

c. Raising agents are used in cake making.

Practice questions

1. Explain why each of the following are good practice:

   a) When using butter to make a cake, make sure the butter is at room temperature. *(2 marks)*

   b) When frying food in oil, keep a metal pan lid or large baking tray nearby. *(2 marks)*

   c) When using fat to make shortcrust pastry, make sure that the fat is chilled. *(2 marks)*

2. Using your knowledge and understanding of the functional and chemical properties of fats, explain the following:

   a) Why vegetable fat spreads sold in tubs and cartons can easily be spread when they are chilled. *(4 marks)*

   b) Why mayonnaise does not separate when it is stored. *(4 marks)*

   c) Why the ability of a fat to aerate a mixture is really important in cake making. *(4 marks)*

2.2.4 Raising agents

What will I learn?

In this section you will learn about:

- why raising agents are used
- what is meant by a raising agent
- how raising agents work.

Why are raising agents used?

- Consumers expect baked products such as bread, cakes and scones to have a light, open, soft and 'spongy' texture.

- To create the desired texture, a **raising agent** is added to the uncooked mixture to introduce lots of **gas bubbles**, which will **expand** when the mixture is baked in the oven.

What is a raising agent?

The gas bubbles in raising agents are air (a mixture of gases), carbon dioxide and steam.

- **Air**, which is a mixture of gases, is trapped in a mixture as it is creamed, rubbed-in, beaten, whisked or rolled and folded. The air is also trapped in flour when it is **sieved**.

- **Carbon dioxide (CO_2) gas**, which is given off by:
  - **yeast** in bread
  - **bicarbonate of soda** added to cake and scone mixtures

Key term

Raising agent: an ingredient or process that introduces a gas into a mixture so that it rises when cooked

- **baking powder**, which has **bicarbonate of soda** in it and is added to **self-raising** flour by food manufacturers.
- **Steam**, which is water in a gaseous state.

Gases are introduced into mixtures in three ways:

1. **Chemical:** by using baking powder or bicarbonate of soda to produce CO_2 gas.
2. **Mechanical:** by whisking, beating, sieving, creaming, rubbing in, folding to trap air or adding moisture (which turns to steam).
3. **Biological:** by using yeast to produce CO_2 gas.

How do raising agents work?

- The action of **moisture, heat** or **acidity** (or a combination of all three) triggers a reaction with the raising agent to produce the gas bubbles.
- As a cake mixture, batter or dough cooks, the gas bubbles given off by the raising agent make it **rise** by **expanding** and pushing it upwards and outwards.
- The gas bubbles then become set in it and provide the soft, sponge-like texture.

The following sections explain how each gas is introduced into a mixture.

Air

Air is trapped in mixtures in a variety of ways. Here are some examples of how this happens.

Creaming (used in cake, sponge and biscuit mixtures)

- When fat and sugar are beaten together with the wooden spoon (a process called **creaming**), lots of little air bubbles are trapped in the mixture.
- Each bubble is surrounded by a **thin layer of fat.**
- The mixture changes colour during creaming (it becomes lighter) as the trapped air creates a **foam**.
- Egg is added to the mixture to **coagulate** and form a wall round the air bubbles, so they can expand and raise the mixture without breaking and allowing the air to escape.

The mixture sets as the **egg proteins coagulate** and the **starch granules** in the flour completely expand and, as it sets, the air eventually escapes from the mixture.

Whisking (used in gas(air)-in-liquid foams (see pages 114–115), for recipes such as meringue, whisked sponges and savoury roulades)

See page 142 for a whisked sponge recipe.

Savoury roulade with watercress and cheese filling

Practical tip

One of the reasons that sugar is added to a cake mixture is to soften and tenderise the gluten.

Be careful!! Adding too much sugar to a cake mixture causes the gluten to soften too much.

The cake will rise really well, but will suddenly collapse because the gluten is too soft and will not set, so it cannot support the expanding gas bubbles.

The finished cake will be very hard and chewy, because the excess sugar will caramelise and set like toffee.

Swiss roll

Method:

1. Heat the oven – Gas 6/200°C (190°C if you are using a fan oven).

2. Grease and line a Swiss roll tin.

3. Place the eggs and sugar in a bowl and whisk at medium speed until the mixture is light, thick and creamy, and leaves a visible trail for at least 5 seconds when the whisk is removed.

4. Sieve the flour twice and fold it very gently into the mixture with a metal spoon in a figure of 8 movement, until there is no visible flour – do not beat it in or use a whisk, as the air will come out.

5. Pour the mixture into the tin and tip it until the mixture goes evenly into the corners.

6. Bake for 10–12 minutes until the Swiss roll is well risen, spongy to the touch and starting to shrink away from the edges of the tin.

7. Remove from the oven and STRAIGHT AWAY tip the sponge away from you onto a sheet of non-stick paper.

8. Carefully remove the paper that lined the tin.

9. Trim a little off the edges of the sponge with a sharp knife (they are crisp and may stop the sponge rolling up properly) and spread the softened jam (stir it with a spoon) over the sponge.

10. Roll up the sponge tightly and leave to cool.

Ingredients:
(serves 8 people)
3 eggs
75g caster sugar
75g plain flour

Filling
3 tbsp jam

Storage instructions:
Allow to cool then store in an air tight tin or box for up to 2 days. Can be frozen for up to 3 months.

What is the science behind this recipe?

Whisking eggs and sugar together: traps air bubbles as the protein from the egg stretches and surrounds the air bubbles to form an air-in-liquid foam.

Heat transfer

Convection	Heating oven to bake the Swiss roll
Conduction	Heat passing through the baking tin into the sponge

---

Which cooking methods and practical skills does this recipe use?

Cooking methods	**Practical skills**
Baking	Whisking method – trapping air in the eggs and sugar
	Rolling the baked Swiss roll

What is the nutritional profile of this recipe?

Macronutrients

Which ingredient(s)?

Protein	
	HBV
	LBV
Fat	
Carbohydrate	
	Starch
	Sugars *(intrinsic)*
	Free sugars
	Dietary fibre

Micronutrients

Which ingredient(s)?

Vitamins	
	Vitamin A:
	Beta carotene
	Retinol
	Vitamin B group:
	Thiamine B1
	Riboflavin B2
	Niacin B3
	Folic acid B9
	B12
	Vitamin C
	Vitamin D
	Vitamin E
	Vitamin K
Minerals	
	Calcium
	Fluoride
	Iodine
	Iron
	Phosphorus
	Sodium

Eatwell Guide

Activity

Using the nutritional information you have learned so far, fill in the nutritional profile details for the Swiss roll recipe.

Rolling and folding (used in flaky and puff pastry)

- The baked texture of some doughs (e.g. flaky or puff pastry, Danish pastries) get their texture from the dough being rolled out and folded several times.

- This process traps air.

- During baking, the fat (in between the layers of dough) melts, leaving a space that is filled with steam (from the water and fat added to the pastry), which also acts as a raising agent, and the trapped air bubbles expand.

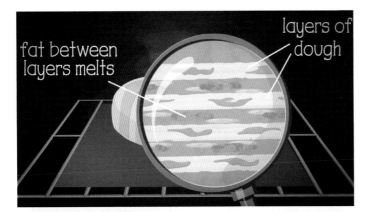

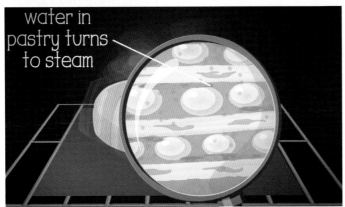

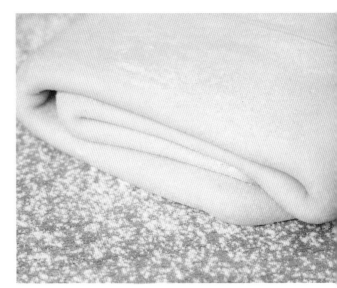

Folded puff pastry

Cooked puff pastry

This causes light, crisp and thin layers of pastry to develop.

On page 144 is a recipe to show the use of puff or flaky pastry.

Puff pastry cheese twists

Ingredients:
(makes approximately 12–15 cheese twists)

250g puff pastry – ready-made or home made

150g finely grated parmesan cheese **OR** 150g finely grated cheddar cheese **OR** 75g finely grated parmesan cheese **and** 75g finely grated strong cheddar cheese

1 tsp paprika

½ tsp Cayenne pepper

1 egg, beaten

Storage instructions:
Best eaten on the day they are made.

OR allow to cool then cover and store in an air tight tin or box for up to 2 days.

Freezer: Can be frozen raw for up to 3 months, then bake from frozen in a hot oven, allowing an extra 5 minutes on the baking time.

Method:

1. Set the oven to Gas 6/200°C (190°C if you are using a fan oven).

2. Stir the paprika, cayenne pepper and grated parmesan/cheddar cheese together in a mixing bowl with a fork, or your fingers, until well mixed.

3. Roll out the puff pastry dough to about ½cm thickness, in a rectangle approximately the size of an A4 piece of paper.

4. Brush the top with egg wash and then sprinkle the cheese mixture on top. Press it down to make it stick to the pastry.

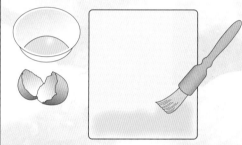

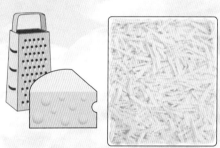

5. Turn the rectangle of puff pastry over and repeat the processes in point number 4 above, on the other side of the pastry.

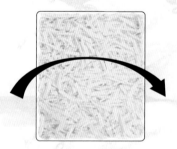

● Press the cheese mixture onto the pastry again, so that it sticks to it on both sides.

● Some of the cheese will fall off when you turn the pastry over, but that is quite normal.

6. Cut the pastry into strips about 2cm wide across the width of the rectangle.

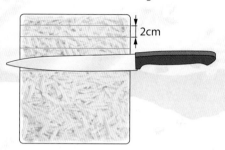

7. Twist each of the strips all the way down their length.

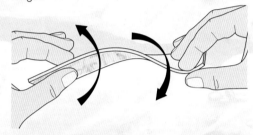

8. Place the cheese twists on a baking tray covered with baking paper and bake for about 15–20 minutes until they have puffed up and become crisp on the outside.

9. Place the baked twists on a cooling tray. They will become firmer and crisper when they cool down as the melted cheese hardens.

Which ingredient(s)?

Macronutrients

Protein

Cheese, egg	HBV
Flour	LBV

Fat

Butter/vegetable fat spread

Carbohydrate

Flour	Starch
–	Sugars (intrinsic)
–	Dietary fibre

Eatwell Guide

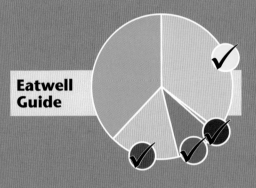

Which ingredient(s)?

Micronutrients

Vitamins

	Vitamin A:
–	Beta carotene
Butter/vegetable fat spread, cheese	Retinol
	Vitamin B group:
White flour, cheese	Thiamine B1
Cheese	Riboflavin B2
Cheese	Niacin B3
Cheese	Folic acid B9
–	B12
Cheese, butter/vegetable fat spread	Vitamin C
–	Vitamin D
Vegetable fat spread	Vitamin E
Cheese	Vitamin K

Minerals

Cheese, flour	Calcium
–	Fluoride
Cheese	Iodine
White flour	Iron
All ingredients	Phosphorus
Cheese	Sodium

Which cooking methods and practical skills does this recipe use?

Cooking methods

Baking

Practical skills

Using and shaping puff pastry

What is the science behind this recipe?

Raising agents: the fat in the pastry melts and is absorbed by the starch in the flour, which makes it form crisp layers. Steam is produced from the water added to the pastry, which makes the pastry puff up in the hot oven. As the pastry has been rolled and folded, air is trapped and expands on heating making the pastry puff up.

Heat transfer

Convection Heating oven to bake the twists

Conduction Heat passing through the baking tin into the twists

Stretch and challenge activity

Investigate the following:

1. Why is puff pastry often just put on the top of pies, such as meat or fish pies, rather than being used underneath as well?

2. Why is filo pastry often used as a healthier substitute for puff pastry?

3. What would prevent puff pastry from rising properly in the oven?

4. Investigate the different methods that are used to incorporate the fat in puff pastry and flaky pastry.

Carbon dioxide (CO_2)

Carbon dioxide gas is produced by **bicarbonate of soda** and **yeast**.

Bicarbonate of soda

Bicarbonate of soda is used as a raising agent in cakes, scones and biscuits.

Bicarbonate of soda produces **CO_2 gas** when it is heated.

In a mixture, the CO_2 gas bubbles that are produced help to expand any air bubbles in the mixture and enable the mixture to rise.

If bicarbonate of soda (which is an **alkali**) is used on its own in a cake or scones, they would rise well, but the taste of the washing soda that is produced in the reaction would be very unpleasant.

This is the reaction:

Bicarbonate of soda + heat   →   washing soda + carbon dioxide gas + water

Alkali + heat   →   **Alkali (soapy taste)**

Disgusted

To prevent this, the bicarbonate of soda is mixed with an **acid** called 'cream of tartar' to make **baking powder.** If you put an acid with an alkali, CO_2 gas will be produced, but the acid and alkali will **neutralise** each other, so that you do not get washing soda produced.

This is the reaction:

Bicarbonate of soda + cream of tartar + heat → sodium potassium tartrate + carbon dioxide gas + water

Alkali + Acid + heat → Neutral (no taste)

Baking powder is added to plain flour to make **self-raising flour**.

Bicarbonate of soda is only used on its own in strong tasting mixtures such as gingerbread, where the flavour of the spices cover up the washing soda taste.

On pages 147 and 148 are two recipes to show the use of bicarbonate of soda and baking powder.

Gingerbread cake

Ingredients:
(serves 10–12 people)
225g plain flour
½ tbsp ground ginger
½ tbsp baking powder
½ tsp bicarbonate of soda
100g Demerara sugar
85g butter or vegetable fat spread
85g black treacle
85g golden syrup
125ml milk
1 small egg, beaten

Storage instructions:
Allow to cool then cover and store in an air tight tin or box for up to 7 days.
Can be frozen for up to 3 months.

Method:

1. Grease and line a shallow baking tray, approximately 22 × 26cm.

2. Sieve the flour, ginger, baking powder and bicarbonate of soda together into a mixing bowl.

3. Melt the butter or vegetable fat spread, sugar, syrup and treacle in a saucepan over a low heat – do not let the mixture boil.

4. Remove the melted mixture from the heat, and leave it to cool for a few minutes.

5. Whisk the egg and milk together and add it to the melted mixture. Pour the liquid into the flour and mix well with a wooden spoon until it is smooth.

6. Pour the mixture into the tin and bake at Gas 3/170°C (160°C if you are using a fan oven) for 25–35 minutes, until well risen and spongy to the touch.

7. You can put crystallised ginger on the top half way through baking the gingerbread if you wish.

What is the science behind this recipe?

Raising agents: bicarbonate of soda in the baking powder produces CO_2 gas in the heat of the oven, which forms bubbles that expand when heated. The strong flavours of the spices cover the washing soda residue formed from the bicarbonate of soda.

Heat transfer

Convection	Heating oven to bake the buns
Conduction	Heat passing through the baking tin into the buns

What is the nutritional profile of this recipe?

Macronutrients

Which ingredient(s)?

Protein	
Milk, egg	HBV
Flour	LBV
Fat	
Butter/vegetable fat spread	
Carbohydrate	
Flour	Starch
–	Sugars (intrinsic)
Sugar, treacle, golden syrup	Free sugars
Flour if wholemeal used	Dietary fibre

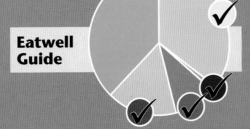

Eatwell Guide

Micronutrients

Which ingredient(s)?

Vitamins	
–	Vitamin A:
Butter/vegetable fat spread, milk, egg	Beta carotene
	Retinol
White flour, milk, egg	Vitamin B group:
	Thiamine B1
Milk, egg	Riboflavin B2
Milk, egg	Niacin B3
–	Folic acid B9
–	B12
–	Vitamin C
Milk, butter/vegetable fat spread	Vitamin D
Vegetable fat spread	Vitamin E
–	Vitamin K
Minerals	
Milk, flour	Calcium
–	Fluoride
Milk	Iodine
White flour, black treacle, egg yolk	Iron
All ingredients	Phosphorus
Baking powder, bicarbonate of soda	Sodium

Which cooking methods and practical skills does this recipe use?

Cooking methods
Baking

Practical skills
Making a melted cake mixture

Section 2: Food Science

Cheese and herb scone round

Ingredients:
(serves 8 people)
225g self-raising flour – white or
 wholemeal or 50% of each
½ tsp baking powder
¼ tsp cayenne pepper
50g strong flavoured cheddar
 cheese – finely grated **OR** 50g
 grated parmesan cheese
1 tsp mixed dried herbs
25g pumpkin seeds or sunflower
 seeds (optional)
50g butter or vegetable fat spread
150ml milk

Storage instructions:
Best eaten on the day it is made.
OR allow to cool then cover and
 store in an air tight tin or box for
 up to 2 days.
Can be frozen for up to 3 months.

Method:

1. Set the oven to Gas 6/200°C (190°C if you are using a fan oven).

2. Sieve the flour, baking powder and cayenne pepper together into a mixing bowl.

3. Stir in the dried herbs.

4. Rub in the butter or vegetable fat spread with your fingertips until the mixture looks like breadcrumbs.

5. Stir in ¾ of the grated cheese and seeds.

6. Make a well in the centre and add the milk.

7. Stir the mixture together with a wooden spoon until it forms a soft dough.

8. Knead the dough lightly on a floured worktop and shape into a round either with your hands or a rolling pin, about 16–18cm diameter and 2cm thick.

9. Grease or line a baking sheet and place the scone round on it.

10. With a knife, mark the scone round into eight pieces – cut down so that the marks are clearly visible and will hold their shape when it is baked. Brush the top with some milk.

11. Sprinkle the remaining ¼ of the grated cheese on top.

12. Bake the scone round for 15–20 minutes until golden, well-risen, spongy to the touch but **not doughy in the middle – check with a skewer**.

13. Cool on a wire rack and cut into eight pieces where you marked it before baking.

14. Serve warm with soup or cheese/ham and pickles.

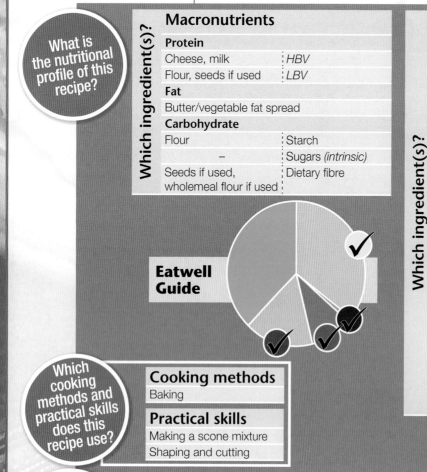

What is the nutritional profile of this recipe?

Which ingredient(s)?

Macronutrients

Protein	
Cheese, milk	*HBV*
Flour, seeds if used	*LBV*
Fat	
Butter/vegetable fat spread	
Carbohydrate	
Flour	Starch
–	Sugars *(intrinsic)*
Seeds if used, wholemeal flour if used	Dietary fibre

Eatwell Guide

Which ingredient(s)?

Micronutrients

Vitamins		
–		Vitamin A:
		Beta carotene
Butter/vegetable fat spread, cheese, milk		*Retinol*
		Vitamin B group:
White flour, milk, cheese		*Thiamine B1*
Milk, cheese		*Riboflavin B2*
Milk		Niacin B3
Cheese		*Folic acid B9*
–		B12
–		Vitamin C
Milk, cheese, butter/vegetable fat spread		Vitamin D
Seeds if used, vegetable fat spread		Vitamin E
Cheese		Vitamin K
Minerals		
Milk, cheese, flour		Calcium
–		Fluoride
Milk, cheese		Iodine
White flour		Iron
All ingredients		Phosphorus
Cheese, baking powder		Sodium

Which cooking methods and practical skills does this recipe use?

Cooking methods
Baking

Practical skills
Making a scone mixture
Shaping and cutting

What is the science behind this recipe?

Raising agents: bicarbonate of soda in the baking powder produces CO_2 gas in the heat of the oven, which forms bubbles that expand when heated. The crust goes golden brown due to the dextrinisation of the starch in the flour.

Heat transfer	
Convection	Heating oven to bake the scone
Conduction	Heat passing through the baking tin into the scone

Yeast

- Yeast is a type of microscopic, single-celled fungi and is related to mushrooms. There are different types and specific ones are produced for use in bread making.

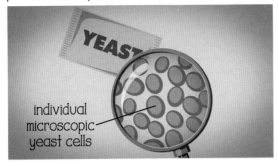

individual microscopic yeast cells

- If given the right conditions of **warmth, moisture, food** (sugar or starch) and **time**, yeast will use the sugar or starch for energy and produce **carbon dioxide (CO_2) gas** and **alcohol** as by-products.

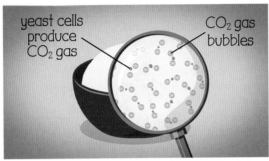

yeast cells produce CO_2 gas

CO_2 gas bubbles

- This whole process is called **fermentation**.
- The CO_2 gas makes the bread dough expand and rise when it is left in a warm place for a period of time.
- Yeast cells will only grow and produce CO_2 gas very slowly if the temperature is too cold.
- When bread is made and the dough is left to rise (prove), the yeast cells multiply by a process called **budding**.
- This means that there are more yeast cells available to produce more CO_2 gas, so the bread will expand and rise very well.
- When the bread dough is put into the hot oven, the CO_2 gas bubbles expand with the heat, and steam and alcohol are produced as the dough heats up.

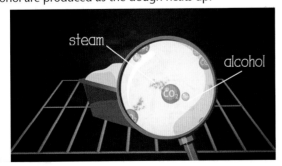

steam

alcohol

CO_2

- The alcohol evaporates in the heat of the oven when the loaf is baked so that there is no alcohol left in it when the bread comes out of the oven.
- Yeast cells will die if they come in direct contact with salt or boiling water.

On page 150 is a recipe for Chelsea buns to show the use of yeast as a raising agent.

Section 2: Food Science

Chelsea buns

Method:

1. Warm the milk and mix it with the yeast and 1 tsp sugar – leave it to activate (go frothy) for a few minutes.

2. Rub the butter into the flour with your fingertips and add the sugar.

3. Whisk the eggs and yeast liquid together – remember you need a total of 300ml of liquid.

4. Mix to a soft dough using a wooden spoon.

5. Knead the dough for 5 minutes, until it becomes stretchy and smooth.

6. Roll out the dough into a rectangle approximately 30 × 25cm.

7. Brush the dough with the melted butter and scatter the fruit, spice and sugar over it.

8. Roll up the dough lengthways and cut it into eight even-sized pieces.

9. Place the pieces in a greased and lined round sandwich tin and leave to rise in a warm place for at least 30 minutes.

10. Bake the buns at Gas 6/200°C (190°C if you are using a fan oven) for 15–20 minutes, until well risen and golden brown.

11. Take them out of the oven and brush them with the glaze while they are still hot, and then separate them by tearing apart gently.

Ingredients:
(serves 8 people)
450g strong plain white or wholemeal bread flour
2 tsp (10g) dried yeast
50g caster sugar
50g butter or vegetable fat spread
2 eggs
approx. 250ml warm milk (you need 300ml liquid altogether including the eggs)

Filling:
1 level tsp mixed spice
100g mixed dried fruit
25g melted butter
2 tsp Demerara sugar

Glaze:
2 tbsp water, 2 tbsp milk, 2 tbsp caster sugar – mixed together and boiled for 3 minutes.

Storage instructions:
Best eaten on the day they
OR allow to cool then cover and store in an air tight tin or box for up to 2 days.
Can be frozen for up to 3 months.

What is the science behind this recipe?

Raising agents: yeast produces CO_2 gas when warm and given food (starch and sugar). CO_2 bubbles expand in the heat and cause the dough to rise. Gluten: stretches as the dough rises and helps the dough to set. The crust goes golden brown due to the dextrinisation of the starch in the flour and the caramelisation of the sugar in the dough.

Heat transfer

Convection	Heating oven to bake the buns
Conduction	Heat passing through the baking tin into the buns

Which cooking methods and practical skills does this recipe use?

Cooking methods
Baking

Practical skills
Making a bun mixture
Kneading, shaping and rolling dough

What is the nutritional profile of this recipe?

Macronutrients

Which ingredient(s)?

Protein	
Milk, eggs	*HBV*
Flour	*LBV*
Fat	
Butter/vegetable fat spread	
Carbohydrate	
Flour	Starch
Dried fruit	Sugars *(intrinsic)*
Caster and demerara sugar	Free sugars
Wholemeal flour if used	Dietary fibre

Micronutrients

Which ingredient(s)?

Vitamins	
–	Vitamin A:
Butter/vegetable fat spread, milk, eggs	*Beta carotene*
	Retinol
White flour, milk, eggs	Vitamin B group: *Thiamine B1*
Milk, eggs	*Riboflavin B2*
Milk, eggs	Niacin B3
–	*Folic acid B9*
–	*B12*
–	Vitamin C
Milk, butter/vegetable fat spread, eggs	Vitamin D
Vegetable fat spread	Vitamin E
–	Vitamin K
Minerals	
Milk, flour	Calcium
–	Fluoride
Milk	Iodine
White flour, dried fruit	Iron
All ingredients	Phosphorus
–	Sodium

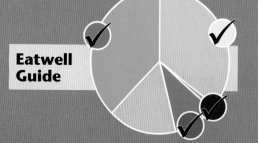

Eatwell Guide

Steam

- Steam is used as a raising agent in batters (e.g. Yorkshire puddings, choux pastry and flaky or puff pastry). It also helps other mixtures rise, such as bread and cakes.

broken hydrogen bonds

- When water (H_2O) is a liquid, the molecules join together with hydrogen bonds. When water is heated to 100°C, the hydrogen bonds gradually break and its molecules of H_2O start to break free and go into the air as **steam**, which is a gas (also known as **water vapour**). This happens because the hydrogen bonds break and the water molecules move away from each other very fast and form steam.

- If there is liquid present in a mixture during baking, then steam will be produced as the heat rises, but it is a slower reaction than that of gas expansion.

- Steam is therefore only suitable as a raising agent for mixtures that contain a lot of water (e.g. batters, choux pastry, puff pastry).

- The oven temperature must be high in order to raise the liquid rapidly to boiling point.

steam

- Water vapour expands to 1,600 times its original volume and is therefore an effective raising agent.

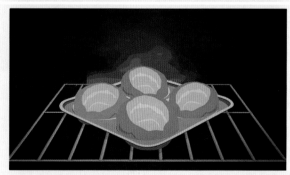

Yorkshire puddings risen as a result of steam

On page 152 is a recipe for sweet and savoury choux pastry to show the use of steam as a raising agent.

Ingredients:
(Éclairs – serves 10 people
Profiteroles – serves 6 people)

Choux pastry – basic mixture:
150ml water
50g butter or block vegetable fat
  spread
60g flour (strong plain bread flour
  is best)
2 medium eggs

**For chocolate éclairs, in
addition to the basic choux
mixture, you need:**

Filling:
200ml double or whipping cream
  – whipped until thick
To make Chantilly cream, add ½ tsp
  vanilla essence and 2 tbsp caster
  sugar after the cream is whipped.

Topping:
150g plain cooking chocolate –
  melted in a bowl over a pan of
  simmering water

**For profiteroles, in addition to
the basic choux mixture, you
need:**

Filling:
200ml double or whipping cream
  – whipped until thick

Chocolate sauce:
150ml milk
1½ tbsp cocoa powder
1 tbsp sugar
1 tbsp golden syrup
10g butter or margarine

**For savoury éclairs, in addition
to the basic choux mixture,
you need:**
75g strong flavoured cheddar
  cheese or parmesan cheese –
  grated
120g cream cheese mixed
  together with 1 tbsp chopped
  mixed fresh herbs

Storage instructions:
Best eaten on the day they are
  made
OR cover and store in a
  refrigerator in an air tight tin or
  box for up to 2 days.
The éclairs can be frozen for up
  to 3 months, either as just the
  pastry shells or filled.

Choux pastry

Method:

Making the choux pastry

1. Heat the oven to Gas 6/200°C (190°C if you are using a fan oven) – you will need to use the top shelf in a gas oven.

2. Bring the water and butter (or vegetable fat spread) to the boil in a saucepan – make sure all the fat has melted.

3. Turn off the heat and, straightaway, add the sieved flour and carefully mix it in with a wooden spoon and then beat it until a ball of **choux paste** is formed in the pan (you are developing the gluten strands when you beat it, which will help the choux pastry stretch when it rises).

4. Allow the choux paste to cool for a few minutes.

5. Gradually add the beaten eggs, a little at a time – **you may not need them all** – beating the mixture well. The paste should be a 'dropping' consistency – it must not be runny.

Filling and finishing

Finishing the chocolate éclairs:

6. Fill each with whipped cream, either with a teaspoon or by piping the cream.

7. Melt the chocolate in a bowl over a pan of simmering water and dip the éclairs into it and leave them to set on a cooling tray.

Piping the mixture

For the éclairs:

8. Pipe the mixture into éclair shapes onto a greased or lined baking tray. Allow some room for them to expand.

For the profiteroles:

9. Pipe the mixture into small, regular shaped mounds onto a greased or lined baking tray. Allow some room for them to expand.

For the savoury éclairs:

10. Add the grated cheese to the mixture and beat well. Pipe the mixture into éclair shapes onto a greased or lined baking tray. Allow some room for them to expand.

Baking the choux pastry

Baking the éclairs (chocolate or savoury):

11. Bake for 15 minutes, then turn the temperature down to Gas 5/190°C (180°C if you are using a fan oven) for another 10 minutes – DO NOT OPEN THE OVEN DOOR WHILE THE ECLAIRS ARE BAKING, OTHERWISE THEY WILL COLLAPSE, BECAUSE THEY ONLY SET IN THE LAST FEW MINUTES OF BAKING.

12. The éclairs should be crisp and well risen – make a slit along the length of each éclair at the side and let it cool. Carefully scrape out any doughy bits that are inside.

Baking the profiteroles:

13. Bake for 15 minutes until well risen and crisp and make a slit in the side of each one and allow to cool.

Finishing the profiteroles:

14. Make the chocolate sauce. Put all the ingredients into a medium saucepan and heat gently until the butter has melted. Bring to the boil, then simmer gently for approx.15–20 minutes to reduce the sauce until it is thick and glossy.

15. Carefully arrange 4–5 profiteroles into a serving bowl, then pour over a quantity of chocolate sauce and serve.

Finishing the savoury éclairs:

16. Fill each éclair with a mixture of cream cheese and fresh chopped herbs or another filling of your choice.

What is the nutritional profile of this recipe?

Which ingredient(s)?

Macronutrients

Protein	
Eggs, cheese	HBV
Flour	LBV
Fat	
Butter/vegetable fat spread	
Carbohydrate	
Flour	Starch
–	Sugars (intrinsic)
Chocolate, sugar, syrup	Free sugars
Wholemeal flour if used	Dietary fibre

Which ingredient(s)?

Micronutrients

Vitamins	
	Vitamin A:
–	Beta carotene
Butter/vegetable fat spread, cream, eggs	Retinol
	Vitamin B group:
White flour, eggs, cream, milk	Thiamine B1
Cream, eggs, milk	Riboflavin B2
Milk, eggs	Niacin B3
–	Folic acid B9
Cheese	B12
–	Vitamin C
Cream, butter/vegetable fat spread, milk, eggs	Vitamin D
Vegetable fat spread	Vitamin E
Cheese	Vitamin K
Minerals	
Cream, milk, flour	Calcium
–	Fluoride
Milk	Iodine
Cocoa, chocolate, egg yolk, white flour	Iron
All ingredients	Phosphorus
–	Sodium

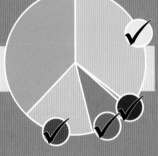

Eatwell Guide

Which cooking methods and practical skills does this recipe use?

Cooking methods
Baking

Practical skills
Making a choux paste
Piping choux paste

What is the science behind this recipe?

Starch in flour absorbs melted fat and boiling water and gelatinises. Gluten in flour stretches and helps paste to rise. Steam is the raising agent and is formed in the hot oven. Protein in eggs and gluten enable pastry to set.

Heat transfer

Convection	Heating oven to bake the choux
	Boiling the water to make the choux paste
Conduction	Heat passing through the baking tin into the choux
	Heat passing through the pan to boil the water to make the choux paste

Stretch and challenge activity

Choux pastry is used for a variety of decorative pastry recipes, such as choux swans, Croquembouche, beignets, Gateau St. Honore, churros and gougere. Investigate where these recipes come from and how they are made. If possible, have a go at making one of them to stretch your skills.

Study tip

Make sure you understand the role of all the ingredients in a recipe and how they help raising agents to work,
- e.g. the gluten in flour which stretches to allow gas bubbles to expand;
- e.g. the egg, which when whisked, has the ability to surround and lock in the air bubbles with denatured and coagulated protein molecules;
- e.g. the fat, which when beaten with sugar has plasticity, which allows it to trap lots of tiny air bubbles.

Activity

Complete the chart below to show which raising agents are used to raise each mixture:

Mixture		Which raising agent(s)?
Choux pastry (chocolate éclairs, profiteroles)		
Puff pastry		
Whisked sponge cake (e.g. Swiss roll)		
Creamed sponge cake (e.g. Victoria sandwich)		
Batter (e.g. Yorkshire puddings)	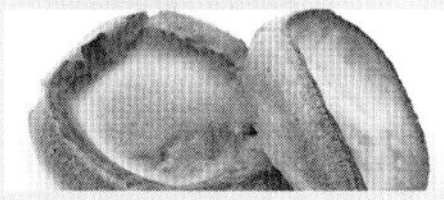	
Bread rolls		
Scones		
Gingerbread		

Practice questions

1. State three ways in which air can be introduced into a baked food product. Give an example for each. *(6 marks)*

2. Explain, in detail, how bread rises and why the following are important in bread making:

   a) Using strong plain flour. *(3 marks)*

   b) The correct temperatures for making and baking the bread dough. *(3 marks)*

   c) The importance of kneading a bread dough. *(3 marks)*

3. Explain, giving reasons, what the cause(s) of the problems could be when these baked food products were made:

   a) A loaf of bread is very heavy, dense and solid, and has risen very little. *(3 marks)*

   b) A Swiss roll has come out of the oven very flat and will not roll without breaking. *(3 marks)*

   c) Yorkshire puddings have not risen. *(3 marks)*

   d) Puff pastry rectangles are flat and there is a lot of melted fat on the baking tray around them when they are taken out of the oven. *(3 marks)*

Differentiated teaching and learning activities

For Section 2.2.1 Proteins.

Activity

Complete the chart below to show your understanding of what happens when you use proteins in cooking.

Look at this picture	Describe what is happening to the food/ingredients in the picture and why it is happening	Answer these questions
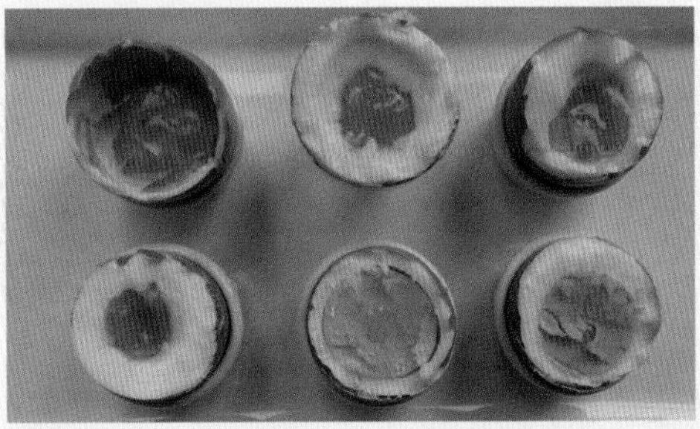 Boiled eggs		• Why are eggs number 5 and 6 the most suitable for making egg sandwiches? • Why might it not be safe to give eggs number 1 or 2 to very young children to eat?
 Bread dough		• Why is it important to knead the bread dough? • What will the texture of the bread be like when it has finished baking in the oven? • Why does this happen?
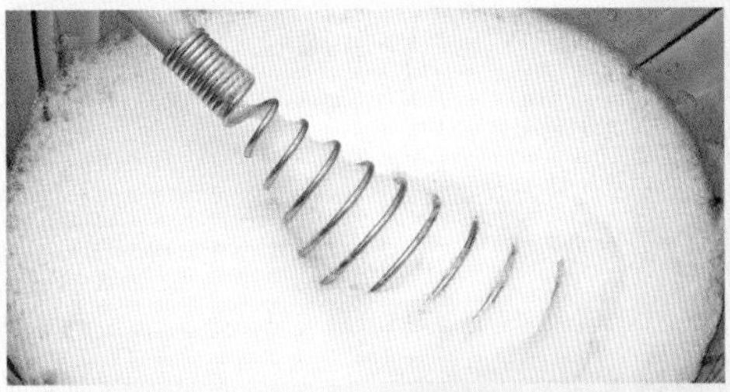  Egg whites and sugar		• Why is a whisk used for this food preparation method? • Why is it important that the mixing bowl is dry and free of fat/grease? • What will happen to the mixture if it is whisked for too long after the sugar is added?

Section 2: Food Science

For Section 2.2.2 Carbohydrates.

Activity

Complete the chart below to show your understanding of what happens when you use carbohydrates in cooking.

Look at this picture	Describe what is happening to the food/ingredients in the picture and why it is happening	Answer these questions
 Raw (A) and boiled (B) pasta		• What will happen if you over cook the pasta? • Why does this happen?
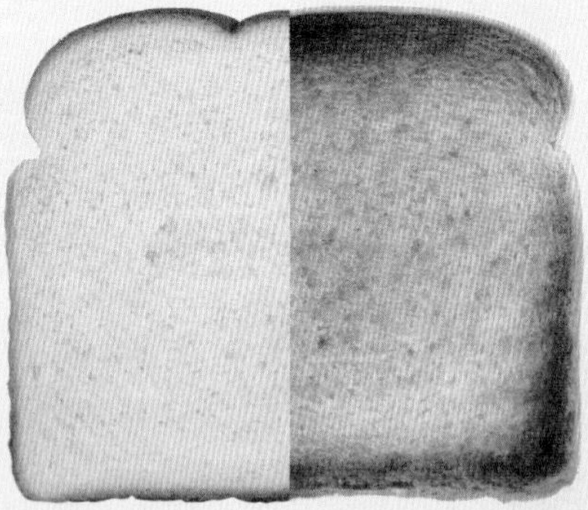 Bread		• What will happen if you leave the bread too long under the grill? • Why does this happen?
 Sautéed onions		• Why do you need to sauté the onions gently? • What happens to the flavour of the onions? • Why does this happen?

For Section 2.2.3 Fats and oils.

Activity

Complete the chart below to show your understanding of what happens when you use fats and oils in cooking:

Look at this picture	Describe what is happening to the food/ingredients in the picture and why it is happening	Answer these questions:
 Butter		• Why is the method of preparing the food like this used to make a biscuit base for a cheesecake or flan? • What happens to the biscuit base when it goes into the refrigerator for a while? • Why does this happen?
 Butter and flour		• Why is the person using their fingertips? • Why is the method of preparing the ingredients like this used to make pastry? • What will the texture of the pastry dough be like when the water is added?
 Butter and sugar		• Why is the method of preparing the ingredients like this used to make cakes? • What will the texture of the cake be like when it has finished being baked in the oven? • Why does this happen?

Chapter 5 Food spoilage and contamination

3.1.1 Micro-organisms and enzymes

What will I learn?

In this section you will learn about:

- what is meant by the word micro-organisms
- which micro-organisms can spoil food and make it unsafe to eat
- the conditions that micro-organisms need in order to live and multiply
- what is meant by the word enzyme
- how enzymes can spoil the palatability of foods.

Key terms

Micro-organisms: tiny forms of life, both plants and animals, only visible under a microscope

Food spoilage: making food unfit and unsafe to eat

Contaminate: making a food unsafe to eat by allowing it to come into contact with micro-organisms that will grow and multiply in it

Pathogenic: something that is capable of causing illness

Food poisoning: an illness caused by micro-organisms contaminating food

High-risk foods: foods that contain a lot of moisture and nutrients, especially protein (e.g. milk, cream, eggs, meat, fish), and easily support the growth of pathogenic micro-organisms, particularly bacteria. Also called **perishable foods**

Enzyme: the name given to natural substances in living things that speed up chemical reactions

Catalyst: a substance that speeds up the rate of a chemical reaction

Introduction

In Chapters 1–4 of this book, you have learned about why we need food, the functional and chemical properties of ingredients, and how and why we cook food.

In Chapter 3 (part 2.1.1), you learned that one of the main reasons we cook certain foods is to destroy the food poisoning bacteria they could contain and make them safe to eat.

Food poisoning is a common and unpleasant illness, which can lead to serious health complications in some people, e.g. babies and the elderly. Anyone who prepares and cooks food needs to know what causes food poisoning and should understand and follow the rules and safe procedures to prevent it from happening.

In Chapters 5 and 6 of this book, you will learn about bacteria and other things that can spoil the palatability of food (how it tastes, looks and feels, and how acceptable it is to someone to eat it) and make it unsafe to eat, and how you can prevent this from happening.

Micro-organisms

- **Micro-organisms** are tiny forms of life, both plants and animals. They can only be seen under a microscope. They are sometimes called **microbes.**

- Micro-organisms are found in many different places:

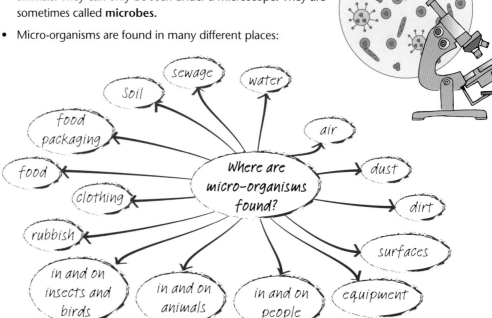

- Micro-organisms **spoil** food and make it unfit and unsafe to eat because they **contaminate** it with their **waste products**, their physical presence (being in the food) and the toxins (poisons) that they produce.

Micro-organisms that make food unsafe to eat and can cause food poisoning are called pathogens. There are lots of different **pathogenic** bacteria, moulds and yeasts.

Which micro-organisms can spoil food and make it unsafe to eat?

- There are three groups of micro-organisms that you need to know about that spoil foods and cause **food poisoning**: **bacteria, moulds** and **yeasts**.

- Each of these three groups has thousands of different types, but only some of them spoil food and make it unsafe to eat.

- Each type of micro-organism will be discussed in the following parts of this chapter.

Mould growing on bread

What conditions do micro-organisms need in order to live and multiply?

- All micro-organisms need suitable conditions in which to grow and multiply.

- Their growth and multiplication can be controlled by changing or preventing the conditions that allow these to happen, as the table below explains.

Suitable conditions needed by micro-organisms	Reason	How to control their growth and multiplication
1. A suitable **temperature** 	• Most micro-organisms grow and multiply the most rapidly when the temperature is warm (around 37°C is their **optimum** [best] temperature). • If the temperature is too hot, it will destroy them. • If the temperature is too cold, their growth and multiplication will slow down until it stops and they become **dormant**, which means they are still alive, but not active.	• Cook food thoroughly and for long enough at high enough temperatures to destroy micro-organisms. • Do not leave food out in a warm room for a long period of time. • Cool down left-over cooked food quickly and refrigerate it between 0°C and below 5°C, or freeze it at –18°C or below.
2. A supply of **moisture** 	• Micro-organisms need water for all their biological processes. • If there is not enough moisture in the food to supply water, they cannot grow or multiply.	• Preserve the food by drying it (e.g. dried milk, dried soups, dried fruit). • Preserve the food with high concentrations of either sugar (e.g. jam making) or salt (e.g. salted fish), which removes water from the micro-organisms' cells by a process called osmosis.

Suitable conditions needed by micro-organisms	Reason	How to control their growth and multiplication
3. A supply of **food** 	• Micro-organisms need nutrients and energy from food to enable them to grow and multiply.	• Prevent them from coming into contact with and contaminating food, by keeping the food covered and away from sources of micro-organisms (e.g. dirt, animals and flies).
4. Enough **time** 	• It takes time for micro-organisms to grow and multiply, and the more suitable the conditions, the quicker they will do so. • Most micro-organisms multiply every 10–20 minutes.	• Store, cook and cool foods thoroughly and correctly in order to avoid giving micro-organisms the time to grow and multiply. • Use food by its use-by date.
5. The right **pH** (acidity or alkalinity) 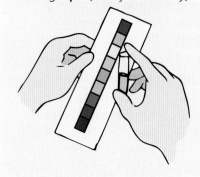	• If conditions are too acidic or too alkaline, this may affect whether they can grow and multiply.	• Preserve the food in acid (e.g. vinegar in pickles and chutneys) to prevent micro-organisms from growing and multiplying.

• Micro-organisms, particularly bacteria, will grow very easily in certain foods (e.g. meat, fish, seafood, poultry, milk, cream, cheese, cooked rice and eggs, and food products containing any of these) because they have lots of moisture and nutrients in them, especially protein. These foods are known as **high-risk foods** or **perishable foods**. Many of these foods are ready-to-eat and do not require any further heat treatment or cooking.

Enzymes

• **Enzymes** are natural substances (mostly proteins) that are found in foods and all living things.
• They are called **biological** **catalysts**, which means they have the ability to speed up chemical reactions.
• Enzymes cause fruits and vegetables that have been harvested to ripen (e.g. bananas) and eventually break down the cells and tissues in them.
• Enzymes cause the tissues of meat and fish and other animal foods to break down once the animal has been killed.
• Enzymes are proteins, so their action can be controlled by causing them to **denature** (e.g. by heat or acids), as explained in the next part of this chapter.

Study tip

To help you learn the meanings of the various key terms for the section on Food Safety, make a set of revision cards to test yourself and other people.

Stretch and challenge activity

According to the Food Standards Agency, there are more than one million cases of food poisoning in the UK every year.

Investigate which foods and micro-organisms are mainly responsible for this and why cases of food poisoning have increased in the last few decades.

Explain what actions food manufacturers, food retailers and consumers can take to help prevent food poisoning.

Practice questions

1. a) State two types of micro-organism that can spoil foods. *(2 marks)*

   b) Explain how micro-organisms make food unfit and unsafe to eat. *(3 marks)*

   c) State three conditions that micro-organisms need in order for them to grow and multiply. *(3 marks)*

2. a) Explain what enzymes are and describe what they do. *(2 marks)*

   b) Explain how enzymes affect fruits and vegetables when they have been harvested. *(2 marks)*

3. Explain what is meant by a high-risk food and give two examples of these. *(4 marks)*

3.1.2 The signs of food spoilage

What will I learn?

In this section you will learn about:
- how enzymes affect foods
- how moulds affect foods
- how yeasts affect foods.

How enzymes affect foods

Ripening

- Enzymes cause foods such as fruits to **ripen**.
- In the pictures below, you can see that both the tomatoes and bananas have ripened because they have gradually changed **colour** – it is the **enzymes** in the fruits that have caused this.
- What you cannot see is that other enzymes have also changed the **texture, flavour** and **aroma** of the fruits.
- In the tomatoes, they will gradually become sweeter, juicier and softer and have a typical tomato aroma.

Key term

Ripening: the process of a fruit or vegetable maturing so that it is ready to eat

The stages of ripening in tomatoes caused by enzymes

- Green bananas have very little flavour; they will be hard and will contain a lot of starch. As the enzymes start to ripen them, they will become sweeter, because the enzymes gradually break down the starch molecules into glucose molecules. They will become softer in texture and will develop a typical banana flavour and texture.

- Eventually bananas will turn a dark brown colour. They will be very soft and syrupy inside and very sweet. They will still be edible, but may not look so nice to eat. They would be perfect, however, to make a banana bread, so would not need to be wasted.

Activity

Investigate and evaluate the appearance, taste, texture and aroma of the different bananas from the list below:

1. A green banana.
2. A banana left at room temperature for a week.
3. A banana left at room temperature for two weeks.
4. A banana stored in the refrigerator.

Key terms

Enzymic browning: the discolouration of a fruit or vegetable due to the reaction of enzymes with plant cell substances and oxygen from the air

Oxidation: when substances combine with (pick up) oxygen

Germinate: this is the process that happens when a spore from a mould starts to grow on a food

Enzymic browning

- When you cut, bite, crush, grate, bruise or peel certain fruits and vegetables, they develop a brown/black/grey discolouration.

- These include apples, potatoes, avocados, mushrooms, aubergines (egg plants) and bananas. This is how it happens.

Task Tip:

As part of the NEA Task 1: Food Investigation you may be required to study and explain the process of enzyymic browning in different fruits and vegetables.

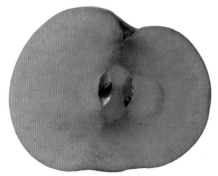
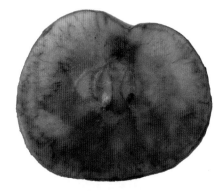

Apple gradually changing appearance due to enzymic browning

- Plant cells contain storage vacuoles (spaces) in the centre, which contain a variety of natural substances. Around the outside of the vacuole is cytoplasm which contains substances called **enzymes**.
- When the cell is broken open, the **enzymes** in the cytoplasm and **oxygen** from the air mix with the substances in the vacuole. When substances combine with (pick up) oxygen, it is called oxidation. This makes the substances join together and change colour.
- The discoloured substances make the food less appetising to eat, but it is possible to delay or prevent them from forming in the following ways.
  – By adding an acid (e.g. lemon juice), which **denatures** the **enzyme protein** – this is often done when making a fresh fruit salad containing apples and pears.
  – By cooking the food, so that the heat denatures the enzyme protein.
  – By putting the food into cold water, which prevents the oxygen mixing with the enzymes and substances in the plant vacuoles.
  – By **blanching** vegetables before they are frozen. Blanching means:
    - to plunge (quickly put in) the vegetables into boiling water for a very short time (to denature the enzyme protein);
    - then drain the vegetables through a colander or sieve;
    - then plunge the vegetables into iced or very cold water to stop the heating process, so that they retain their colour and flavour;
    - then drain them again and freeze them.

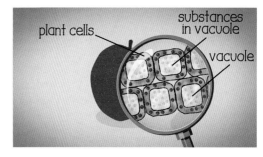
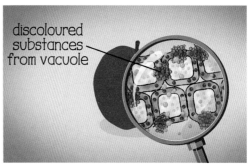

How moulds affect foods

- Moulds are a type of micro-organism. They are related to mushrooms and there are many types.
- Some types of mould can contaminate food by growing and multiplying in it and producing waste products or toxins (poisons), which spoil the appearance, smell, texture and flavour of food and can cause food poisoning.
- In order to prevent moulds from multiplying in food, it is important to understand how they grow and multiply.
- Moulds are small but, when they grow on foods, it is possible to see them because they grow on the surface of the food and have a furry appearance.
- Like all micro-organisms, moulds need suitable conditions to grow and multiply: the right temperature, moisture, food, time and pH.
- Moulds multiply by sending out tiny airborne spores that land on food and germinate (start to grow) if conditions are right. You need a microscope to see the individual spores.
- If the conditions are right, the spores will land on some food and germinate.
- The germinated spores will send down roots into the food (called a mycelium, which you cannot see without a microscope) and will send up thousands of 'shoots' with a fruiting body on the top of each, which is what you can see as mould.

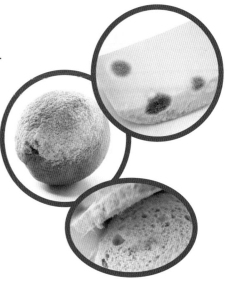

Examples of mouldy foods

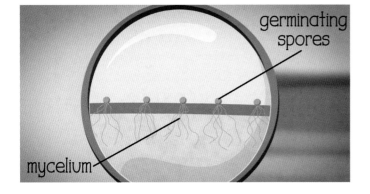
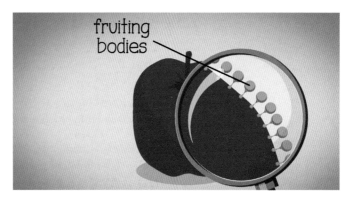

- When they are ripe, the fruiting bodies will burst and send out a shower of spores, which will travel through the air to other foods, thus repeating the life cycle of the mould.
- Foods that have gone mouldy during storage (e.g. Cheddar cheese) will often look alright inside if the mould is cut off the surface. However, harmful waste substances produced by the mould (which we cannot taste or smell) may spread into the food through the mycelium and may be harmful to us if we eat them.

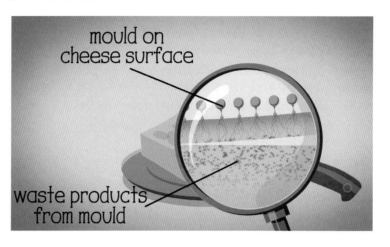

How yeasts affect foods

- There are many species of wild yeasts and they can spoil foods, especially those that contain sugar, such as fresh and dried fruits (e.g. grapes, apples, strawberries).
- Like moulds, they will settle on the food and start to grow, and then **ferment** the sugar to produce CO_2 gas and alcohol.
- Yeast spoilage appears as a pale brown, spotted growth on the skin of the fruit, which becomes brown and mushy as the yeast continues to grow.

Yeasts growing on a piece of fruit

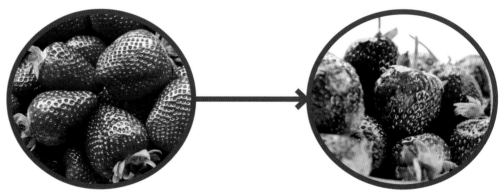

Practice questions

1. Explain the reasons for the following:
   a) When making a fresh fruit salad, it is important to add some fresh lemon juice to the fruit.
   b) When storing bread, it is important to keep it in a cool, dry storage area in a covered container.
   c) Why it is best practice to throw away cheese if it becomes mouldy during storage, rather than scrape off the mould and eat the remaining cheese? *(9 marks)*

2. Explain why it is important to regularly check food items in a refrigerator and food cupboard, and to use them up in rotation (use oldest first and newest last). *(6 marks)*

Micro-organisms in food
3.1.3 production

What will I learn?

In this section you will learn about:

- micro-organisms that are used in the production of different food products
- micro-organisms used in the production of Cheddar cheese
- micro-organisms used in the production of bread
- micro-organisms used in the production of yogurt.

Micro-organisms used in the production of different food products

- So far in this chapter, you have learned that there are many types of micro-organisms, some of which need to be prevented from growing in food because they are **pathogenic** and can cause food poisoning.

- It is important to know and understand that there are also many types of micro-organisms that are **non-pathogenic** and do not cause food poisoning, and are, in fact, used to make a variety of familiar food products.

- In this part of the chapter, you will learn about a few of these.

Micro-organisms used in the production of cheese

- When cheese is made, two types of micro-organisms are used – **bacteria** and **moulds**.

- In Cheddar cheese, just bacteria are used, but in blue cheeses such as Stilton, Danish Blue and Gorgonzola, moulds are also used to give the blue colour and distinctive flavour.

- The following table shows you how Cheddar cheese is produced. The process is similar for other cheeses.

Key terms

Pathogenic: a micro-organism that is harmful to humans and can cause food poisoning

Non-pathogenic: a micro-organism that is **not** harmful to humans and **does not** cause food poisoning

Pasteurisation: this means heating fresh milk to 72°C for 15 seconds in order to kill pathogenic micro-organisms that may be in it

Homogenised: forcing milk under high pressure through a fine sieve, in order to break up the fat into tiny droplets. This means that the droplets stay suspended in the milk and do not separate out into a layer of cream

Production stage	What happens	Reason and explanation
1. The milk is pasteurised 	Milk is pasteurised, which means it is heated to 72°C for 15 seconds then cooled to 30°C in a large tank.	• Milk is a perfect food for bacteria to grow and multiply. • Fresh milk contains many types of safe bacteria and also some pathogenic (harmful) bacteria. • Pasteurisation kills the pathogenic bacteria.

Production stage	What happens	Reason and explanation
2. A special **bacteria culture** is added to the milk 	The bacteria turns the **lactose sugar** (in the milk) into **lactic acid**.	The **lactic acid** does several things for the cheese: • It **coagulates** the protein in the milk. • It adds **flavour** and **texture** to the cheese. • It helps to **preserve** the cheese.
3. An enzyme called **rennet** is added 	The **rennet** also **coagulates** the protein.	• **Rennet** turns the milk into a **semi-solid** called **curds** and a **liquid** called **whey**.
4. Cutting the **curds** 	The solid **curds** are cut up finely using special knives.	• This helps to release the liquid **whey**.
5. Draining off the liquid **whey** 	The **whey** is collected and used to make ricotta cheese and as an additive in other food products such as bread, biscuits and pastries (look for the words '**whey protein**' in the ingredients list).	• The **whey** contains high biological value (HBV) protein (see page 2) so is a valuable by-product of the cheese-making process.

Production stage	What happens	Reason and explanation
6. Drying the **curd** 	The **curd** is stacked into slabs that are turned over at regular intervals. Notice that the familiar colour of the cheese is starting to develop.	• Stacking helps more **whey** to drain off.
7. Milling the **curd** 	The slabs of **curd** are heated and put through a curd mill, and cut into small pieces.	• Cutting the **curd** into small pieces helps to form the final texture of the cheese.
8. Pressing the cheese 	Salt is added and then the **curds** are put into a shape (mould) and pressed tightly overnight, either in traditional round-shaped cheese moulds or in modern rectangular-shaped cheese moulds.	• Salt adds flavour and helps preserve the cheese. • Pressing makes the cheese become a solid block.
9. Ripening/maturing the cheese 	The cheese is placed on shelves for a few weeks or months in a special room where the temperature and humidity (moisture in the air) is carefully controlled.	• The bacteria in the culture added at the beginning help to **ripen** the cheese, which means to develop the flavour, texture and colour of the cheese. • **Mature** cheeses are ripened for a long time so that they develop strong flavours. • Cheese is stored in a cool place to control the growth of moulds and other bacteria that may contaminate and spoil it.

Activity

How to make soft cheese

It is easy to make your own soft cheese by following the instructions below. When you have finished making the soft cheese, evaluate the texture, flavour and appearance.

Ingredients
500ml whole milk
1 lemon
A pinch of salt

Flavouring
Chives
Chopped pineapple
Peeled and crushed garlic

Equipment
Saucepan, large bowl, knife, lemon squeezer, piece of muslin cloth, sieve

Method:

1. Pour the milk into a saucepan and stir in a pinch of salt. Bring to the boil over medium heat, stirring occasionally.

2. Squeeze the lemon to extract the juice.

3. When the milk begins to boil, turn off the heat. Stir the lemon juice into the milk and the milk will curdle (turn into curds and whey).

4. Line a sieve with muslin cloth and pour the milk through the cloth to catch the curds. What is left in the muslin cloth is the **curd**. The liquid is the **whey**. Gather the cloth around the cheese, and squeeze out as much of the whey as you can.

5. Open the cloth and add flavouring to the soft cheese.

Shape the cheese into a round and cover and store it in the refrigerator. Eat the cheese within a few days of making it. You can use the whey to make scones, or pancake batter.

Stretch and challenge activity

Halloumi cheese has become very popular as an ingredient in cooking and can be used in a variety of ways.

Investigate how halloumi is made, how it is traditionally prepared and eaten in its country of origin and the science behind why it is able to be heated to high temperatures without melting and losing its shape.

Plan, prepare and cook a variety of dishes using halloumi and evaluate the cheese and the overall dishes for texture, flavour and appearance.

Blue cheeses

Blue cheeses such as Stilton, Gorgonzola and Danish Blue use special moulds to give them their distinctive blue pattern and flavour.

Blue Stilton cheese is a very traditional English cheese and is made in a similar way to Cheddar cheese, except for a few differences, as explained below.

1. The spores of a special mould are added to the pasteurised milk with the bacteria culture in stage 2 (see page 166).

2. In stage 8, the curds are put into a cylinder-shaped mould for a while, but they are not pressed. They are taken out of the moulds and allowed to continue to drain during the ripening process in stage 9.

3. When the cheese has developed its traditional crust (rind), it is pierced with stainless steel needles to allow air into the cheese. This enables the mould spores to germinate and spread inside the cheese to form blue 'veins' and a distinctive flavour.

Blue veined Stilton cheese

Moulds used in cheese making

- Non-pathogenic (harmless) moulds are also used to ripen cheeses and add flavour to them.

- For example, in cheeses such as Brie and Camembert, special **mould spores** are either sprayed onto the cheese or it is dipped into a liquid containing them.

- By carefully controlling how the cheese is stored while it is ripening (which only takes a few weeks), this type of cheese will develop a white surface mould, as you can see in the picture, and a special flavour.

Ripened Camembert cheese

Activity

Use your sensory analysis skills to carry out some cheese tasting. Evaluate the sensory characteristics of five cheeses and discuss how they have been produced, for example:

- Cheddar

- Cheshire

- Brie

- Blue Stilton

- Goat's cheese.

Micro-organisms used in the production of bread

Recap

- When bread is made, a specially cultivated, non-pathogenic variety of the micro-organism **yeast** is used.

- In Chapter 4, part 2.2.4 (see page 149), you learned about yeast as a raising agent in baking.

- Yeast is a type of microscopic, single-celled fungi and is related to mushrooms.

- Specific types of yeast are produced for use in bread making.

- If given the right conditions of **warmth, moisture, food** (sugar or starch) and **time**, yeast will use the sugar or starch for energy and produce **carbon dioxide (CO_2) gas** to make bread and other yeast doughs rise, and **alcohol** as by-products.

- This whole process is called **fermentation**.

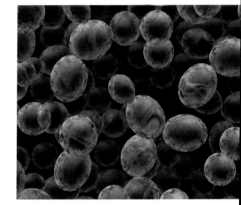

Photograph of yeast cells greatly magnified

Fresh yeast – dissolved and activated with warm water and sugar before adding to flour

Dried yeast – this has larger granules (dissolved and activated with warm water and sugar before adding to flour)

Fast acting, instant dried yeast – this has very fine granules (added directly to flour)

Micro-organisms used in the production of yogurt

- Yogurt is made from milk that has been **fermented** by two types of non-pathogenic bacteria.
- The following table shows you how yogurt is produced.

1. Preparing the milk

What happens	Reason and explanation
Heat-treated, whole, semi-skimmed or skimmed milk can be used to make yogurt. The milk is **homogenised** – this is a process that breaks the milk fat into tiny droplets.	Heat treatment destroys pathogenic bacteria. Homogenisation ensures that the fat droplets stay suspended in the milk and do not separate out, as show in the diagram below. 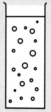   Raw milk Cold raw milk after 1 hour Homogenised milk during storage Fat droplets suspended in non-homogenised milk gradually rise to the surface This gives the yogurt a smooth and consistent texture. 42°C is the right temperature for the bacteria that are added in stage 2 to grow and ferment the lactose in the milk.

2. Adding the bacteria culture

What happens	Reason and explanation
- The milk is held at 42°C while the bacteria ferment the lactose sugar in the milk and produce lactic acid. - When the pH (measure of acidity) reaches 4.5, the milk is cooled to 7°C. 	- The lactic acid denatures and coagulates the milk proteins, which makes the milk become semi-solid. - The lactic acid and other natural substances that are produced give the yogurt its distinct, traditional flavour. - Cooling the milk to 7°C stops the fermentation process. - This produces natural yogurt. 

3. Flavouring the yogurt

What happens	Reason and explanation
Fruit or other flavours (e.g. honey, coconut, fudge, ginger) are added. 	There are lots of different flavours and ingredients added to yogurt to give a wide variety of choice. 

Practice questions

1. a) Outline the difference between a pathogenic and a non-pathogenic micro-organism. *(2 marks)*

   b) Name **two** food products where micro-organisms are used in their manufacture. *(2 marks)*

2. Explain why micro-organisms are used in the manufacture of the following foods:

   a) Stilton blue-veined cheese. *(3 marks)*

   b) Bread. *(3 marks)*

   c) Yogurt. *(3 marks)*

[3.1.4] Bacterial contamination

What will I learn?

In this section you will learn about:

- food poisoning
- the main types of bacteria that cause food poisoning
- how bacteria grow and multiply
- how foods become contaminated with bacteria
- how to control and prevent bacterial contamination.

Food poisoning

Recap

In part 3.1.1 of this chapter, you learned that:

- food poisoning is a very common and unpleasant illness, which can lead to serious health complications in some people
- micro-organisms make food unfit and unsafe to eat because they contaminate it with their **waste products**, their **physical presence** (being in the food) and the **toxins (poisons)** that they produce
- micro-organisms that make food unsafe to eat and cause food poisoning are called pathogens
- there are many different pathogenic bacteria, moulds and yeasts
- **bacteria** are the micro-organisms that most commonly cause food poisoning.

What happens to the body if you have food poisoning?

- Most **pathogenic bacteria** cause food poisoning inside the **digestive system**, particularly in the intestines, which are in the area of the body called the **abdomen**.

- The **symptoms of food poisoning** can include:

- bad abdominal pain (stomach ache)
- diarrhoea

- nausea (feeling sick)
- vomiting (being sick)

- headache
- dizziness

- a raised body temperature
- feeling cold and shivery

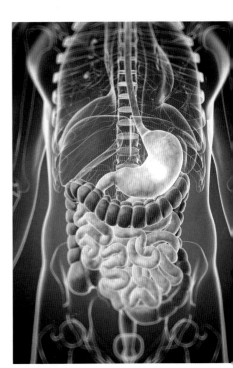

The abdomen, showing the stomach, small and large intestines.

Study tip

Learning the names of bacteria can be challenging. Try to learn the names of the examples given in the tables below and how they make people ill. You can shorten the name Staphylococcus aureus to S.Aureus if that helps.

- Some pathogenic bacteria can work their way out of the digestive system and into the **bloodstream**, where they go round the body and **damage vital body organs**, such as the kidneys and liver.

- Food poisoning is particularly dangerous for **babies** and **young children**, **pregnant women**, **elderly people** and **people who have a weak immune system**.

- Usually, the **onset** of food poisoning (the time it takes between eating contaminated food and the symptoms of food poisoning appearing) can be anything from a few hours to a few days. In some cases it can be longer than this, which can make it difficult to identify which food caused the illness, as it is hard for people to remember what they ate and drank several days ago – (for example, try to remember everything that you ate and drank 7 days ago!).

Main types of bacteria that cause food poisoning

- There are many different types of **pathogenic** bacteria that cause food poisoning.

- The table below shows the names of some pathogenic bacteria you need to know, which foods they are found in and the typical symptoms of food poisoning for each.

Campylobacter

Foods/drinks/places where it is often found	Symptoms of food poisoning
• Raw poultry and meat • Milk • Untreated (dirty) water  	• Diarrhoea (often with blood in it) • Abdominal pain • Nausea • Fever
	Incubation time **(how long it takes for the symptoms to appear)** 48–60 hours

E. coli

Foods/drinks/places where it is often found	Symptoms of food poisoning
• Beef (especially minced beef) and other meat • Raw milk (milk that has not been heat treated) • Untreated (dirty) water  	• Diarrhoea • Abdominal pain • Vomiting • Fever • Kidney damage or failure
	Incubation time **(how long it takes for the symptoms to appear)** 12–24 hours (sometimes longer after 12–24 hours)

Salmonella

Foods/drinks/places where it is often found	Symptoms of food poisoning
• Raw and undercooked poultry, eggs and meat • Raw milk (milk that has not been heat treated) 	• Diarrhoea • Abdominal pain • Vomiting • Fever

Incubation time (how long it takes for the symptoms to appear)
12–36 hours

Listeria

Foods/drinks/places where it is often found	Symptoms of food poisoning
• Soft cheeses • Cheese made from unpasteurised milk • Salad vegetables • Pâtés 	• Flu-like symptoms • Can cause miscarriage in pregnant women or infect the unborn baby

Incubation time (how long it takes for the symptoms to appear)
1–70 **days** (which is why it is often difficult for people to remember what might have caused their illness)

Staphylococcus aureus

Foods/drinks/places where it is often found	Symptoms of food poisoning
People – especially on their hands, in their nose and mouth, on the skin, in cuts and skin infections, raw milk, cold cooked meats, dairy products 	• Abdominal pain • Vomiting • Low body temperature

Incubation time (how long it takes for the symptoms to appear)
1–6 hours

How do bacteria grow and multiply?

- There are thousands of different types of bacteria.
- Under the microscope, it is possible to see that they come in different shapes and sizes.
- Bacteria are so small that **several hundreds of thousands** of them can fit into an area which is the size of the **full stop** at the end of this sentence.

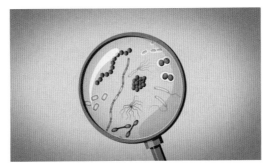

Colonies (large groups) of millions of bacteria

- Because they are so small, it is impossible to see them in some food by just looking at it, which makes it very difficult to know if a food is **contaminated** or not.
- Like all micro-organisms, bacteria need the right **conditions** to grow and multiply: a suitable **temperature**, **food**, **moisture**, and **time**.
- The picture below shows how different temperatures affect the growth rates of bacteria.

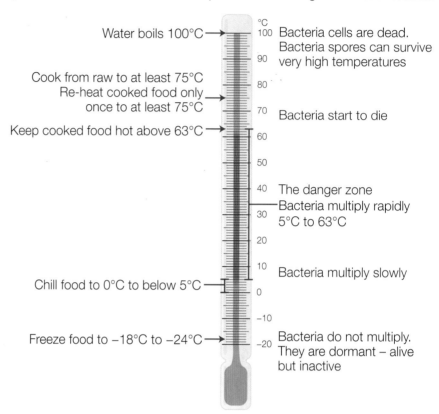

Water boils 100°C → 100 Bacteria cells are dead. Bacteria spores can survive very high temperatures

Cook from raw to at least 75°C
Re-heat cooked food only once to at least 75°C
Keep cooked food hot above 63°C →

70 Bacteria start to die

40 The danger zone
Bacteria multiply rapidly
5°C to 63°C

10 Bacteria multiply slowly

Chill food to 0°C to below 5°C

Freeze food to −18°C to −24°C → −20 Bacteria do not multiply. They are dormant – alive but inactive

Key terms

Danger Zone: the range of temperatures (5°C to 63°C) that are just right for bacteria to multiply rapidly

Spore: a special protective coating that some types of bacteria grow if the conditions are not right for them to multiply

Germinate: when the conditions become right, the protective spore breaks open and the bacteria becomes active again

Contamination: making a food unsafe to eat by allowing it to come into contact with micro-organisms that will grow and multiply in it

Cross-contamination: how bacteria are spread from one source onto some food

The **Danger Zone** (5°C to 63°C) on the thermometer is the range of temperatures that are just right for bacteria to multiply, and they do so very rapidly, which is why it is important to store food below 5°C and to heat it and keep it hot above 63°C.

- If the conditions are right, bacteria multiply about every 20 minutes. Each bacteria cell divides into two new bacteria cells, in this way:

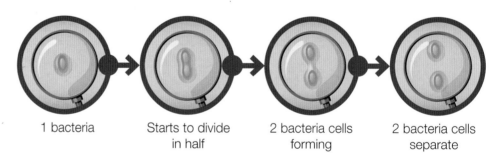

1 bacteria   Starts to divide in half   2 bacteria cells forming   2 bacteria cells separate

- Therefore one bacteria cell can give rise to millions more in just a few hours. There are various video clips that show this (speeded up) on the Internet, e.g. www.youtube.com/watch?v=zrx7Xg0gkQ4
- There would never be only one bacteria cell to start with in some food – there would be many thousands; so you can see just how many bacteria could be produced and why it would be so easy to get food poisoning.
- A few types of bacteria are really dangerous, because if the conditions are not right for them to multiply, they will produce **spores**.

- Spores are a protective coating in which the bacteria remain inactive until the right conditions return, then they **germinate** (the spore breaks open and the bacteria becomes active again).

- As they germinate, the bacteria spores produce deadly poisons (toxins).

- Spores can be very resistant to heat and acids.

conditions too cold too dry no food

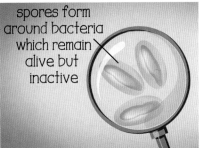

spores form around bacteria which remain alive but inactive

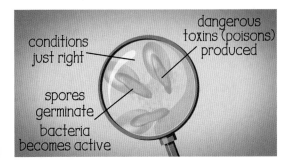

conditions just right

dangerous toxins (poisons) produced

spores germinate bacteria becomes active

Activity

Using a calculator, work out how many bacteria will be produced from just one bacteria cell in 8 hours. Remember, you need to double the number for every 20 minutes (three times for each hour). Write down the number you end up with and then try to say it!

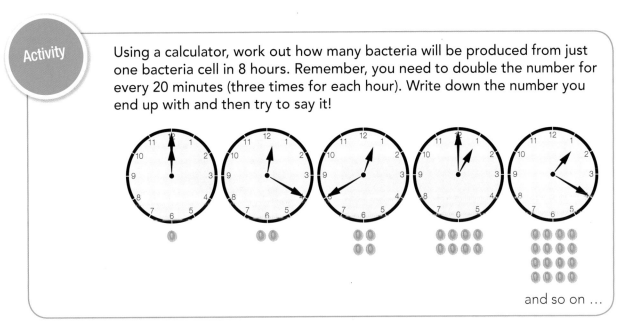

and so on …

How foods become contaminated with bacteria
and how to control and prevent bacterial contamination

Recap

- In part 3.1.1 of this chapter, you learnt that micro-organisms, including bacteria, are found in many different places (see the mind map on page 158).

- You also learned that food can become **contaminated** by micro-organisms.

- Contamination means making a food unsafe to eat by allowing it to come into contact with micro-organisms that will grow and multiply in it.

- Cross-contamination is a term used to describe how bacteria are spread from one source (e.g. a work surface, knife, chopping board, some raw chicken, a dirty dishcloth or someone's hands) onto some food.

- The following chart shows:
  - the different **sources** of bacterial contamination,
  - the ways in which food can become **contaminated** by bacteria,
  - how contamination can be **controlled** and **prevented**.

Sources of bacterial contamination

Other contaminated foods (e.g. raw meat, poultry or fish, raw eggs, vegetables or fruits, pâté, cream, soft cheese, cooked meats, gravy)

How does contamination happen?

- Storing raw foods (e.g. meat, poultry or fish) next to cooked foods.

- Allowing raw meat, poultry, fish or other high-risk foods to drip onto other foods.

- Storing or preparing and allowing egg shells to come into contact with other high-risk foods.

- Storing unwashed vegetables with soil still on them next to high-risk foods such as meat, poultry, fish, eggs and dairy products.

- Adding a contaminated, high-risk food, such as gravy, cream or **pâté**, to other foods in a meal.

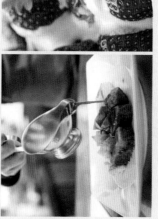

Using the same chopping boards, knives and other equipment for different foods (e.g. raw and cooked meat, poultry or fish, eggs, cream), without thoroughly washing and drying them in between. This is why different coloured chopping boards and other equipment are used for different foods in the catering industry.

Chopping board colour codes

Red	**Raw meat/poultry**
Yellow	**Cooked meat poultry/fish**
Blue	**Raw fish**
Brown	**Root vegetables**
Green	**Leafy vegetables/ salads/fruit**
White	**Bakery items/ dairy foods**

How to control and prevent bacterial contamination

- Separate raw and cooked foods.

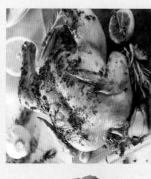

- Store high-risk foods in sealed containers, food packaging or on solid trays in a refrigerator, so they cannot drip onto other foods.

- Wash hands after handling high-risk foods.

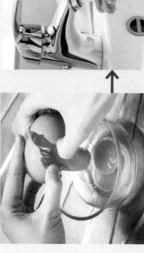

- Make sure all high-risk foods are stored correctly and cooked thoroughly for the right amount of time and to the correct core temperature of at least 75°C for 2 minutes.

- Use separate equipment for different foods or wash equipment thoroughly in between using it for different foods.

Sources of bacterial contamination

Work surfaces and equipment

How does contamination happen?

- Failing to thoroughly wash, rinse and dry work surfaces and equipment after using them for food preparation and cooking.

- Using the same equipment or work surfaces for different preparation and cooking processes and foods without washing and cleaning them thoroughly in between.

- Using dirty dishcloths and drying cloths to clean equipment and work surfaces.

- Not using hot water and detergent to clean properly.

- People putting dirty shoes or other objects onto surfaces used for food preparation.

- Allowing animals and insects to walk/sit/land on work surfaces and equipment.

How to control and prevent bacterial contamination

- Clear away, wash work surfaces and equipment regularly – 'Clean as you go'.

- Allow heavily soiled equipment to soak in hot water and detergent to make it easier to clean later.

- Use **HOT** water and detergent to wash up equipment and regularly replenish (replace) with clean water.

- Dishwashers are used in many catering establishments and homes. They heat the water to a very high temperature, which removes food residues and micro-organisms very effectively from equipment, cutlery and crockery.

- Disposable cloths and wipes can be used for cleaning purposes.

- Leaving equipment to dry in the air avoids the use of drying-up cloths, which can be a source of cross-contamination if they are not regularly replaced and cleaned.

Sources of bacterial contamination

People preparing, handling, cooking and serving food

How does contamination happen?

People failing to wash their hands thoroughly:

- before, during and after preparing, handling, cooking and serving food. (Look at the pictures of hands below each of the following activities to see how many bacteria collect on the hands before they are washed.)

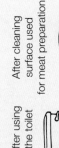
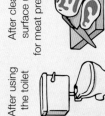
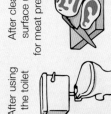

After handling raw chicken

After handling a dirty dishcloth

After using the toilet

After cleaning surface used for meat preparation

BEFORE WASHING

- after using the toilet
- after disposing of food waste in a bin.
- Touching/picking their nose, mouth and face whilst preparing, handling, cooking and serving food.
- Licking their fingers or equipment they are using, then touching the food or putting the equipment back into the food.
- Coughing, sneezing or spitting on or near food.
- Wearing dirty clothing when preparing, handling, cooking and serving food.
- Not following the rules of food safety and hygiene.

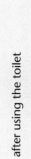
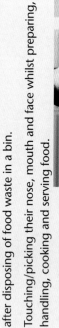
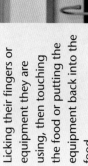
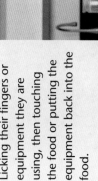

How to control and prevent bacterial contamination

- Wash your hands regularly when handling, preparing, cooking and serving food. Scrub your nails to remove dirt deposits.
- Wash your hands thoroughly.

1. Wet your hands   **2.** Liquid soap   **3.** Lather and scrub 20 sec

4. Rinse 10 sec   **5.** Dry your hands   **6.** Turn off tap

- Tie your hair back and wear clean clothes (apron, chef's whites) when cooking.

- Do not cough, sneeze or spit near food.
- Cover up cuts and sores on the skin with a detectable, blue, waterproof plaster.

- Do not lick your fingers or utensils when cooking.
- Remove jewellery from your hands and wrists.
- Remove false nails or wear disposable gloves when you cook.

Sources of bacterial contamination

Pests including flies and other insects, rodents (rats and mice), birds, pet animals such as cats and dogs

How does contamination happen?

- Pests and pet animals carry bacteria and other micro-organisms in and on their bodies and in their waste products (urine and faeces).
- They can contaminate food by urinating and defecating (going to the toilet) on it, and by landing on it, walking over it and eating it.
- Flies lay eggs in food, which then hatch into maggots and contaminate the food.

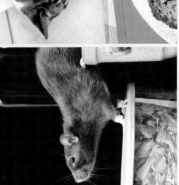

How to control and prevent bacterial contamination

- Cover food to protect it from flies.
- Make sure that pests cannot easily get into the kitchen by using deterrents (e.g. fly screens, food nets and insect umbrellas, metal grilles over drains and holes in the walls, electric fly killers).

- Keep pet animal feeding bowls and utensils separate from those used by people.
- Do not allow pets onto kitchen work surfaces.

Section 3: Food Safety

Sources of bacterial contamination

Waste food and rubbish

How does contamination happen?

- Waste food and rubbish can quickly start to decompose in a warm kitchen, and bacteria and other micro-organisms will grow in it.

- Waste bins attract pests.

- Waste bins that have been allowed to become dirty with food spills will quickly become contaminated with bacteria.

- In the UK each year, about **15 million tonnes** of food is wasted and thrown away. Almost 50% of this wasted food comes from our homes (source: http://england.lovefoodhatewaste.com/node/2163).

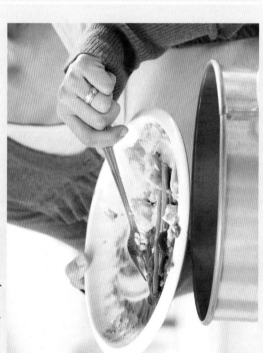

How to control and prevent bacterial contamination

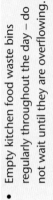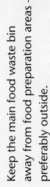

- Empty kitchen food waste bins regularly throughout the day – do not wait until they are overflowing.

- Keep the main food waste bin away from food preparation areas – preferably outside.

- Regularly wash the waste bin with detergent and hot water.

- Wash your hands after throwing rubbish away.

- Try to avoid wasting food.

- Recycle food scraps and waste where possible so it can be turned into compost to grow more food.

Sources of bacterial contamination

Food packaging

- Food packaging that is not stored correctly in a factory or kitchen may become contaminated by bacteria if pests (e.g. flies and mice) are able to land or walk on it and drop their waste products onto it, or if the packaging gets dirty.

- Canned foods can become damaged if they are dropped or badly stored and may develop tiny splits, which could allow bacteria into the canned food inside.

- Cans that have gone rusty may develop tiny holes in them, which could allow bacteria in.

- If plastic packaging, such as vacuum packaging (which is where all the air is removed from around a food, such as cold meats and cheeses) becomes damaged, the air can get back in and micro-organisms will contaminate the food.

- Packaging used for long-life foods (e.g. milk, fruit juice, soup) must be tightly sealed to prevent the entry of micro-organisms into the food.

- Once long-life packaging is opened, the food inside must be treated as fresh, refrigerated and used up within a few days.

How to control and prevent bacterial contamination

- Food packaging should be stored in a clean, dry place and protected from pests.

- Always check food packaging and labels for 'use-by' and 'best before' dates that tell you when the food should be eaten by (see page 186).

- Always check that the packaging on food that you buy is not damaged.

- Food factories use computer technology to check packaging for any **flaws** (faults) in it, particularly where the packaging is joined and sealed.

- Do not buy food if you think the packaging is damaged, especially with high-risk foods.

- Remember that once vacuum packaging or long-life food packaging is opened, the food must be treated as fresh food, stored correctly and used up within a few days as it will have become exposed to contamination by micro-organisms.

Practice questions

Section A consists of multiple choice questions.

There are 10 marks available. Answer all questions.

For each question you should shade in **one** box.

1. Cross-contamination of food can be caused by:
   a) Not washing your hands properly ☐
   b) All of these ☐
   c) Storing raw foods next to cooked foods ☐
   d) Using the same equipment for different foods without washing it in between ☐

2. If you have food poisoning, which of the following symptoms are you most likely to have?
   a) Ear ache ☐
   b) Runny nose ☐
   c) Sore throat ☐
   d) Stomach ache ☐

3. What will be the effect on the bacteria in a food if you store it in a refrigerator?
   a) They will stop growing ☐
   b) They will grow very quickly ☐
   c) They will grow fairly slowly ☐
   d) They will all die ☐

4. Which of the following pairs of foods are linked with Listeria food poisoning?
   a) Salad vegetables and egg ☐
   b) Salad vegetables and pâtés ☐
   c) Rice and soft cheeses ☐
   d) Soft cheeses and egg ☐

5. Which of the following food groups are **all** high-risk foods?
   a) Gravy, raw meat, pâté ☐
   b) Raw fish, dairy products, cakes ☐
   c) Cooked meat, eggs, dried pasta ☐
   d) Raw meat, biscuits, vegetables ☐

6. How often should food waste in a kitchen be thrown away into a waste bin outside?
   a) Twice a day ☐
   b) Regularly throughout the day ☐
   c) Only when the kitchen waste bin overflows ☐
   d) Every other day ☐

7. Some bacteria produce spores in which they stay for a while. Why do they do this?
   a) They can multiply easier inside a spore ☐
   b) They want to keep away from the light ☐
   c) The conditions are not right for them to grow and multiply ☐
   d) They want to keep away from the air ☐

8. Which one of the following is important in helping to prevent bacterial contamination?
   a) Clean as you go ☐
   b) Make sure all the lights work ☐
   c) Make sure all the equipment is working ☐
   d) Store heavy equipment in low cupboards ☐

9. Which one of the following statements is TRUE?
   a) Some bacteria are pathogenic ☐
   b) All bacteria are pathogenic ☐
   c) No bacteria are pathogenic ☐
   d) Only bacteria spores are pathogenic ☐

10. In ideal conditions pathogenic bacteria multiply every:
    a) 20 seconds ☐
    b) 2 hours ☐
    c) 60 minutes ☐
    d) 20 minutes ☐

    (10 marks)

Answers on page 184.

Section B: Explain, in detail, why the following practices may result in food poisoning. Give reasons for your answers.

a) Leaving some chicken and salad sandwiches, in a plastic bag, inside a car for 3 hours on a warm day before eating them for lunch. *(4 marks)*

b) Leaving some left-over cooked meat from a roast dinner, uncovered, on a plate in a warm kitchen for a few hours. *(4 marks)*

c) Sneezing over some food when you are preparing it. *(4 marks)*

Stretch and challenge activity

Read the following case study and investigate the food safety issues that occurred by answering the following questions.

Scenario: To celebrate a 16ᵗʰ birthday, a barbeque party for 30 people is held in the garden on a hot sunny day. The food, which is going to be a help-yourself buffet, will include:

MENU

Mains
- Barbequed chicken joints
- Sausages
- Beef burgers
- Vegetarian burgers

Salads
- Green salad
- Tomato and mozzarella
- Bean salad
- Rice and prawn salad

Sides
- Bread rolls
- Jacket potatoes
- Various cheeses *including Brie, Camembert, unpasteurised goat's cheese, Cheddar and blue Stilton*

Desserts
- Fresh cream and fruit-filled meringues
- Fruit salad
- Banoffee pie
- Fresh cream filled profiteroles with chocolate sauce

At 12 noon, the food is put out, uncovered, on tables for people to help themselves and two people start to cook the chicken, sausages and burgers on the barbeque. The chicken and sausages were stored in the freezer and have not fully defrosted, but they decide to cook them anyway. They use their hands to pick up the raw food to place it on the barbeque, then serve it at the end, without washing their hands in between.

Cooking the food on the barbeque is slow and takes nearly two hours, because there are problems with fitting everything onto the barbeque. Some of the chicken and sausages appear to cook fast and start to burn on the outside, so they are set aside on a plate, ready for serving, while the rest are cooked.

The food is finally served two and a half hours after it was put out on the tables.

Within two to three days, ten of the guests who went to the barbeque start to vomit (be sick), have severe abdominal pains, diarrhoea and a fever. Another four guests have similar symptoms, but with shivering and a low body temperature. Two weeks later, another guest develops flu-like symptoms which makes her feel ill for several days.

In your investigation, examine closely and explain in detail:

1. What caused several people to become ill after the barbeque? *(2 marks)*
2. Why did some people have different symptoms from others? *(3 marks)*
3. Which foods were likely to have been the source of the micro-organisms? *(4 marks)*
4. Which micro-organisms are likely to have caused the illnesses? *(3 marks)*
5. What mistakes were made at the barbeque party that probably caused the illnesses? *(5 marks)*
6. How could the illnesses have been prevented? *(3 marks)*
7. What are the safety rules that should be followed when barbequing food? *(4 marks)*

Practice questions

Answers to practice questions on page 182.

1b	3c	5a	7c	9a
2d	4b	6b	8a	10d

Chapter 6 Principles of food safety

3.2.1 Buying and storing food

What will I learn?

In this section you will learn about:

- food safety advice when buying and storing food
- what to look for when buying food
- types of food storage
- temperature control in food storage.

Buying food

Introduction

Most people in the UK buy their food from supermarkets and store it at home in refrigerators, freezers and kitchen cupboards.

There are other places to buy food, including:

- street and covered markets
- small independent shops
- farm shops and farmers markets
- home delivery companies.

Key terms

Shelf-life: how long a food product will last before it becomes unsafe/unpalatable [unpleasant] to eat

Use-by date: the date by which high-risk/perishable foods should be eaten. After the use-by date the food may not look or taste different, but it will be unsafe to eat

Best before/best before end (of month or year) date: after this date, a non-high-risk food will still be safe to eat, but not be at its best quality, e.g. have begun to go stale (changed in appearance, texture and flavour)

Ambient: ordinary room temperature; average between 19°C and 21°C, but variable according to the season

Tainted: when a food picks up the smell or flavour of another food nearby, which spoils its palatability

Food safety advice when buying food

Wherever you buy food, there are a number of checks you can do to make sure that the food you buy is in good condition and safe to eat.

The chart below shows you what to check for.

The food shop/market stall/workers

What to look for when buying food	Why this is important
• Are the premises clean and are the workers wearing clean and appropriate clothing? • Is the food displayed well and kept at the right temperature (i.e. not in the Danger Zone – see page 174)? • Do the shop workers handle the food hygienically? • If the food is delivered to you, does it arrive in good condition and are the chilled (0°C to below 5°C) and frozen foods (–18°C to –24°C) at the correct temperature?	• If the shop/market stall is clean, contamination by micro-organisms will be more easily kept under control. • If the food is displayed and stored properly, it will be safe to eat. • If the shop workers follow food hygiene rules, there will be less chance of cross-contamination. 

The food packaging

What to look for when buying food	Why this is important
• Is it intact (complete and undamaged)? • Is it clean? • Is it possible to read the label clearly?	• If the packaging is intact and undamaged there is less risk of the food being contaminated by micro-organisms. • If the packaging is clean, it shows that it will have been stored well.

County Foods
Strawberry Yogurt
Made with fresh strawberries

Suitable for vegetarians
150g
Store in a refrigerator
Between 0°C and 5°C
Use by 2 May
Produced in the UK by
County Foods Ltd.
Brintown

It should be possible to read all the information about a food product clearly so that you know:

• what ingredients it contains

• the **shelf-life** of the food product (how long it will last before it becomes unsafe/unpalatable [unpleasant] to eat)

• how to store it

• how to cook it.

The **use-by date** or **best before/best before end (of month or year) date** on the food label or packaging.

• The use-by date applies to high-risk foods, such as fish, meat, eggs and cream, that are most likely to become contaminated with pathogenic micro-organisms, and is the date by which the food should be eaten.

• The use-by date also applies to perishable foods that spoil easily and quickly, such as strawberries and other soft fruits.

• The best before/best before end (of month or year) date applies to low-risk and non-perishable foods such as canned foods, biscuits, breakfast cereals, bottled foods, dried pasta and rice.

• The best before/best before end (of month or year) date means that after this date, the food will still be safe to eat, but the quality may have changed (e.g. it may have begun to go stale and changed in texture and flavour).

• If the foods on sale are all in date, this shows that the shop is careful to sell the foods in rotation – this means they sell the oldest foods first before they go out of date.

What to look for when buying different types of food

The following mind maps show you what to look for when buying different types of foods.

Fresh fish should have these qualities:

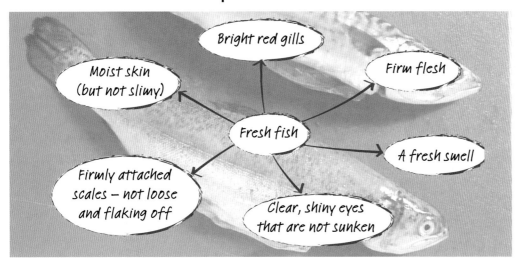

Bright red gills

Moist skin (but not slimy)

Firm flesh

Fresh fish

A fresh smell

Firmly attached scales – not loose and flaking off

Clear, shiny eyes that are not sunken

Fresh meat should have these qualities:

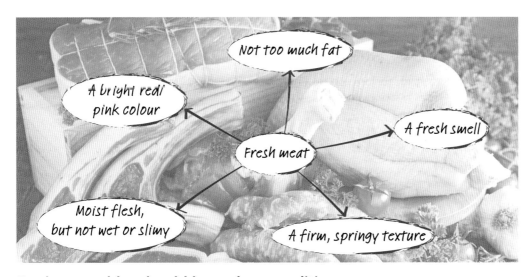

Not too much fat

A bright red/ pink colour

A fresh smell

Fresh meat

Moist flesh, but not wet or slimy

A firm, springy texture

Fresh vegetables should have these qualities:

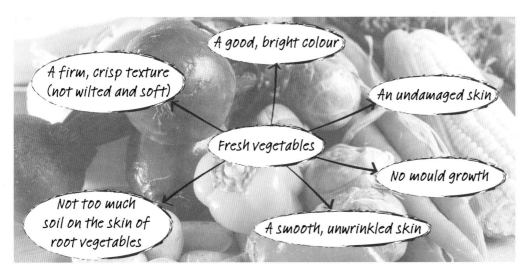

A good, bright colour

A firm, crisp texture (not wilted and soft)

An undamaged skin

Fresh vegetables

No mould growth

Not too much soil on the skin of root vegetables

A smooth, unwrinkled skin

Study tip

Vegetables that are misshapen or not perfect can still be eaten. Many organic vegetables are not perfect shapes. It is important not to waste food because it is not a perfect shape. See page 268.

Unripe passion fruit – the skin is very tight

Ripe passion fruit – the skin is wrinkly

Study tip

When handling food, these are the key temperatures to learn related to temperature control (see page 176):
Freezing: −18°C to −24°C
Chilling 0°C to below 5°C
Cooking and reheating: 75°C
Danger Zone: 5°C to 63°C

Fresh fruits should have these qualities:

A good, bright colour

A good texture – not too soft

An undamaged skin

Fresh fruits

An unwrinkled skin – apart from passion fruit which become wrinkly as they ripen

No mould/yeast growth (mentioned in previous chapter)

Food storage

Introduction

It is important that food is stored properly in order to:

- preserve the flavour, appearance and nutritional value of the food
- prevent the food from becoming spoiled and unsafe to eat
- prevent food wastage.

Types of food storage

Different foods can and need to be stored in different ways to keep them fresh and good quality.

The chart below shows:

- the types of food storage
- the types of food to be stored
- the temperatures used to store food.

Food safety advice when storing food

Type of storage	Types of food stored	Special points
Dry foods storage	**Canned and bottled foods** (e.g. fish, beans, sauces). **Packaged foods** (e.g. breakfast cereals, biscuits, cakes, pasta, rice). **Ingredients** (e.g. flour, sugar, cornflour, dried fruits, spices, dried herbs). *Temperature control when storing food this way* Dry foods should be stored at **ambient** temperature (ordinary room temperature) – usually between 20°C and 21°C.	• Cupboards should be well ventilated to prevent a build-up of moisture from steam in the kitchen, which may get trapped inside food cupboards and cause mould to grow. • Cupboards need to be protected from pests (e.g. flies, mice, ants). • Once food packets are opened, dried foods should be stored and securely sealed in airtight containers (e.g. tins, plastic boxes, glass or ceramic jars) to protect them from moisture, dust, airborne micro-organisms and pests. • Regularly check best before dates and use up older food products first.

Type of storage	Types of food stored	Special points
Refrigerated foods storage	**High-risk foods**, including raw and cooked meat, fish, seafood, poultry, milk, cheese, eggs, yogurt, cream (and any food products containing these foods, e.g. cream cakes, sausage rolls, scotch eggs, quiche, custard tarts, mousses, trifle); fresh soups, sauces (e.g. mayonnaise); defrosted (previously frozen) foods. **Perishable foods**, including soft fruits (e.g. strawberries, raspberries and blueberries); cucumbers, tomatoes, salad leaves. *Temperature control when storing food this way* The temperature inside a refrigerator should be between **0°C and below 5°C**.  At these temperatures, the rate at which bacteria grow and multiply **slows down**. Refrigeration does not kill bacteria. Thermometers can be used to monitor refrigerator temperatures.	• Foods need to be protected from moisture loss and becoming **tainted** with the smell/flavour of other foods in a refrigerator, by covering, wrapping, sealing or storing them in suitable containers. • There should be spaces between the stored foods to allow the air to circulate and remove the heat from the refrigerator efficiently. • Foods should be grouped together as shown below. 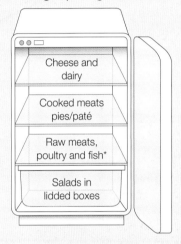 *Raw meats, poultry and fish should be in sealed containers to prevent them dripping onto the salad below.
Frozen foods storage	*Temperature control when storing food this way* The temperature inside a freezer should be between –18°C and –24°C. At these temperatures, bacteria stop growing and multiplying and become **dormant (inactive/'asleep')**. Freezing does not kill bacteria. Once the food is **defrosted** and warms up, the bacteria start to grow and multiply again. *Star ratings for refrigerator ice compartments and freezers* These star ratings are seen on refrigerators with an ice box/frozen food compartment and freezers. They indicate how long frozen foods can be safely stored. You may also see the star ratings on frozen food packaging. * For making ice cubes and keeping food cold enough for 3–4 days (usually only in refrigerators with an ice box) ** For storing already frozen food for 15–20 days at –12°C (usually only in refrigerators with an ice box) *** For storing already frozen food safely for up to 3 months at –18°C (usually on in freezers) **** For freezing and storing fresh and pre-cooked foods safely for several months at –18°C to –24°C (only in freezers)	• Foods need to be protected from moisture loss and becoming tainted with the smell/flavour of other foods in a freezer, by wrapping, sealing or storing in suitable containers. • Foods also need to be protected from freezer burn, which damages the food and happens if the packaging is too thin and the food is exposed to the freezing air in the freezer. 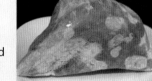 Freezer burn in a joint of meat • Food can become dried out and discoloured. • Foods should be clearly labelled to show what they are (it can be difficult to identify frozen food), with the date they were frozen. • Frozen food can gradually change flavour, texture and colour if it is frozen for too long. • Some foods do not freeze well because they have a high water content and become mushy and watery when they defrost (e.g. cucumbers, lettuce, strawberries). • Check food date labels regularly and use up older foods first. • Regularly clean and defrost the freezer so that it works efficiently.

Suitable materials for food storage

There are many different types of materials available in which to store foods.

They include:

Paper – e.g. greaseproof and silicon paper for wrapping foods

Plastics – e.g. cling film, plastic bags (different thicknesses), storage boxes, take-away containers

Food storage

Glass – dishes and containers, some of which are suitable for freezing

Metal – e.g. aluminium foil wrap, aluminium foil containers, stainless steel boxes

Ceramic/china – dishes and containers, some of which are suitable for freezing

Study tip

When you compare and contrast two things, make sure you:
- arrange the information you are going to include into separate topics
- answer one topic at a time
- summarise what you have compared and contrasted, and give your conclusion about which is the best.

Activity

Compare and contrast the pictures of the two refrigerators below, by giving detailed comments about:

- food safety risks
- bacterial contamination
- palatability of the foods being stored
- the efficiency of the refrigerator.

Refrigerator A

Refrigerator B

Stretch and challenge activity

Chris works in a small company that makes sandwiches to sell at lunchtime to local businesses in the area.

Chris's job is to organise the storage of all the ingredients used to make the sandwiches.

Using the following chart as a guide, explain how Chris should store the ingredients to make sure that they are safe to eat and remain in good condition.

Ingredient(s)	State where the ingredients would be stored (include temperatures)	Explain where and how the ingredient(s) would be stored
Sliced bread		
Vegetable fat spread		
Mayonnaise		
Salad vegetables (lettuce, tomatoes and cucumber)		
Chutney		
Cheddar cheese		
Cooked prawns		
Cooked ham		
Hummus		
Raw eggs (for hard boiled eggs)		
Canned tuna		

Practice questions

1. a) Explain why it is important to use suitable containers to store food in a freezer. *(3 marks)*

   b) Explain why it is a good idea to tightly wrap or place strong-smelling foods, such as cheese and garlic, in containers with lids in the refrigerator. *(3 marks)*

   c) Explain why it is important that cupboards that are used to store dry foods should be well ventilated. *(3 marks)*

   d) Explain how and why eggs should be stored in a refrigerator. *(3 marks)*

2. State four qualities you would look for when buying each of the following foods:

   a) Fresh vegetables. *(4 marks)*

   b) Fresh fish. *(4 marks)*

3. Explain why use-by dates are put on high-risk and perishable food products. *(2 marks)*

4. State what a 'best before date' means on a food product. *(2 marks)*

Stretch and challenge activity

In a busy professional kitchen, responsibility for organising the storage of food is often given as a specific job role for a member of staff.

a) Identify and illustrate, with examples, the key tasks that this job would involve. *(6 marks)*

b) Comment on the importance of correct food storage in such an organisation. *(6 marks)*

Preparing, cooking and

3.2.2 # serving food

What will I learn?

In this section you will learn about:

- the food safety principles when preparing and cooking food
- preventing cross-contamination
- controlling microbial growth and multiplication.

Food safety principles (rules) when preparing, cooking and serving food

Introduction

In this section, you will learn how to make sure that any food you prepare and cook is safe for people to eat and will not put them at risk of food poisoning.

Most of the instructions should be common sense (such as washing your hands before handling food), but people often forget or do not know how easy it is to contaminate food with bacteria without realising it, and do not always follow basic hygiene rules.

If you work in the food industry, you are required **by law** to follow the food safety and hygiene rules, and there could be serious consequences if you did not.

When you prepare food for yourself and other people at home, these rules still apply, but are not enforced by law, so you need to think and act responsibly. This section will show you how.

Preventing cross-contamination

Recap

In part 3.14 of Chapter 5, you learned:

- the different ways in which food can become contaminated with bacteria
- about **cross-contamination** and how bacteria are easily spread from one source then onto food
- how to prevent cross-contamination.

Personal hygiene

- One of the main sources of cross-contamination is the **people** who handle food.
- In this section you will learn about why it is important to follow the rules of personal hygiene when handling food.
- It is vital that people who handle food and cooking equipment are very careful about their personal hygiene.
- The picture below shows where the main concentrations of bacteria are found in and on the human body.

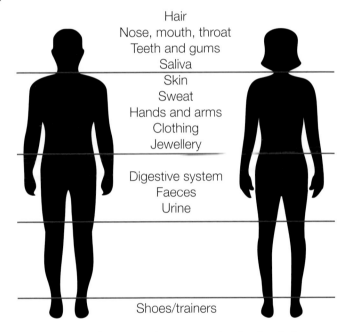

Hair
Nose, mouth, throat
Teeth and gums
Saliva
Skin
Sweat
Hands and arms
Clothing
Jewellery

Digestive system
Faeces
Urine

Shoes/trainers

Key terms

Personal hygiene: following certain routines to make sure that a person does not contaminate food with bacteria from their body

Core temperature: the temperature in the centre of a piece of food

In order to prevent bacteria from these areas from contaminating food, these **personal hygiene rules** should be followed when preparing and cooking food:

Personal hygiene rules when preparing and cooking food	Reason
• Tie back and cover long hair.	• Hairs from the head naturally fall out every day and should not be allowed to drop into food.
• Do not cough, spit, pick your nose or sneeze over food. • Do not put your fingers into the food and lick them, then put them back into the food. • Do not 'double dip' when checking the flavour of some food you have made (i.e. do not lick the spoon then put it straight back into the food without washing it). • Always use a clean teaspoon for taste testing or sensory analysis.	• The mouth, throat, nose, teeth, gums and saliva contain billions of bacteria, some of which are pathogenic. • Sneezing sends out many thousands of bacteria from the nose, throat and mouth into the air for a distance of several metres. 

Section 3: Food Safety

Personal hygiene rules when preparing and cooking food	Reason
• Cover outdoor clothing with a clean apron or chef's jacket. • Do not wear jewellery on your hands, round your neck or in your ears. 	• Clean clothing forms a clean barrier between the food and your own clothes, which will have picked up bacteria from outside the kitchen. • Jewellery can become clogged with dirt and food residues, which will transfer bacteria to food. • Jewellery could also drop unnoticed into foods and become a **physical hazard** (someone could choke on it or it could break a tooth or puncture their tongue or mouth).
• Do not allow sweat to drop into food.	• Sweat contains bacteria from the skin's surface.

• Wash and dry your hands thoroughly:
  – before handling food and regularly during preparation and cooking
  – after using the toilet
  – on your return from going outside of the kitchen
  – after handling raw eggs, rubbish and waste food, food bins, raw meat, fish and poultry, soiled vegetables.

	• Damp hands carry many more bacteria than dry hands.
	• Urine and faeces carry billions of bacteria, and toilet paper **does not** prevent some of them from contaminating your hands.
	• If you go outside the kitchen and touch door handles, stair rails and other surfaces, you will pick up a lot of bacteria on your hands.
	• Meat, fish, poultry and eggs all have bacteria on them, which will transfer to your hands.
	• Rubbish bins and waste food will transfer bacteria to your hands.

• Keep fingernails short and clean. Nail brushes can be used to clean nails, but the brushes must be kept clean, as bacteria can collect in the bristles. • Do not wear false nails or nail varnish.	• Dirt, bacteria and other debris collect under fingernails. • False nails trap dirt and bacteria and may come off and become a physical hazard to someone who may accidentally eat them. • Nail varnish flakes off and contaminates food.
• Do not put your feet/shoes onto work surfaces where food is prepared.	• Soil and dirt on the ground contains billions of bacteria. • Shoes pick up dirt and bacteria from the ground. • When working in the food industry, outdoor shoes are not allowed in the factories. 

Activity

Look at the picture below, which shows two people cooking.

Explain, giving reasons, how one of the two people **is** following the personal hygiene rules when cooking and how the other person **is not**.

A   B

Preparing food

Recap

In parts 3.1.1 and 3.1.4 of Chapter 5, you learned:

- about which micro-organisms can spoil food and make it unsafe to eat
- that some foods are high-risk, because micro-organisms grow very easily in them.

In this section you will learn about how to handle foods correctly when you are preparing food.

The following **food preparation rules** should be followed to prevent cross-contamination of bacteria.

Food preparation rules	Reason
<ul><li>Keep raw and cooked foods separate.</li><li>Use separate work surfaces for raw and cooked foods. This is the law in food premises (e.g. butchers). See page 176 for more information on different coloured chopping boards.</li><li>Use separate preparation equipment for raw and cooked foods.</li></ul>	<ul><li>Any pathogenic bacteria on the raw food will be alive and will contaminate cooked food that is going to be eaten.</li></ul> 
<ul><li>Cover prepared food to protect it from pests and dust.</li><li>Insect umbrellas are widely available.</li></ul> 	<ul><li>Pests and dust carry micro-organisms and transfer them to food.</li></ul> 

Food preparation rules	Reason
• Defrost frozen foods thoroughly (e.g. chicken) in a cool place (refrigerator) on a tray or in a dish (covered with cling film or a lid), to catch any liquid that leaks from them.   Chicken covered with cling film ready for storage in refrigerator	• If not defrosted properly and then cooked, the temperature inside the food may not become hot enough to kill pathogenic bacteria and they will multiply in the under-cooked food. • Liquid leaking from defrosting food will contain bacteria, which will contaminate other food.
• Wash your hands thoroughly after handling raw meat, poultry, fish, eggs and other high-risk foods.	• Washing hands will prevent cross-contamination of bacteria to other foods you will handle.

Controlling microbial growth and multiplication

Recap

In parts 3.1.1 and 3.1.4 of Chapter 5, you learned:

- that micro-organisms need suitable conditions in which to grow and multiply:
  - a suitable temperature
  - moisture
  - food
  - time.
- that different temperatures affect the growth rates of bacteria and other micro-organisms.

In part 3.2.1 of Chapter 6, you learned:

- that foods need to be correctly stored to control microbial growth and multiplication.

In this section you will learn about being responsible for making sure that the growth and multiplication of micro-organisms is controlled by the correct storage and cooking of food.

Storing food

The following rules should be followed to make sure that food is safely stored.

Food storage rules	Reason
• As soon as possible after the food has been bought, store it away in the appropriate places, at the right temperature (see page 174).  • Do not leave high-risk/ perishable foods standing for any length of time in a warm place such as a kitchen or car. • Check use-by and best before dates regularly.	• Chilling high-risk/perishable foods will slow down microbial growth. • Bacteria will grow and multiply more quickly as the temperature of the food increases in a warm place. • Check the label to see if a food is suitable for freezing. Some foods have already been frozen and are not suitable for freezing again (e.g. prawns in a refrigerated section).

Food storage rules

- Regularly check the internal temperature of your refrigerator to make sure it is between 0°C and below 5°C, and also your freezer (–18°C to –24°C).
- Check that the door seals on the refrigerator and freezer are sealing it shut properly so no warm air gets in.
- Defrost refrigerators and freezers regularly. If they are very frosted inside, they will not work efficiently.
- If possible, place the refrigerator/freezer as far away from the cooker as possible to make sure it does not become too hot, otherwise it will not work efficiently.

This freezer needs defrosting and will not work efficiently

- Store foods correctly and label them clearly if necessary.

- Use up the oldest foods first before opening new ones, but check the label to make sure they are within date.

Reason

- Refrigerators and freezers work fairly quietly so you might not know or hear if they stop working.
- Door seals will become weaker after a period of time and can be replaced.

- Careful storage will minimise the risk of cross-contamination (see page 175).

- This avoids food wastage.

Cooking, cooling down and serving food

The following rules should be followed to make sure that food is safely cooked.

Food cooking rules

Food should be cooked thoroughly for the correct time, so that its **core temperature** is **75°C or hotter** for at least 2 minutes, when measured with a **food probe**.

Reason

High temperatures will kill most pathogenic micro-organisms.

Section 3: Food Safety

Food cooking rules	Reason
Cooked food that is kept hot must be **63°C** or above. 	• If the temperature drops below **63°C**, any pathogenic bacteria that were not killed in the cooking process may start to grow and multiply, and the food will drop into the Danger Zone (between 5°C and 63°C). • The minimum serving temperature of foods in schools, restaurants, takeaways, etc., is 63°C, but the food must have first reached a core temperature of 75°C for at least 2 minutes when it was cooked.
• **Left-over food** should be cooled to **5°C** or cooler within **1½–2 hours**. • The quickest way to cool the food is by placing it in a covered shallow tray, in a cool and well-ventilated place.	• If the food is left for longer, any pathogenic bacteria left in it will start to grow and multiply. • A shallow tray will give the food a large surface area, so it will cool down more quickly.
• **Left-over food** must only be re-heated **once**. • It should be re-heated to a minimum **core temperature** of **75°C** for at least 2 minutes. • Use different utensils to serve different foods. 	• If the food is re-heated more than once, bacteria will have more of a chance to grow and multiply, which will lead to food poisoning. • Using different utensils will avoid cross-contamination.

Food probes

- Food probes are designed to give you an accurate reading of the core (centre) internal temperature of the food you are cooking.
- Using a food probe correctly means that you can be confident that the food has been cooked thoroughly and safely.

Here are some instructions for using a food probe correctly.

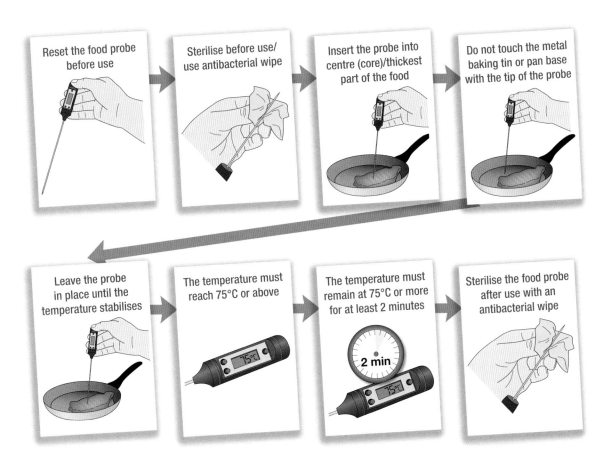

Reset the food probe before use

Sterilise before use/ use antibacterial wipe

Insert the probe into centre (core)/thickest part of the food

Do not touch the metal baking tin or pan base with the tip of the probe

Leave the probe in place until the temperature stabilises

The temperature must reach 75°C or above

The temperature must remain at 75°C or more for at least 2 minutes

Sterilise the food probe after use with an antibacterial wipe

Activity

These are all words to do with food safety and hygiene.

Find out and write down what they mean on some flash cards to help you remember them:

- Ambient temperature
- Pathogenic
- Defrost
- Dormant
- Contamination
- Perishable
- Rodent
- Tainted
- Enzyme
- Toxin
- Germinate
- Use-by
- Maggot
- Core temperature.

Stretch and challenge activity

Explain why each of the foods shown in the chart below is high-risk and give details as to how you can prevent them from causing food poisoning when buying, storing, preparing and cooking food.

Food – why is it high-risk?	How would you prevent it from causing food poisoning when buying and storing?	How would you prevent it from causing food poisoning when preparing and cooking?
Chicken 		
Fresh cream cake 		
Egg 		
Minced beef 		
Liver pâté 		

1. a) State five personal hygiene rules that people should follow when preparing and cooking food. *(5 marks)*

   b) Explain why it is important to store high-risk foods at low temperatures. *(2 marks)*

   c) Explain why left-over food should only be re-heated once. *(2 marks)*

2. Using the words and numbers below to help you, fill in the gaps in the following paragraph about food safety.

   When preparing food, keep raw and _____ foods separate from each other.

   Defrost _____ _____ thoroughly (e.g. chicken) in a cool place such as the refrigerator.

   Chilling high-risk/ _____ foods will slow down microbial growth.

   Regularly check the internal temperature of your refrigerator to make sure it is between _____ _____ _____ and also your freezer (−18°C to −24°C).

   Food should be cooked thoroughly for the correct time, so that its _____ _____ is _____ or hotter for at least 2 minutes, when measured with a _____ _____.

   Cooked food that is kept hot must be 63°C or above.

   Left-over food should be cooled to 5°C or cooler within _____ ___ _____.

   Left-over food must only be re-heated _____.

   It should be re-heated to a minimum core temperature of 75°C for at least ____ _____.

75°C	frozen foods	perishable	1½–2 hours
0°C and below 5°C	core temperature		2 minutes
cooked	food probe		once

3. Explain, giving reasons and examples, how the following can help people to store, prepare and cook food safely, especially in a restaurant kitchen.

   a) A food probe. *(4 marks)*

   b) A refrigerator thermometer. *(4 marks)*

   c) A well-organised refrigerator. *(4 marks)*

   d) Different-coloured chopping boards. *(4 marks)*

Chapter 7 Factors affecting food choice

4.1.1 Factors that influence food choice

What will I learn?

In this section you will learn about:

● the factors that may influence what we choose to eat.

Key terms

Lifestyle: the way in which people live, their attitudes, activities, likes and dislikes, beliefs, etc.

Seasonality: the time of the year when a particular food crop is ready to harvest and is at its best for flavour, colour and texture. It is also usually cheaper and fresher because there is a lot of it available to buy.

Food miles: the distance travelled by all the ingredients in a food product until it reaches our plate

Factors that may influence what we choose to eat

There are many factors that influence what we choose to eat:

In this section, you will learn about how the following factors influence food choice:

- Healthy eating and Physical Activity Level (PAL).
- **Lifestyle**, income, time available to prepare and cook food.
- Cost of food.
- Time of day and eating habits.
- Food availability and **seasonality**.
- Enjoyment, celebrations, preferences and social aspects of food.

In Section 4.1.2, you will learn about how religion, culture, ethical and moral beliefs and medical conditions influence food choice.

Healthy eating and Physical Activity Level (PAL)

Which factors/sources of information help people choose what to eat?	Questions to consider and discuss	
Their knowledge of food, nutrition, healthy eating and cooking from being educated about these: • At home. • In school. • In the community.	• How important is it to have the opportunity to be taught about food and how to prepare and cook it?	
Their desire to eat healthily: • For themselves. • For their family.	• Why is it important to consider what you eat every day and over a long period of time? • Why is it important that parents encourage their children to eat healthily and set them a good example?	
Their nutritional needs at a particular stage of life: • As babies and young children. • As children and teenagers. • As adults. • As elderly people.	• Why is making good food choices particularly important for children and teenagers?	
Their state of health: • Whether they have an allergy or intolerance to certain foods (see pages 216–219). • Whether they need to increase or decrease their intake of a particular nutrient. • Whether they have a long-term health condition that affects what they can and cannot eat.	• Why is it important that food labels give clear information about what the food product contains?	(B3), Iron, Pantothenic Acid (B5), Vitamin B12, Vitamin B6, Riboflavin (B2), Thiamin (B1), Folic Acid (B9), Vitamin D]], Raisins (11%) [Raisins, Sunflower Oil], **Oat Flakes**, Diced Dates (2.6%) [Dates, Rice Flour], **Flaked Almonds (Nut)** (1.3%). Allergy Advice! for allergens, including cereals containing gluten, see ingredients in bold. **May also contain traces of other nuts and peanuts. Not suitable for milk allergy sufferers.**

Which factors/sources of information help people choose what to eat?	Questions to consider and discuss
Their Physical Activity Level (PAL): • The amount of energy they need every day. • Whether they are physically active or mostly sedentary (inactive), which will affect how much energy they need from food every day.	• Why are some foods more energy dense than others? • Why is it easy to consume too much energy from food? 
Food labels, which give information about: • Nutrition. • Ingredients. • Food allergies. • Energy value. • Food manufacturers' claims about their food products.	• Are food labels easy to read? • Are food labels easy to understand? • How much should you believe food manufacturers' nutrition and health claims about their food products? 
The media: • TV documentaries and cookery programmes about food, nutrition and health. • Magazine and newspaper articles. • Internet websites and articles. • Social media. • Advertisements for food. • Supermarket information.	• Does the media give mixed messages about food, nutrition and health? • If the information or the food product is endorsed (supported) by media or sport celebrities, how does this influence food choice? 
Scientific and medical research and discoveries: • About the effects of particular foods and diets on short- and long-term health. • About how nutrients work in the body. • About which foods are the best sources of nutrients.	• Why are so many people in the world obese? • Why are so many people developing Type 2 diabetes? • Why are there serious concerns about the amount of sugar, fat and salt that people consume? 

Lifestyle, income, time available to prepare and cook food

Which lifestyle factors influence what people choose to eat?	Questions to consider and discuss	
The work they do: • Physically active (e.g. construction workers, nurses, sport instructors). • Sedentary (e.g. office workers, delivery drivers). • The level of stress or boredom caused by work. • Home-made packed lunch or takeaway food?	• Why are stress and boredom at work a potential problem when it comes to choosing food? • How can a person doing a physically active job that requires a lot of energy eat healthily?	
Cooking their food at home: • Having the motivation to cook and clear up afterwards. • The level of skills and confidence that someone needs and has to cook. • The amount of time a person has available to cook. • The amount of time a person thinks it will take them to cook a meal.	• Why is having the confidence to cook important? • Is it possible to prepare and cook healthy, enjoyable meals in a short time? How would you do it?	
Social life: • The frequency of eating out and eating at home. • The choice of foods for eating out.	• What are the advantages and disadvantages of eating out and eating at home?	
Income: • How much income is available to spend on food. • How much it costs to eat healthily. • How much it costs to cook your own food compared to buying it ready-made.	• Why is it good practice for someone on a low income to plan their week's meals, write a shopping list and stick to it when shopping for food? • Why is there an increase in people using food banks in the UK?	

Cost of food

Which factors influence what people choose to eat?

Cost of food:

- The prices charged by supermarkets/open markets/online shopping/independent shops.
- Whether special offers are value for money.
- The cost of ready meals/fast food compared to home-made food.
- The cost of convenience foods.
- Buying foods that are in season.
- Price differences between value brands or top end brands of food.
- How much packaging a food product has, because this adds cost to it and contributes to environmental problems.
- The advantages of home grown food.
- The amount of food wasted by shops.

Questions to consider and discuss

- What is the advantage of checking the price per kilogram/100g or price per litre/100ml when deciding which product to choose from range of similar food products (e.g. cheese, fruit juice)?
- How can people avoid throwing money away by wasting food they have bought and not used?
- What are the advantages and disadvantages of preparing and cooking your own food compared to buying ready-made/convenience foods?

Large amounts of food are wasted every year in the UK

Time of day and eating habits

Which factors influence what people choose to eat?

Eating habits:

- Meal times.
- Eating with others/eating alone.
- Snacking/grazing.
- Each family member's preferences for different foods.
- Dashboard dining (eating on the move in the car).
- Keyboard dining (eating at a work desk).

Questions to consider and discuss

- What are the potential problems with eating snacks throughout the day rather than regular meals?
- How can families save time but provide healthy, appetising and quick meals during busy weekdays?
- What are the benefits of a family sitting down together to share a meal?

Which factors influence what people choose to eat?

Family and personal timetable:

- What times people are at home to have a meal, which may mean that members of a family have to eat at different times.
- How often they go out of the home for social and recreational activities, which may mean they need a snack or have to take a packed meal.
- Who will prepare the meals – how much time do they have, what skills do they have?

Questions to consider and discuss

- How can all members of a family contribute to everything that is involved in providing meals throughout the week (shopping, preparing, cooking, clearing up)?
- How can you ensure that packed meals are economical and healthy?

Availability of food and seasonality

Which factors influence what people choose to eat?

Food grown and produced in the UK:

- Whether it is locally grown or transported long distances (**food miles**).
- Whether it is only available at certain times of the year (seasonality).
- How it was grown or reared, harvested or slaughtered.
- The choices (e.g. how many different varieties of apples, types of cheese, flavours of biscuits) are available.
- How well the farmer who grew the food is treated by the food industry.
- How people feel about the amount of food wasted by consumers and the food industry.

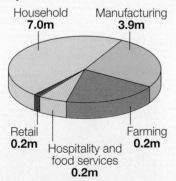

Household
7.0m

Manufacturing
3.9m

Retail
0.2m

Hospitality and
food services
0.2m

Farming
0.2m

This pie chart shows how many million tonnes of food are wasted on average each year in the UK by consumers and different parts of the food industry. Figures produced by www.lovefoodhatewaste.com

Questions to consider and discuss

- How much do you know about how your food is produced?
- What are the advantages and disadvantages of intensively produced food (where one type of food is produced in very large numbers in one place, e.g. lettuces in a field, chickens in a large shed or salmon in a fish farm)?
- What are the advantages and disadvantages of being be able to buy foods, such as strawberries, all the year round?
- Does it matter if fruits and vegetables grow in uneven sizes and shapes?

Section 4: Food Choice

Which factors influence what people choose to eat?

Food imported from other countries:

- The environmental and energy costs of transporting and distributing food for long distances.
- The wider choice of foods that are available all year round, many of which would be out of season in the UK at certain times of the year.
- How well the farmer who grew the food is treated by the food industry.

Climate and soil:

- The fertility of the soil, which affects the growth of plants and how much food they produce.
- The amount of rain/water and sun available to make the plants grow and ripen.
- The effects of pests and diseases on the amount of good quality food produced.

Questions to consider and discuss

- How far has the food you buy travelled (how many food miles)? See **www.foodmiles.com** to calculate this.
- Why is it important to consider how far food has travelled?
- Does it matter who makes a profit when food is produced? Look at the example of a banana below, which shows what proportion of the cost of each banana goes to each group of people involved in its production and sale:

BANANA SPLIT

Who gets what in the banana chain

- Worker
- Plantation owner
- Shipper
- Wholesaler/importer
- Ripener
- Retailer

- Why are lots of pesticides used on food crops?
- What are the advantages and disadvantages of using pesticides on food crops?
- What is the impact on the environment if lots of artificial fertiliser is added to the soil?

Enjoyment, celebrations, preferences, occasion and social aspects of food

Which factors influence what people choose what to eat?

Special meals and foods associated with family celebrations and traditions:

- Weddings.
- Birthdays.
- Anniversaries.
- Funerals.
- Bar mitzvahs.
- Calendar events (e.g. Chinese New Year, Hogmanay, Thanksgiving).

Questions to consider and discuss

- Why is food so important in celebrations and traditions?

- What are the challenges for caterers producing food on a large scale for big celebrations with lots of different people invited?

Which factors influence what people choose what to eat?

Special meals and foods associated with national celebrations and traditions; e.g., here are some examples from the UK throughout the year:

January: Breakfast week

February: Bramley apple week

Fairtrade fortnight

March: National salt awareness week

British pie week

May: British sandwich week

National vegetarian week

June: National picnic week

National fish and chip day

National cucumber week

September: British food fortnight

National cupcake week

Organic September

Scottish food and drink fortnight

Harvest festival

October: Apple day

British egg week

National baking week

National curry week

November: Bonfire night 5 November

Sharing food with other people:
- Sharing food at school or in the workplace.
- Entertaining people at home.
- Going out to eat together.
- Trying foods from other cultures.

Questions to consider and discuss

- Why are particular foods celebrated and showcased at certain times of the year?

- Why is food an important part of friendship groups and social gatherings?
- What are the advantages of trying foods from different cultures and traditions?

Which factors influence what people choose what to eat?

Preferences:

- Personal likes and dislikes for different foods and drinks.
- Personal preference for following a particular diet (e.g. vegetarianism).
- Food aversions (foods that people avoid because they associate them with something bad, e.g. being ill, being unhappy).

Questions to consider and discuss

- How can young children be encouraged to try a variety of foods?

Practice questions

1. a) State three factors that influence what people choose to eat. *(3 marks)*

    b) State three reasons why it is important to encourage very young children to try a variety of foods. *(3 marks)*

2. Families are often very busy during the week.

    a) Explain how a busy lifestyle influences what people choose to eat. *(5 marks)*

    b) Discuss ways that busy families can ensure that they eat a range of healthy and appetising meals. *(3 marks)*

Stretch and challenge activity

Scenario: The Parent Teacher Association at a primary school is planning an event to raise money to develop a school garden, to teach the children how to grow food and about where food comes from. They are planning to have a buffet and expect about 150 people (adults and children) will attend the event.

Plan a buffet menu for the event to include ten savoury and five sweet dishes.

Explain, in detail, the criteria you will use to plan the menu and the reasons for your choices of dishes, explaining how your menu will take into account:

- the needs of different age groups of people
- special dietary needs
- environmental sustainability.

4.1.2 Food choices

What will
I learn?

In this section you will learn about:

How food choices are related to:

- religion and culture
- ethical and moral beliefs
- medical conditions.

Food choices related to religion and culture

- Religious and cultural texts and teachings are considered by various religions and cultures to be the core of their tradition.
- In many religions and cultures, the texts include instructions, rules and advice (sometimes called 'dietary laws') according to which foods should and should not be eaten.
- The table below describes the dietary laws for a variety of religions and cultures.

Buddhism
Principles and beliefs in relation to food
The Buddha instructs Buddhists to stop and think about the foods they are eating in five ways: 1. What food is.   2. Why we eat food.   3. Where food comes from.   4. When food should be eaten.   5. How food should be eaten.   Buddhism considers living beings to be sacred and this belief means that many Buddhists are vegetarian or vegan.   Violence towards animals is considered to cause human aggression, so most Buddhists follow the principle of **ahimsa** (non-violence or harmlessness) and avoid all foods related to processes where animals were harmed.
Foods that cannot be eaten
• Some Buddhists avoid meat and dairy products while others avoid only meat.   • Buddhists also avoid the consumption of alcohol.
Special occasions linked to food
Buddhist monks fast (do not eat any food) during the afternoons.   

Section 4: Food Choice

Christianity

Principles and beliefs in relation to food

- Food and drink is regarded and celebrated as part of God's creation.
- The freedom to eat and drink healthily is regarded as part of the salvation that Jesus brought to men and women.
- There are no strict rules about food and drink that modern Christians are expected to obey.
- Fasting is practised by some Christians as a way of remembering people who are starving or malnourished.

Foods that **cannot** be eaten

No restrictions

Special occasions linked to food

Shrove Tuesday (Pancake Day): this occurs in February or March on the day before Ash Wednesday, which is the first day of Lent.

Traditionally on Shrove Tuesday, people use up the foods that are not allowed to be eaten during Lent, including ingredients used to make pancakes: butter, cream and eggs.

Lent: for forty days and nights before the celebration of Easter, Christians avoid consuming certain foods and drinks.

Good Friday: some Christians avoid eating meat. Hot cross buns are eaten to celebrate the end of Lent and remind Christians of the crucifixion of Jesus and the spices that were put onto his body afterwards.

Easter: Easter eggs are eaten to celebrate new life and represent Jesus' empty tomb.

Christmas: special foods and meals are eaten to celebrate the birth of Jesus, including mince pies, roasted turkey or goose, roasted potatoes, carrots, roasted parsnips, Brussels sprouts, cranberry sauce, chestnut stuffing, sausages wrapped in bacon (called 'pigs in blankets'), gravy, Christmas pudding and mulled wine (red wine with spices and fruits added and served warm).

Hinduism

Principles and beliefs in relation to food

- Food is believed to contain particular energies that people take in when they eat.
- Many Hindus are vegetarian, but it is not compulsory not to eat meat.
- Some Hindu communities practise fasting.

Foods that **cannot** be eaten

Beef: The cow is held in high regard as a symbol of abundance and so it is not eaten by Hindus. The cow is seen as sacred.

Onions and garlic are avoided or only eaten occasionally as they are thought to affect the search for spiritual enlightenment. This also applies to alcohol.

Special occasions linked to food

Holi: this festival celebrates the start of spring. There is much dancing and singing and the throwing of coloured powder paint.

Diwali: (the festival of lights). This happens in October/November. Many Indian sweets called 'mithai' are eaten. Savoury Diwali snacks (often deep fried) are also made and their ingredients include chickpeas, rice, lentil flours, spices, sesame seeds, fresh fenugreek leaves or coconut. Other foods include puris, dhals, pakoras and vegetable curries.

Special foods are eaten including:

Gujiyas (pastries filled with shredded coconut, dates, sultanas, nuts).

Colourful sweets made from milk, sugar and condensed milk.

Kachoris, which are round puff pastry filled with spices and lentils.

Savoury rice coloured with saffron, sweetened and garnished with nuts, sultanas and cardamom.

Islam

Principles and beliefs in relation to food

- Muslim dietary laws are found in the Qur'an (the Islamic holy book).
- The laws state what is lawful (halal) and require that poultry birds and meat animals have to be slaughtered in a special ritual called Zibah.

Foods that **cannot** be eaten

Pork, pork products (e.g. gelatine).

Alcohol

Special occasions linked to food

Ramadan: held in the ninth month of the Islamic calendar (lunar calendar). Each day during Ramadan, Muslims must fast (not eat or drink anything) from dawn to dusk. One meal is eaten before sunrise and another after sunset.

Eid-ul-Fitr: a big celebration held at the end of Ramadan. A wide variety of foods are eaten in many different countries:

- Sheer khurma – a breakfast dish made from vermicelli (a type of pasta), whole milk, sugar and dates, with other ingredients added, such as cardamom, pistachios, almonds, saffron, raisins and rose water.
- Baklava – a rich pastry made from layers of filo pastry filled with chopped nuts, honey or syrup.

Judaism

Principles and beliefs in relation to food

- Jewish foods laws are called 'Kashrut'.
- Food that is allowed to be eaten is called 'Kosher', such as fish that have scales and fins, animals that chew the cud (i.e. eat grass) and have cloven (split) hooves such as sheep and cows.
- Saturday is called the Sabbath, when no work may be done, so food (e.g. a stew) is prepared the day before and left to cook slowly, so it can be eaten on the Sabbath.

Foods that **cannot** be eaten

Pork.

Shellfish.

Dairy foods and meat must not be prepared or eaten together.

Special occasions linked to food

Yom Kippur (the day of Atonement): Jews must fast (not eat or drink) for 24 hours.

Passover and Rosh Hashanah: celebrate the birth of the Jewish nation and the New Year.

A Seder plate is prepared and contains specific foods that remind Jews of the Passover story:

A roasted bone – symbolises the Pesach offering Jews brought to the Holy Temple in Jerusalem.

A hard-boiled egg – symbolises another offering brought to the Holy Temple.

Horseradish root – symbolises harsh suffering and bitter times endured when Jews were slaves.

A mixture of ground up chopped apple, walnuts and red wine – symbolises bricks and mortar, reminding Jews how hard they had to work when they were slaves.

Onion, boiled potato or parsley dipped into salt water – symbolises the tears Jews cried when they were slaves.

Romaine lettuce – symbolises harsh suffering and bitter times endured when Jews were slaves.

Gefilte fish: this dish is made from a poached mixture of ground deboned fish, such as carp or whitefish, and is usually eaten as an appetiser.

Rastafarianism

Principles and beliefs in relation to food

- Rastafarians follow the dietary rules of I-tal.
- Food must be natural and clean and include plenty of fruit, vegetables and herbal teas.

Foods that **cannot** be eaten

Pork.

Fish longer than 30cm.

Many do not drink alcohol, milk and coffee.

Special occasions linked to food

Ethiopian Christmas (7 January): this includes a large feast, where the food eaten is often vegetarian or vegan.

Sikhism

Principles and beliefs in relation to food

Many Sikhs are vegetarians.

Foods that **cannot** be eaten

Some Sikhs do not drink alcohol, tea or coffee.

Gurpurbs: these are festivals associated with the lives of Gurus (spiritual teachers). There are several Gurpurbs throughout the year and food is an important feature of them.

The picture shows children eating laddoos at a Sikh festival. Laddoos are sweets made of flour, minced dough and sugar.

Food choices related to ethical and moral beliefs

Ethical and moral beliefs relate to what people believe to be **right** or **wrong**.

Many people are concerned about how food is produced and will only choose foods that have been produced by methods they consider to be ethically and morally right.

Here are some of the concerns that people may have about how food is produced.

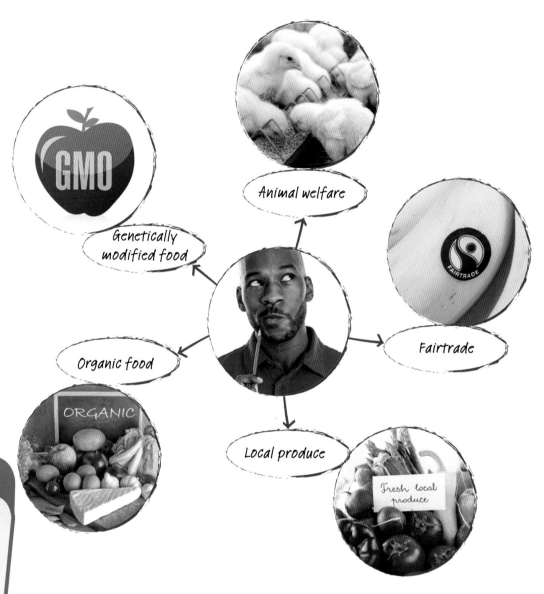

In Chapter 11, you will find more information about each of these methods of food production.

Food choices related to food intolerances and allergies

Some people have medical conditions that affect which foods they can and cannot choose to eat, for example someone who has high blood pressure may need to limit the amount of foods they eat that contain salt.

There are two medical conditions that are directly related to food choice:

- food intolerance
- food allergy.

Key terms

Food intolerance: a long-term condition where after several hours or days, certain foods cause a person to feel unwell and have a range of symptoms, but it is usually not life threatening and does not involve the immune system

Food allergy: this happens to some people when their immune system has a very sensitive reaction to specific foods, which causes severe and potentially life-threatening symptoms that happen very quickly after the food is eaten

Food intolerance

This is sometimes called food sensitivity and is a condition where, for some reason, a person becomes sensitive to particular foods and develops a range of uncomfortable symptoms that make them feel weak and unable to carry out everyday activities effectively.

The symptoms of food intolerance include:

- constant tiredness and weakness
- muscle and joint aches and pain
- nausea (feeling sick)
- pain and bloating (swelling due to fluid or gas) in the abdomen
- diarrhoea
- eczema and dry skin conditions

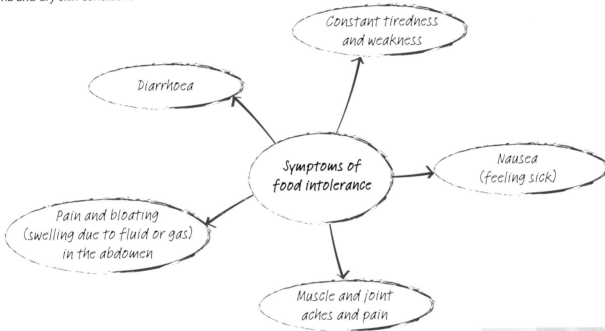

It is hard to diagnose food intolerance, but there are two particular forms of it that are well known:

- lactose intolerance
- coeliac disease.

Lactose intolerance

Lactose is a natural disaccharide sugar (see page 17) that is found in milk and milk products. Most people can digest lactose without any problems.

People who are lactose intolerant cannot digest it and bacteria that live in the large intestine break it down, which causes a large amount of gas to be produced (flatulence), abdominal pain, diarrhoea and nausea. This can make someone feel very unwell.

The only way to prevent the symptoms from occurring is to avoid drinking milk, eating milk products (e.g. cheese, butter, cream, yogurt) or any food product that contains milk or a milk product in its ingredients list. This means that food labels must be carefully read and the person must become familiar with the words associated with milk, such as whey protein, buttermilk, dairy protein, galactose (a monosaccharide that makes up one part of the lactose molecule – see page 17).

It is possible to buy dairy products where the lactose content has been reduced or even removed completely, as shown in the picture on the right.

There are also dairy free 'milks' made from nuts, soya beans, rice or oats.

Coeliac disease

- Coeliac disease is an intolerance to the protein **gluten** (see pages 110–111). Someone who has coeliac disease is referred to as a coeliac.

- Gluten is found in wheat, barley, oats and rye and food products that contain them.

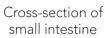

Cross-section of
small intestine

In the body, food is broken down during **digestion** and individual nutrients are released, ready to be absorbed in the **small intestine**.

The small intestine is lined with thousands of tiny projections – a bit like fingers – called **villi**, as shown in the picture of a cross-section of the small intestine.

- The villi have a **large surface area**, so they can absorb lots of nutrients and send them into the bloodstream to go round the body, as shown in the diagram below of the villi in the small intestine of a healthy person.

Small intestine

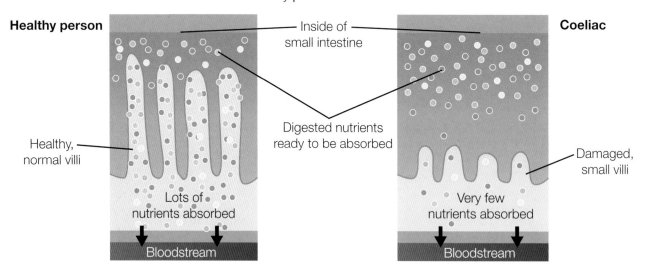

In coeliac disease, gluten damages the villi so they become very short, as shown in the diagram above of the villi in the small intestine of a coeliac.

- The damaged, short villi cannot absorb many nutrients and so the person with coeliac disease becomes **malnourished** and shows signs of **nutrient deficiency**, which results in these symptoms:
  - anaemia – due to the poor absorption of iron and vitamin C
  - lack of energy, tiredness
  - loss of weight
  - diarrhoea
  - poor growth in children – due to the poor absorption of protein, calcium, vitamin A, etc.

– general malnutrition – which will affect their ability to fight infections, develop strong bones, etc.

Once the person has been diagnosed as having coeliac disease, they have to avoid any foods that contain wheat, barley, oats and rye.

Coeliacs can eat any of the following foods: agar (from seaweed), almonds, amaranth, buckwheat, carageenan, cassava (manioc/tapioca), chestnuts, corn (maize), linseeds (flax), gram flour, millet, mustard, polenta, potato flour, peas, beans, lentils, quinoa, rice, sago, sorghum, soya flour, and urd/urid (lentil flour).

Food manufacturers now produce a wide range of food products that are gluten free, including breads, pasta, breakfast cereals, biscuits and cakes.

There are symbols to look out for on food labels to indicate this.

Food manufacturers are required to place a warning on food labels if gluten is present in the ingredients.

Gluten free bread on sale

Food allergy

Having a food allergy means that someone has an allergic (serious) reaction to certain foods or ingredients in food. An allergic reaction can happen within a few seconds up to a few hours after the food is eaten and, in some people, can result in life-threatening symptoms.

The allergic reaction involves the immune system and makes the body produce a substance called **histamine** and other chemicals, which lead to a variety of symptoms.

- skin rashes – usually raised, red patches called 'hives'
- itchy skin and eyes
- runny, itchy nose
- wheezing, coughing
- swollen lips, eye lids, face.

100% gluten free food label

People who have a very serious allergy can go into **anaphylactic shock**. This is usually sudden (within seconds or minutes) and is very serious, because of the symptoms, which include:

- swelling of the mouth and throat
- not being able to swallow, speak or breathe properly.

Someone suffering from anaphylactic shock must be given medical treatment quickly, as it can lead to death.

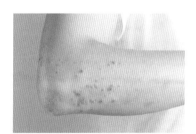

Hives caused by an allergic reaction

Food allergens

The most common foods that cause food allergies are:

- eggs
- milk
- fish
- crustaceans (e.g. crab, shrimp, prawn)
- molluscs (e.g. mussels, squid)
- peanuts
- tree nuts, including almonds, hazelnuts, walnuts, cashews, pecans, brazils, pistachios, macadamias
- sesame seeds and other seeds
- soya
- celery and celeriac
- mustard
- lupin
- sulphur dioxide and sulphites (these are preservatives that make the food last longer)
- fruits such as kiwi, strawberries, oranges.

Common foods that can cause an allergic reaction

People who are allergic to a food should avoid eating it in any form, and they need to pay close attention to food labels and ingredients lists when they are choosing their food.

These lists also include those on medicines and supplements because the ingredients might contain an allergen, such as arachis oil (from peanuts).

If a food contains a **known allergen** (an ingredient that may give some people an **allergic reaction**), the law now requires that it is shown clearly on a food label.

Practice questions

1. Discuss some of the main issues that affect the food choices of each of the following people:

   a) A student at university. *(4 marks)*

   b) An elderly person living on their own. *(4 marks)*

2. Explain the importance of food labelling for the following people:

   a) Someone with a serious food allergy to nuts. *(3 marks)*

   b) Someone who follows the Muslim faith and someone who follows the Jewish faith. *(4 marks)*

Stretch and challenge question

Discuss how food choices can be influenced by different religious, cultural, moral and ethical beliefs. *(12 marks)*

4.1.3 Food labelling and marketing influences

What will I learn?

In this section you will learn about:

- why food labels are used and how they influence food choice
- what the law says about food labelling
- how to interpret (read and understand) nutrition information on a food label
- how food marketing influences food choice.

Key terms

Target group: a specific group of similar people, e.g. all the same age, with similar jobs, such as students

Nutritional profile: the types and amounts of different nutrients a food contains

Marketing: advertising and promoting a food product to encourage people to buy it

Why food labels are used and how they influence food choice

- Food labels are designed to give consumers a **range of information** about individual food products, to **inform** them about what they are choosing to buy.

- Some of the information they give is **mandatory (required by law)** and some is not.

- Food manufacturers want their labels to attract consumers to buy the product, so they are **designed** to be **colourful, eye-catching** and **appealing** to **different target groups** of consumers.

- The use of specific **colours, words, phrases** and **slogans** (short and attention-grabbing or memorable phrases used in advertising) on food products can influence food choice.

Small group activity

Here is a selection of chocolate bars, which are sold in the UK, divided into four sets. Look at the features of each of the labels, and discuss the following:

a) Who are the target groups for each set of chocolate bars?

b) Which features have the label designers used to appeal to these target groups?

Set A	Set B

Set C	Set D

The purpose of food labels

- They inform and educate consumers about food products they choose to buy.
- They protect the consumer, manufacturer and retailer by requiring certain information to be provided on the label by law (e.g. what the ingredients are, how to safely store the product and prepare it for eating, etc.).
- Some food labels are written in multiple languages.

Potential problems with food labels

- The limited amount of space on food labels can make them difficult to read, especially on small food products, such as snack foods.
- They can be difficult for some people to understand because of the amount and different types of information they contain.

What the law says about food labelling

- Consumers, food manufacturers and retailers are all protected by law in relation to food labelling.
- There are several laws and regulations that have to be followed:
  - The **European Union (EU)** issues mandatory **Food Information for Consumers regulations (FIC)** for general and nutritional labelling, which has to be followed in the UK.
  - EU food labelling regulations have recently been revised, with most of the revisions taking place in 2014. Nutritional labelling will become mandatory (required by law) in 2016.
  - The UK Government also issues mandatory **food labelling and packaging guidance and regulations** for food manufacturers, caterers and retailers.
  - The UK **Food Standards Agency (FSA)** is responsible for overseeing and enforcing labelling in relation to food safety.
  - The UK **Department of Health (DoH)** has responsibility for nutritional labelling.

The **UK Government** says that food labels should be:

- clear and easy to read
- permanent (the information cannot be erased)
- easy to understand
- easily visible (the information must not be 'hidden' or the font [printed words] too small to read)
- not misleading (e.g. if a picture of the food product is shown, the product inside must look the same).

The following table shows information that is required to be shown on a food label by law.

Information that is mandatory (must be shown on a food label)	Notes	Examples
The **name** of the food product	• This is given to help the consumer identify the food product. • If it is not obvious to the consumer what the food is from the **brand name**, a **description** of the food must be given underneath the brand name.	# Jingles Crisp, savoury biscuits, mildly flavoured with chilli and mixed herbs and dusted with parmesan cheese
A list of **ingredients** in the food product (for more than two ingredients) and the **amount** of certain ingredients	• These have to be shown in **descending order** of weight, i.e. the ingredient present in the largest amount first, to the ingredient present in the smallest amount last. • This is important information for consumers who may want to know what is in the product (e.g. if they are vegetarian, if they are following a special diet or if they are intolerant to certain foods). • It also enables consumers to identify 'hidden' ingredients, such as sugars (often listed by their chemical name, such as 'maltose' or 'sucrose') and fats (e.g. 'triglycerides'). • Sometimes the amount of an ingredient (usually as a %) is shown.	**Activity** Try to work out what the food product is in each of the ingredients list examples: **Example A:** Ingredients: Water, carrots, onion, lentils, celery, garlic, yeast extract, ground black pepper, salt. **Example B:** Ingredients: Wheat flour, unsalted butter, sugar, dried fruit (contains sultanas, raisins, glacé cherries), whole egg, whole cow's milk, mixed spice, baking powder (contains bicarbonate of soda, sodium potassium tartrate). **Example C:** Ingredients: Potatoes, pollock, farmed salmon, whole cow's milk, prawns, butter, wheat flour, Cheddar cheese, ground black pepper, salt, parsley. **Answers on page 236**

Durum Wheat Semolina 31,7% Eggs. Contains
s: Semoule de Blé Dur, Œufs 31,7%. Contient Glu
en: Hartweizengrieß, Eier 31,7%. Enthält Gluten un
: Sèmola de Trigo Duro, Huevos 31,7%. Contien

ITALIAN MACARONI PRODUCT
MADE IN ITALY

Information that is mandatory (must be shown on a food label)	Notes	Examples
Information about the **net weight, volume,** or **quantity** of the food product	<ul><li>The label must show the **net quantity** (the actual weight or volume of the food inside, *not* including the weight of the packaging materials) in grams (g), kilograms (kg), millilitres (ml) or litres (l) of: – packaged food over 5g or 5ml – packaged herbs and spices.</li><li>It must be possible to see the quantity information when you read the name of the food on the label.</li><li>This information can help the consumer to compare value for money with other similar products.</li></ul> **7.90** (100g = 1.76) <ul><li>Often food shops and products will display the price per kg/100g/litre/100ml on the shelf or on the product to make it easy to compare the prices of similar food products.</li><li>Solid foods that are packed in a liquid must show the drained net weight, i.e. the weight of the food without the liquid.</li><li>The ℮ symbol on food labels tells the consumer that the weight or volume of the product is an **average** amount. – This is because the machines that pack food in a factory are not 100% accurate and many foods contain solid pieces and lumps, so although they have the same volume, they will be a slightly different weight. – This is allowed by law, but there are strict regulations about how much the weight and volume may vary. – The symbol is only used in Europe.</li><li>It is not necessary to show the weight or volume on foods that are sold by number (e.g. six fruit buns) but the consumer must be able to see clearly the number of items inside the packaging.</li></ul>	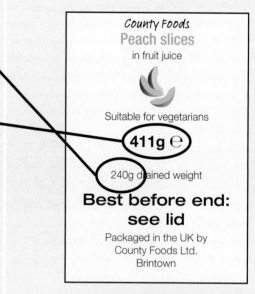 

Information that is mandatory (must be shown on a food label)	Notes	Examples
The **name or business name** and **address** of the food business operator (manufacturer, packer, distributor or seller) **Place of origin** or **provenance** if implied on the label (e.g. 'Greek olives')	• This enables a consumer to find out more about the food product or to be able to notify the manufacturer or retailer if there is a problem with it. • Food labels for beef, veal, fish, shellfish, olive oil, honey, poultry and most fruits and vegetables that have been imported from outside of the EU must show the **country of origin** (where the product was grown [plant foods] or reared [animal foods]).	  
Instructions about how to use, prepare or cook the product	• **Heating and cooking instructions** are particularly important to enable consumers to cook the food correctly and safely to prevent food poisoning. • Oven and microwave cooker instructions are often given and should show oven temperatures/microwave power levels and cooking times.	For best results oven cook from chilled. Do not reheat once cooled. | OVEN COOK	CHILLED	FROZEN
GAS 5, 190°C, FAN 170°C	5 mins	6 mins | **Preheat oven.** Remove naans from packaging and sprinkle with water. Place on a baking tray in centre of oven. Heat until piping hot. Allow to stand for 1 minute. | MICROWAVE	CHILLED	FROZEN
CAT D 800W	50 secs	1 min 30 secs
CAT E 900W	50 secs	1 min 30 secs
CAT E 1000W	40 secs	1 min 20 secs	

Information that is mandatory (must be shown on a food label)	Notes	Examples
Indication of minimum durability (shelf-life) shown by 'use-by date' or 'best before date'	• **Use-by dates** are usually put on to the labels of high-risk, perishable foods (usually refrigerated) that would become a food poisoning hazard if they are stored for too long (e.g. cream, fresh meat and fish). • **Best before dates** are usually put on to the labels of food products that have a long shelf-life and do not need to be refrigerated (e.g. biscuits, canned foods).	
Storage conditions and/or **conditions for the use of the food product**	• **Storage instructions** are given to make sure that the consumer understands how to store the food product in order to keep it safe to eat and avoid food poisoning. • These instructions also protect the manufacturer and retailer because they can prove that they have given the instructions to consumers. • Before the food is purchased by the consumer, it is the responsibility of the manufacturer and retailer to ensure that the food is safely stored at the factory, warehouse, during distribution to shops, and whilst being stored in the shop. • Once the food is purchased from the retailer, it is the responsibility of the consumer to ensure that it is taken home quickly and safely stored at the correct temperature and conditions.	

<table>
<tr><th>Information that is mandatory
(must be shown on a food label)</th><th>Notes</th><th>Examples</th></tr>
<tr><td rowspan="4">Any necessary warnings (e.g. food allergens and additives information)</td>
<td>• There must be a warning given if the product contains Genetically Modified ingredients (see page 259).
• This will enable the consumer to choose whether or not they wish to buy the product.</td>
<td>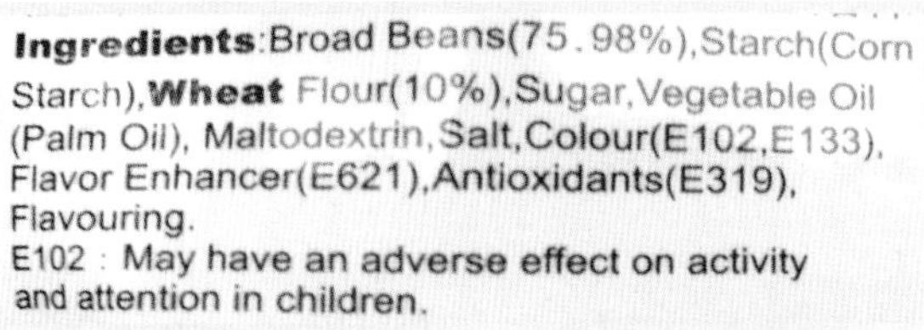
Ingredients:Broad Beans(75.98%),Starch(Corn Starch),Wheat Flour(10%),Sugar,Vegetable Oil (Palm Oil), Maltodextrin,Salt,Colour(E102,E133), Flavor Enhancer(E621),Antioxidants(E319), Flavouring.
E102 : May have an adverse effect on activity and attention in children.</td></tr>
<tr><td>• If the product has been irradiated (this is a type of food preservation), it must show the following symbol:
Irradiation symbol
• This will enable the consumer to choose whether or not they wish to buy the product.</td>
<td></td></tr>
<tr><td>• If the food is packaged using a packaging gas, the words 'packaged in a protective atmosphere' must be shown.
• This will inform the consumer about how the food has been kept fresh and safe to eat.
• Packaging gases are used in a wide range of food products to increase their shelf-life (how long they stay fresh and safe to eat) by excluding oxygen.</td>
<td>Cooked meats and fish, partly baked bread rolls, bags of salad, fruit, sandwiches, fresh pasta, etc.
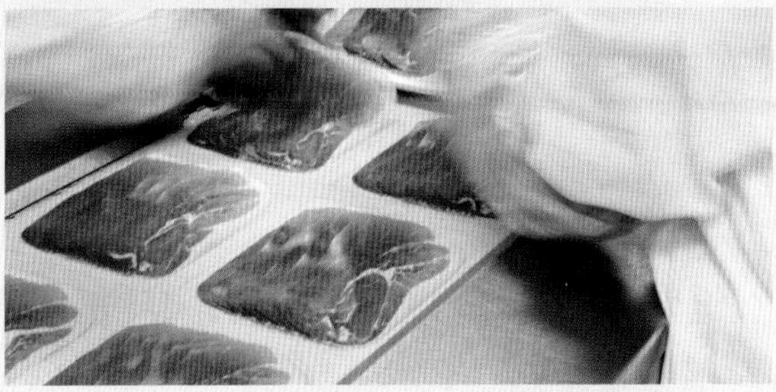</td></tr>
<tr><td>• If the food contains certain ingredients (e.g. food colourings or sweeteners), certain words must be used in the warning. Some examples of this are shown.
• This will help people to identify and understand problems that may arise if they eat certain foods.</td>
<td><table>
<tr><th>Ingredient</th><th>What is it?</th><th>What must be written on the label?</th></tr>
<tr><td>• Allura red (E129)/ quinoline yellow (E104)</td><td>Food colourings</td><td>'May have an adverse effect on activity and attention in children'</td></tr>
<tr><td>• Polyols</td><td>Sweetener</td><td>'Excessive consumption may cause a laxative effect' (may cause diarrhoea-like symptoms)</td></tr>
<tr><td>• Raw milk</td><td>Milk that has not been heat treated before being sold</td><td>'This milk has not been heat-treated and may therefore contain organisms harmful to health'</td></tr>
</table></td></tr>
</table>

Information that is mandatory (must be shown on a food label)	Notes	Examples
	• The label must show if the food contains a **known allergen** (an ingredient that may give some people an **allergic reaction** [see page 219]) • This is essential information for people who have food allergies so that they can avoid the food product.	There is a list of 14 known allergens in the regulations that must be shown: • eggs • milk • fish • crustaceans (e.g. crab, shrimp, prawn) • molluscs (e.g. mussels, squid) • peanuts • tree nuts (e.g. almonds, hazelnuts, walnuts, cashews, pecans, brazils, pistachios, macadamias) • sesame seeds • cereals containing gluten (e.g. wheat, rye, barley or oats). Gluten can lead to a type of **food intolerance** called **coeliac disease** (see page 218) rather than an allergic reaction, but it is included in this list • soya • celery and celeriac • mustard • lupin • sulphur dioxide and sulphites (these are preservatives that make the food last longer).

Mandatory information on a food label (what must be on it by law)

1 Nutrition information (from December 2016)

2 Ingredients that are known food allergens

3 List of ingredients (in descending order)

4 The quantity of certain ingredients

5 The name of the food product

6 A description of the food product if it is not obvious to the consumer from the name what the food product actually is

7 Indication of minimum durability (the shelf-life of the food product) by 'use-by' or 'best-before' date

8 The net weight/quantity of the food product

9 Place of origin (provenance) of the food product or a specific ingredient

10 Cooking or usage instructions

11 Storage conditions and instructions

12 Contact details of food product manufacturer, distributor or retailer

How to interpret (read and understand) nutrition information on a food label

Nutritional labelling is used to inform consumers about the nutritional profile of a food product (the types and amounts of different nutrients it contains).

Nutritional labelling has been used voluntarily for several years by food manufacturers, and consumers have become familiar with seeing nutrient lists or charts on the food label.

New legislation about nutritional labelling will come into force on **13 December 2016** under the **European Union Food Information to Consumers Regulation No 1169/2011 (EU FIC)**.

This will apply to most pre-packed food products and will require manufacturers to show **nutritional information by law**, usually on the back of a food label.

It will need to be clearly shown with a minimum font size so that most people will be able to read it.

The table below shows which nutritional information will be **mandatory (required by law)**.

Which nutrients **must** be shown in 100g or 100ml of a food product (this includes soft drinks)	Which unit of measurement must be used
The **Energy value**	kilojoules (kJ) **and** kilocalories (kcal)
Protein	grams (g)
Fat (total)	grams (g)
Saturated fats (saturates)	grams (g)
Carbohydrate (total)	grams (g)
Sugars	grams (g)
Salt (NOT sodium, because the word salt is more familiar and understandable for consumers)	grams (g)

The table below shows other nutrients that can also be included on the label **voluntarily**.

Other nutrients that, if included, must be shown in 100g or 100ml of a food product (this includes soft drinks)	Which unit of measurement must be used
Monounsaturated fats (monounsaturates)	grams (g)
Polyunsaturated fats (polyunsaturates)	grams (g)
Polyols (sugar-free sweeteners)	grams (g)
Starch	grams (g)
Fibre	grams (g)
Any of the following vitamins if present in significant amounts (i.e. 15% of the DRV* in 100mls/g of a food; 7.5% for a drink)	
Vitamin A	Microgram (μ)
Vitamin D	Microgram (μ)
Vitamin E	Milligram (mg)
Vitamin K	Microgram (μ)
Vitamin C	Milligram (mg)
Vitamin B1	Milligram (mg)
Vitamin B2	Milligram (mg)
Vitamin B3	Milligram (mg)
Vitamin B6	Milligram (mg)
Vitamin B9	Microgram (μ)
Vitamin B12	Microgram (μ)

Other nutrients that, if included, must be shown in 100g or 100ml of a food product (this includes soft drinks)	Which unit of measurement must be used
Any of the following minerals (there are others) if present in the food product in significant amounts (i.e. 15% of the DRV* in 100ml/g of a food; 7.5% for a drink)	
Potassium	Milligram (mg)
Calcium	Milligram (mg)
Iron	Milligram (mg)
Fluoride	Milligram (mg)
Iodine	Microgram (µ)

* Dietary Reference Values (DRVs) (see page 7)

No other nutrients or substances may be included in the nutrition information.

The percentages of **Dietary Reference Values (DRVs)** (see page 7) provided by the food product have to be given for vitamins and minerals.

If a nutrition or health claim is made about a food product (e.g. *'This product is high in Omega 3 fatty acids'*), the amount that is present must be shown near to the nutritional values table.

This is an example of how nutritional information must be presented on a food label under the new rules.

Nutrient	Per 100g	Per serving (150mg)
Energy	586 kJ/140 kcal	879kJ/210kcal
Fat of which:	1.5g	2.25g
Saturates	0.2g	0.3g
Monounsaturates	0.9g	1.35g
Polyunsaturates	0.4g	0.6g
Carbohydrate of which:	50.0g	75.0g
Sugars	2.5g	3.25g
Starch	42.0g	63.0g
Fibre	5.5g	8.25g
Protein	8.0g	12.0g
Salt	0.2g	0.3g

Often food products are sold as a portion or serving (e.g. pots of yogurt, a pie, sandwiches and a bottle of fruit juice), the weight or volume of which may be more or less than 100g/100ml. The food label must show the nutrients per 100g/100ml as well as how much of each are in a portion/serving, so that people know how much of each nutrient and energy they are consuming when they eat it.

In the UK, the Food Standards Agency has designed a simple, visual way called the 'Traffic Light System' for consumers to identify whether food products contain high, medium or low amounts of fat, saturated fat, sugars or salt, using the colours on traffic lights as a guide.

RED means that the food product contains a HIGH amount of fat, saturated fat, sugars or salt.

AMBER means that the food product contains a MEDIUM amount of fat, saturated fat, sugars or salt.

GREEN means that the food product contains a LOW amount of fat, saturated fat, sugars or salt.

Some food manufacturers and retailers have used this system to develop their own colour coding.

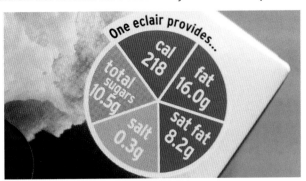

How food marketing influences food choice

Like all products for sale, food products are **marketed** (advertised and promoted) to encourage consumers to buy them.

There are a number of ways in which foods are marketed through different **media**.

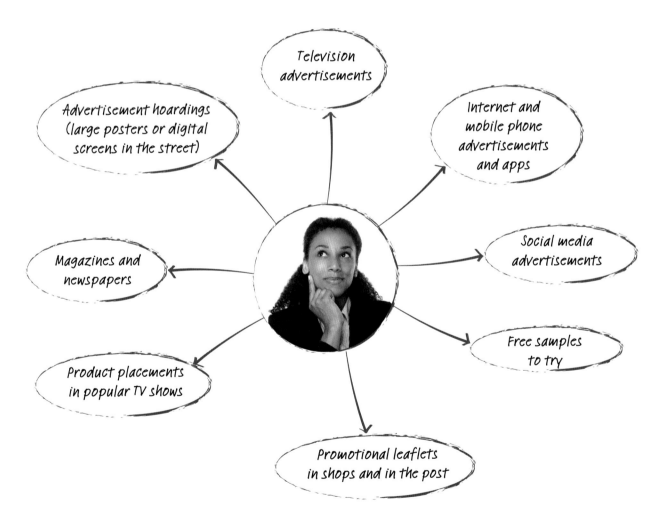

The table on pages 232–234 shows the methods that are often used by supermarkets and food manufacturers to market food products and encourage consumers to buy them.

Methods and examples of how food is marketed

PRICE DEALS AND SPECIAL OFFERS

- Buy one get one free (BOGOF) deals.
- Buy two, get the 3rd free.
- Buy one, get another one ½ price.
- Special buy (e.g. a product bought in by the shop specially at a low price and available until it is sold out).
- Price reduction (e.g. for a product that was previously sold at a higher price for a set amount of time).
- Meal deals (e.g. the choice of three items for a set price).
- Special limited editions, such as a new flavour, size or temporary packaging (e.g. a special biscuit tin), available for a short time only.

- Different price bands for similar products (e.g. top of the range and value/basic food products).

- Loyalty cards in supermarkets, which target consumers with promotional information based on what they buy.

Points to consider and discuss

- Often it is the food producer who has to pay for the cost of these price deals and special offers and not the supermarket who wants to offer the special deal, i.e. the supermarket will reduce the price they pay the producer for the food product, such as strawberries, so that they can give away these 'free' deals without losing their profit.
- Discuss these special offers from the point of view of the producer, the supermarket and the consumer.
- These deals may encourage consumers to buy something they do not really need or to buy more than they need, just because it is cheaper.
- It is important to **check and compare the price per kilogram/litre** between special deals and other similar food products.
- Sometimes the special deal may be more expensive when compared this way.
- Why do supermarkets like to target children and young people in special offers?
- Find out what **'pester power'** means.
- Why are bright colours often used for special offers?

- Why do supermarkets have different price ranges for similar products?
- How do supermarkets reduce the cost of value/basic food products?

- Through the use of IT, supermarkets use the information provided by loyalty cards to find out exactly what consumers buy and to target them with special offers/coupons on those food products.
- Why do supermarkets hold consumers' personal information like this?

Methods and examples of how food is marketed

Points to consider and discuss

LINKING A PRODUCT TO A CELEBRITY OR FAMOUS BRAND

- Food products may be endorsed (approved by) and promoted by being linked to a famous celebrity or brand, such as a:
  - sports personality
  - celebrity chef
  - pop singer
  - film star
  - film company
  - sports clothing manufacturer
  - football or other sports club
  - popular toy
  - popular TV show.

- Why are food products marketed this way?
- Who are often the target groups for these types of food products?

ETHICAL MARKETING

- Food manufacturers are aware of a growing concern amongst consumers about where their food comes from and how it is produced.
- To encourage consumers to buy their food products, they may be marketed to show that they are produced:
  - with a Fairtrade policy
  - organically
  - locally
  - with low carbon pollution
  - with recyclable packaging.

- Why is the ethical trading and marketing of food a concern to many people?

HEALTHY EATING

- Many foods are marketed with a health theme, such as:
  - foods for special diets
  - foods to protect the body from ill-health
  - foods with added nutrients
  - foods with a reduced amount of a particular ingredient, such as fat, salt or sugar.
- Manufacturers have to comply with the law about making health claims for their food products.

- Why is healthy eating such a popular way to market foods?
- Why are nutrition labels and ingredients lists an important feature on food labels?

Methods and examples of how food is marketed	Points to consider and discuss
TIME SAVING • Many people have little time to prepare and cook food, so manufacturers promote food products that save time, effort and energy. 	• Why are ready made and convenience foods so popular? • What are the advantages and disadvantages of these products for consumers? • What are the implications for the environment of these types of food product?

Activity

Collect a variety of food labels and food advertisements from leaflets and magazines.

List the methods and features used by the food manufacturer/retailer to market the food products and make them appealing to consumers.

When you are watching the television, note down any advertisement for food products. Discuss the time the advertisement was shown and who the target audience was.

Practical challenge

Compare similar supermarket own brand food products from different price ranges.

Many supermarkets sell similar own-brand food products in different price ranges to attract different target groups of people. The cheaper ranges are often called 'value' or 'essential' or 'basics', and the most expensive are often called 'best', or 'finest' or 'special'.

Aim: to investigate the similarities and differences between varieties of supermarket own brand food products from different price ranges.

Choose a range of different food products (e.g. cheese, baked beans, a breakfast cereal, yogurt, canned tomatoes, pasta, fresh carrots, bread, etc.) from the top, middle and bottom price range in a supermarket.

Task Tip:

This the type of activity could be carried out for the Food Investigation task.

When carrying out the Food Investigation task, you will need to establish controls when experimenting to ensure a fair test (see page 254). Think about the controls for this investigation to ensure fair and accurate results.

Controls

* You must choose the same type of food in each price range in order to get a realistic comparison (e.g. Cheddar cheese, the same flavoured yogurt, the same type of breakfast cereal).
* Do not show which sample is from the top, middle or bottom price range – code them **randomly** (e.g. XYZ, YZX, XZY, etc.) and keep a record of which is which so that you can analyse the results at the end.
* Keep a record of the price of each product – for a direct comparison, find out the price per 100g/kg or 100ml/litre.

Ask a group of people to conduct a sensory analysis profiling test of each of the samples.

1. Taste each of the samples (taking a sip of water between each to clear your palate).

2. Give each sample a score out of 5 (1 = least preferred/worst, 5 = most preferred/best) for the sensory qualities you want to assess.

Example: PRODUCT: strawberry yogurt

Sensory quality: Sample XYZ	Tester ratings out of 5	Average score Add up each score out of 5 to get a total. Divide the total by the number of people who tasted the food
Appearance		
Flavour		
Texture		

Sensory quality: Sample YZX	Tester ratings out of 5	Average score Add up each score out of 5 to get a total. Divide the total by the number of people who tasted the food
Appearance		
Flavour		
Texture		

Sensory quality: Sample ZYX	Tester ratings out of 5	Average score Add up each score out of 5 to get a total. Divide the total by the number of people who tasted the food
Appearance		
Flavour		
Texture		

Discuss the results as a class.

For each product tested:

- Which sample was the most popular? Why was this?
- Which sample was the least popular? Why was this?
- How did the prices of each product compare? Based on your results, which ones were best value for money?
- Which of the products in the lowest price range do you think are worth buying?

Practice questions

1. a) State three different ways in which supermarkets encourage people to buy their food products. *(3 marks)*

    b) Explain how food manufacturers use food labels to encourage parents to buy food products for their children. *(3 marks)*

2. a) Identify four pieces of information (apart from nutritional information) that are required by law to appear on a food label, and explain why each is there and how it helps the consumer to choose what to buy. *(8 marks)*

    b) Explain why the following appear on nutritional labels on food products:

    (i) The amount of nutrients per 100g or 100ml. *(1 mark)*

    (ii) The amount of nutrients per portion of the food product. *(1 mark)*

    (iii) The amount of salt and not sodium. *(1 mark)*

Activity

Answers to activity on page 223.

A – Lentil and vegetable soup
B – Rock cakes
C – Fish pie

Chapter 8 British and international cuisines

4.2.1 Traditional cuisines

What will I learn?

In this section you will learn about:

- the definition of cuisine
- the features and characteristics of cuisines from Britain and other countries.

Definition of cuisine

The word **cuisine** means:

- a style of cooking and eating that is characteristic of a particular country or region of the world.

Cuisines around the world have developed over many centuries, by using:

- distinctive (particular) ingredients that are usually grown or gathered locally in the area
- specific preparation and cooking methods
- specific cooking equipment
- distinctive presentation and/or serving techniques (practices).

Many cuisines have been influenced by:

- the local geography and climate that influences which foods can be produced
- the immigration of people from other countries, who have settled in a country and brought their traditional eating patterns with them, which have then become part of that country's cuisine.

Key term

Cuisine: a traditional style of cooking and eating that has developed in a country or region of the world

Activity

Consider different countries well known for their food and particular ingredients. Research and produce a concept map of the country to include well-known ingredients, equipment and traditional recipes. Countries you could choose from include: China, Thailand, Japan, America, India, Jamaica, Spain, France, Denmark, etc.

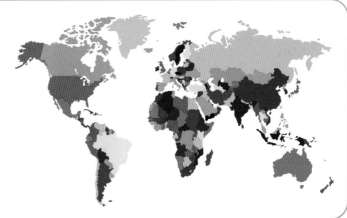

Features and characteristics of cuisines from Britain and other countries

In modern Britain, as in many other countries around the world, people do not only eat their traditional cuisines. Travel abroad, immigration, the importation of foods from other countries and the ready availability of foods from different cuisines in shops and restaurants, mean that many people eat foods and meals from different cuisines very regularly and incorporate these as part of their normal diets – food has become very **multi-cultural**.

British cuisine

The United Kingdom is divided into four countries: England, Northern Ireland, Scotland and Wales. Each has its own distinctive cuisine. The table below describes the traditional cuisine of each British country.

Task Tip:

One of the Food Preparation tasks will be based on British or International Cuisines and therefore a good knowledge of ingredients and recipes from different countries will be advantageous.

Activity

The table below shows some ingredients/recipes associated with each UK country. Carry out research to find other ingredients which could be added to the table.

Traditional ingredients	Examples of traditional British recipes and dishes			
	England	**Northern Ireland**	**Scotland**	**Wales**
Meat (beef, lamb, pork, ham), chicken, game birds (pheasant, grouse, pigeon), game meat (venison, hare, rabbit, wild boar [pig])	Cumberland pork sausage, corned beef, boiled beef, sirloin or fillet steaks, beef casseroles, stews	Irish stew, traditional butcher's sausages, spiced beef, steak and Guinness pie	Haggis, Lorne sausage, Aberdeen Angus beef	Welsh lamb, Welsh beef, cawl (stew with lamb and leeks), faggots (lamb or pork liver meatballs), Glamorgan sausage
Fish, shellfish	Crab, cockles, mussels, winkles, eels, Dover sole	Ardglass potted herring, Lough Neagh eel	Kippered herrings, salmon, trout, haddock, herring Mussels, scallops, oysters, langoustines, spoots (razor clams), buckies (whelks)	Monkfish, steamed cockles
Dairy foods: butter, milk, buttermilk, cream, cheese Duck, goose and hens eggs	Stilton, Cheddar, Wensleydale, etc.	Coolea, Milleens, Crozier Blue, Smoked Knockanore	Bonnet, Crowdie	Caerphilly, Tintern, Y Fenni
Vegetables: potatoes, root vegetables (e.g. carrot, parsnip, swede, turnip), cabbage, green beans, cauliflower, Brussels sprouts, kale, onions, etc.	Asparagus, cauliflower, sprouts, cabbage	Leeks, scallions (spring onions), etc. Seaweed Champ (potato mashed with butter, milk and onions), red seaweed, boxty (potato cake)	Neeps (swede/turnip), tatties (potatoes)	Leeks, laver (seaweed)

Traditional ingredients	Examples of traditional British recipes and dishes			
	England	**Northern Ireland**	**Scotland**	**Wales**
Fruit: apples, pears, strawberries, blackcurrants, blackberries, redcurrants, etc.	Bramley cooking apples, Granny Smith apples, rhubarb	Strawberries, raspberries	Raspberries, strawberries, tayberries (dark red berries – a cross between a raspberry and a blackberry)	Welsh apples (Welsh Cox, Anglesey Pig Snout, Birds Beak)
Cereals: wheat, barley **Cereal products:** bread, cakes, pies, tarts, biscuits	Cottage loaf, English muffin, English crumpet, Lardy cake	Soda breads, Belfast baps, potato bread, wheatens, Ulster Fry	Porridge, oatcakes, Scottish pancakes, plain white bread with a well fired crust, potato ('tattie') scones	Laver bread, Welsh cakes, breads (e.g. Bara Brith), Welsh rarebit

Spices: mostly from other countries

Fresh herbs: often locally grown (e.g. parsley, mint, rosemary, sage)

Sauces: mint, mustard, horseradish, tartare, mayonnaise, salad cream, brown sauce, tomato sauce

Traditional cooking equipment	Traditionally, open fires were used for spit roasting (meat or fish put on a large metal skewer and turned slowly to allow the flames to cook it) and metal or ceramic heating pots for vegetables, soups, stews and sauces. Peat was used in Ireland and Scotland as fuel.
	These have been replaced by electric and gas cookers (hob oven, grill) and modern barbeques.
	Frying and vegetable (sauce) pans for the hob.
	Girdles (griddle) used in Northern Ireland, Scotland and Wales.
	Spurtle – traditional wooden stick for stirring porridge used in Scotland.
Traditional cooking methods	Stewing, boiling, baking, roasting, grilling, griddling, frying, steaming, poaching
Traditional eating patterns	**3 meals a day:** **Morning:** Breakfast **Elevenses:** Mid-morning break – tea or coffee and a cake or scone **Midday:** Lunch (sometimes called dinner) **Afternoon tea:** (tea to drink, plus sandwiches, cake, etc.): used to be traditionally eaten around 4pm in most homes **Evening:** Dinner (sometimes called supper)
Food presentation styles	Meat, poultry or fish with potato and one or two other vegetables, plus a gravy made from meat juices; stews and casseroles Fried foods such as fish, potatoes, pastries and doughs Pies, tarts, flans, pasties Soups and broths (meat and vegetables cooked in stock and thickened by cereals such as barley) Puddings served with sauces such as custards Cakes, biscuits, scones served as individual portions or slices

Examples of traditional British recipes and dishes

England

Roasted meat joints with bones left in, or whole poultry birds (chicken, turkey, goose, duck, pheasant) with roasted potatoes and boiled vegetables (Sunday roast)

Yorkshire puddings, toad-in-the-hole

Bangers (sausages) and mash (boiled and mashed potatoes)

Ploughman's lunch (bread, cheese, pickles)

Fish and chips

Pork pie, cottage pie, game pie, Cornish pasties, steak and kidney pie

Apple pie, jam roly-poly pudding, rhubarb crumble

Lancashire hot pot, scouse, beef cobbler

English breakfast (fried bacon, sausages, eggs, bread, black pudding, mushrooms and tomatoes)

Northern Ireland

Champ – boiled, mashed potatoes with butter, milk and chopped scallions

Dulse – salty snack made from seaweed

Colcannon - cabbage and potatoes boiled and mashed together

Irish stew – meat (lamb or beef), potatoes, carrots, onion in a rich gravy; boiled bacon and cabbage

Farls – breads made with either potato, flour and buttermilk (cooked on a griddle), or soda bread farl, where bicarbonate of soda is added to make the dough rise

Lough Neagh Eel – fried eel in a white onion sauce

Steak and Guinness pie

Meat pasties

Boxty – potato cake made with boiled mashed potatoes and raw grated potatoes (boiled as a whole 'loaf', then cooled, sliced and fried with bacon)

Potted herrings

Scotland

Tatties – (potato scones)

Neeps and tatties (mashed swede/turnip and potatoes)

Arbroath smokies – smoked haddock

Cullen skink – chunky soup made with smoked haddock, potatoes and onions

Scotch pie

Scotch broth – thick soup

Kippers – smoked herrings

Haggis – savoury pudding made from sheep's heart and liver minced with onion, oatmeal, suet, spices, salt and stock and encased in a sheep's stomach

Oatcakes, scones, shortbread

Dundee cake

Wales

Tatws Pum Munud (5 minute potatoes) – a Welsh stew

Welsh rarebit (toasted cheese)

Bara brith – a type of bread

Cawl – lamb and leek stew

Glamorgan sausages – made with cheese, breadcrumbs, and eggs

Faggots – a type of meat ball

Leek and potato soup

Welsh cakes

Cuisines from other countries

There are hundreds of different cuisines throughout the world, and it is interesting to compare them to British cuisines.

The tables on pages 241–242 and pages 244–245 give examples of two cuisines from Italy and Morocco.

ITALY

Italy is divided into different regions, all of which have traditional cuisines, depending on which ingredients are grown in each area.

Traditional foods

Meat – beef, goat

Fish – sardines, tuna, anchovies, squid, sea bream, swordfish

Dairy foods – butter, cheeses (e.g. parmesan, mozzarella, ricotta)

Vegetables and fruit – olives, olive oil, tomatoes, lemons, oranges, aubergines, peppers, fava beans

Cereals – rice and maize (Northern Italy), durum wheat (Southern Italy) – used for making pasta

Cereal products – pasta, pizza, breads, risotto, pastries and cakes

Spices – saffron

Herbs – basil, oregano, coriander

Sauces – tomato sauces for pasta and pizzas

Nuts – e.g. almonds

 Activity

Find out the names of these different shapes of pasta and which ingredients are added to pasta to give it different colours. Answers on page 246.

Traditional eating patterns

Meals tend to have several courses, and Italians like to take their time together with their families to eat the meal.

The Italian Slow Food Movement encourages people to focus on their food and eat it slowly, so that they can enjoy and appreciate all the flavours and textures of well-produced, well-prepared and well-cooked food.

Traditional cooking methods

Stewing, boiling, baking, roasting, grilling, griddling, frying, steaming, poaching

Meal courses in Italian meals

Antipasto – food to start the meal, such as bruschetta (grilled bread, garlic, olive oil and salt)

Primo – first course (e.g. a hot dish such as pasta, risotto, gnocchi or soup)

Secondo – second course (e.g. meat or fish dish)

Contorno – salad or vegetables

Formaggio – fruits and cheese

Dolce – sweet course

Traditional cooking equipment

Pizza ovens, flat pizza trays, pasta maker, electric and gas cookers (hob, oven, grill) and modern barbeques

ITALY

Food presentation styles

Food presentation is simple with many dishes having only 4–8 ingredients:

- pasta with sauces
- variety of salads
- soups
- pizzas
- risotto
- shellfish with sauces or salads
- frozen fruit and cream desserts

Examples of traditional Italian recipes, dishes and food

Antipasto

- Bruschetta
- Prosciutto
- Crostino
- Cured meats (e.g. salami)
- Olives
- Sliced tomatoes and pesto
- Focaccia bread and sardines

A selection of cured meats

Bruschetta with tomato and basil

Secondo

- Lasagne (meat or vegetable)
- Bolognese (meat or vegetable)
- Chicken fettuccini
- Caprese salad
- Chicken scaloppini

Spaghetti neapolitan

Lasagne

Chicken fettuccini

Primo

- Pasta dishes
- Risotto
- Soup
- Gnocci

Risotto and scallops

Ravioli

Gnocchi in a cream sauce

Dolce

- Tiramisu
- Zabaglione
- Panna cotta
- Panettone
- Granita
- Semifreddo
- Gelato
- Cassata

Zabaglione

Tiramisu

Panna cotta

Practical challenge

Making fresh pasta

Ingredients:

200g 00 pasta flour (00 flour has a very high gluten content). Strong plain bread flour can be used instead if you do not have pasta flour

1 egg

1 egg yolk

Method:

1. Weigh the flour and add it to the food processer.

2. Add the egg and the egg yolk.

3. Pulse the machine until the mixture begins to look like breadcrumbs.

4. Process it until the mixture forms a soft ball of dough.

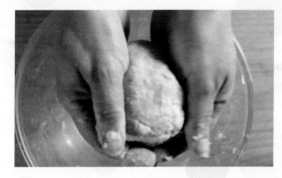

5. Place the dough onto a floured work top and knead it until it is smooth and form it into a ball.

6. Wrap the ball of dough in cling film and leave it to rest in a cool place for 20 minutes before using it. This will allow the gluten to develop and the water from the eggs to be absorbed by the flour. The longer you leave it, the more manageable it will become.

7. Cut the dough into two pieces. Flatten each piece with a rolling pin or your hands until it is about 5mm thick.

8. Fold the dough and pass it through the pasta machine at its widest setting, re-folding and re-rolling several times without changing the setting. Do this until you have a rectangular shape approximately 7.5cm × 18cm. If you do not have a pasta machine, roll thinly using a rolling pin.

9. Repeat with the second piece of dough.

10. To thin the pasta, start with the pasta machine at its widest setting and pass the dough through the rollers.

11. Do not fold the pasta dough, but repeat this process, decreasing the width setting of the roller each time, until you reach the narrowest setting.

12. For most uses, take the pasta down to the thinnest setting – especially for ravioli, as you are sandwiching two layers together when it is folded.

13. The fresh pasta should be wrapped in a damp cloth if you are not using it straight away so that it does not dry out and become difficult to use.

This could be a group activity.

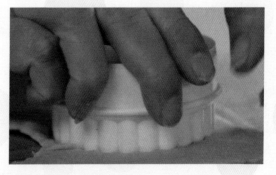

There are a number of other ways to finish pasta, depending what type you are going to make. For example, using a sharp knife or pizza cutter to slice the pasta into strips for tagliatelle or fettuccine, circles for tortellini or squares for ravioli. On most pasta machines, there are attachments that can do this for you.

Activity

1. In small groups make a batch of pasta dough.

2. Investigate adding colour and flavour to the pasta using natural ingredients, e.g. spinach, tomato puree, beetroot, turmeric, mustard, etc.

3. Practice shaping the pasta, e.g. tagliatelle, tortellini, ravioli.

4. Make ravioli and research and experiment with different fillings that could be added.

MOROCCO

Morocco is situated in the north west of the African continent, just below Spain. Moroccan cuisine has been influenced by other cultures over many years, including many from the Mediterranean and Arabic countries, and Andalusian (Spanish region) and Berber (North African) cultures.

Alcohol is not permitted to be drunk by Muslims and pork is not eaten for religious reasons.

Traditional eating patterns

Traditional cutlery (knives, forks, spoons) are used, as well as the hands, for eating food.

Bread is included in most meals.

Most meals start with a selection of **mezze**, which are small dishes served as appetisers (e.g. olives or a selection of cold or cooked vegetable salads with olive oil, cumin and served with a dip and flat bread).

These are then followed by a tagine dish. Lamb and chicken are often eaten.

Couscous with meat and vegetables is often included in the meal.

Fresh fruit or dessert is then served.

Sweet mint tea is usually served at the end of a meal.

Traditional foods

Meat – lamb, beef, goat, mutton, camel, chicken

Fish – squid, calamari, shrimp, scallops, white fish, snapper, etc.

Dairy foods – milk from cows, sheep, goats and camels is used to make a variety of fermented dairy foods, e.g. iben and raib (fermented milk), jben (fresh cheese) and zabda (butter)

Vegetables and fruit – olives, olive oil, tomatoes, lemons, oranges, aubergines, peppers, grapes, apples, strawberries, green beans, onions, potatoes, fava beans, etc.

Cereals – barley, wheat

Cereal products – couscous, khubz (flat breads) made from durum wheat semolina, wholegrain baguettes

Spices – cinnamon, cumin, turmeric, ginger, pepper, paprika, sesame seeds, anise, nutmeg, oregano, cayenne pepper, fennel, cloves, coriander, saffron, mace

Herbs – mint, parsley, coriander, peppermint, marjoram, caraway, verbena

Nuts – e.g. almonds, pistachios

Flavourings – dried fruits, lemon pickle, unrefined olive oil

Food presentation styles

Eating is taken seriously and dining rooms are often elaborately decorated with furnishings and wall coverings, as well as ornamental dishes and utensils on the table.

Dishes of food are placed in the centre of the table. Tagines are often decorated and brightly coloured and are used to serve the food.

People then help themselves to the food.

MOROCCO

Traditional cooking methods

Stewing (slow cooking tagines), baking, roasting, grilling, griddling, frying, steaming, poaching

Traditional cooking equipment

Tagine: a ceramic pot with a pointed lid used for many traditional, slow-cooked Moroccan recipes

Skewers: for making and grilling kebabs

Steamer: for cooking couscous

Copper cooking pots: called maqla, quarda, tanjir and tanjra, used for a variety of cooking methods and foods

Majmar (charcoal brazier): for slow-cooking tagine recipes

Examples of traditional Moroccan recipes, dishes and foods

Mezze

Tagine

Dessert

Dried fruit

Practical challenge

Select a cuisine from a region of the world that interests you to research further.

Make a table, like the two examples from Italy and Morocco earlier in this chapter, and include specific information about the cuisine you are researching.

Choose and prepare one or two typical examples of traditional recipes from the cuisine.

Prepare a recipe card or poster about your chosen cuisine to display with your finished recipes, so that people can learn more about your chosen cuisine.

You could set up a tasting session to get feedback about your chosen recipes.

How does your chosen cuisine compare to British cuisine?

Stretch and challenge question

What might be the environmental impact of making recipes that include ingredients imported from different countries?

Practice questions

1. a) Give a definition of what the word 'cuisine' means. *(1 mark)*

    b) Describe three ways in which cuisines develop and change over the years. *(3 marks)*

    c) Name one type of cuisine of your choice. List three recipes and cooking methods typical of that cuisine. *(6 marks)*

2. Explain why the food eaten in modern Britain is considered to be multicultural, giving examples in your answer. *(12 marks)*

Activity

Answers to activity on page 241.

1 – spaghetti   6 – penne

2 – tagliatelle   7 – farfalle

3 – macaroni   8 – fusilli tricolore

4 – ravioli   9 – rigatoni

5 – conchiglie   10 – cannelloni

Chapter 9 Sensory evaluation

4.3.1 Sensory evaluation

What will I learn?

In this section you will learn about:

- how senses influence food choice
- how we taste food
- sensory testing methods used to evaluate food products
- how to set up a food tasting panel.

How senses influence food choice

Eating good food is one of the pleasures of life and its enjoyment is dependent on the body's **senses** working together.

There are five senses involved in the choice and enjoyment of food: **sight, smell, taste, touch** and **sound**.

The enjoyment of food is the result of a mixture of all these senses working together.

If one of the senses is not working correctly, it can affect the whole eating experience.

To enable people to enjoy their food, it is important that the choice, preparation, cooking and serving of food is carried out well so that it is **appetising** (makes you want to eat it) and appeals to the senses, which is why when you are learning to cook you need to develop good skills in each of these areas.

When tasting food it is important to use descriptive words such as 'moist texture', 'crunchy', 'sweet flavour', etc. Avoid using words such as 'nice', 'horrible', etc., as these are your opinion and not descriptions of the food you are tasting.

The table below shows how each of the senses influence the choice and enjoyment of food.

Key terms

Senses: the ability of the body to react to things through sight, taste, hearing, smell (aroma) and touch

Appetising: food prepared, cooked and served so well that you want to eat it

Sense: sight
How does this sense influence food choice?
Does the appearance of the food look **appetising** (you want to eat it) or repulsive (you want to avoid it)? 

What influences the enjoyment of the food?	**How can you make the food enjoyable?**
Colour, pattern, shape, quantity, neatness, presentation, cleanliness, how it is served on a plate. 	Decorate and garnish food neatly, creatively and with colour. 

Sense: smell

How does this sense influence food choice?

Does the aroma of the food smell appetising or off-putting? Does it have a good **aroma**?

What influences the enjoyment of the food?

Fresh ingredients, correct cooking, combinations of aromas (smells), expectations (people expect foods to smell a particular way), temperature of the food (aromas are released when food is heated).

How can you make the food enjoyable?

Make sure food is fresh.

Do not overcook foods.

Sense: taste

How does this sense influence food choice?

Does the food have an enjoyable and delicious **flavour**?

What influences the enjoyment of the food?

Freshness (stale food loses its flavour), correct cooking, combinations of flavours, expectations (people expect foods to taste a particular way), temperature of the food (flavours are released when food is heated).

How can you make the food enjoyable?

Make sure food is fresh.

Cook carefully to preserve the flavour of foods such as vegetables, fruits and spices.

Use cooking methods that develop flavours such as sautéing vegetables, making stock, etc.

Experiment with combining a few different flavours.

Make use of natural flavours such as citrus fruit zest, fresh herbs and spices (e.g. fresh ginger and lemongrass).

Sense: touch

How does this sense influence food choice?

Does the food have a nice **texture** and **mouthfeel** (how food or drink feels in the mouth)?

What influences the enjoyment of the food?

Freshness (stale food loses its texture), correct preparation and cooking to avoid unexpected items in the food such as lumps in a sauce, egg shell, fish bones, fruit stalks, etc.

How can you make the food enjoyable?

Make sure food is fresh, especially vegetables, fruits and fish, as their textures can quickly change in a short period of time.

Prepare foods carefully to remove inedible parts such as bones and egg shells.

Cook at the correct temperature and for sufficient time to develop textures (e.g. melting chocolate, raising a sponge cake, baking bread).

Avoid lumpy sauces by stirring them constantly when cooking.

Sense: hearing

How does this sense influence food choice?

Does the food sound right (e.g. crunchy, crispy, fizzy)?

What influences the enjoyment of the food?

Freshness (stale food will lose its crispness, crunch and fizziness), correct cooking.

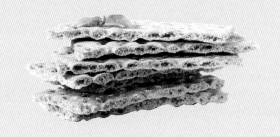

How can you make the food enjoyable?

Make sure food is stored correctly to keep it fresh and maintain its texture.

Salad foods stay crisp in a cool place.

Store dry foods away from moisture.

How we taste food

To enjoy the flavours of food, the senses of **taste** and **smell** have to work together.

The flavours of food are detected by thousands of taste buds on the surface of the tongue (you can feel them as lots of little bumps).

Taste buds have tiny sensitive hairs (called microvilli) that send messages to the brain about the flavour of food.

Five different groups of flavours are detected by all taste buds on the tongue, which the brain identifies as **salt**, **sweet**, **bitter**, **sour** and **umami** (this is how you say it: oo-ma-mee) (savoury).

Most foods are combinations of many different chemicals that make up their unique flavour, for example the flavour of fresh blueberries is made up of 24 different natural chemicals.

Lots of different natural chemicals are released from food, especially when it is cooked. These are detected by our nose and stimulate our appetite (make us want to eat). When we put food into our mouth and chew it, these chemicals go up into the nose, where special olfactory (smell) receptors pick them up and send messages to the brain about what they smell like.

Different areas in the brain then combine the information from the taste buds and the olfactory receptors to give us the sensation of different flavours. About 80% of what you taste as flavour actually comes from the information provided to the brain by the olfactory receptors in your nose.

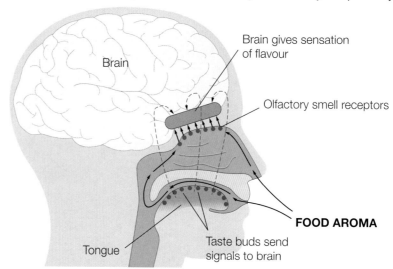

If you have a cold and your nose is blocked up, the flavour of the food you are eating will not be as strong as usual because the olfactory receptors cannot pick up the chemicals from the food to send the messages to the brain. You can put this to the test by holding your nose when you eat something and seeing what effect this has on the flavour.

Sensory testing methods used to evaluate food products

Sensory analysis is a way of measuring the sensory qualities of food and is used by food manufacturers, chefs and retailers to test the popularity of new food products and existing ones that may have been changed in some way.

It takes a lot of work and time to develop new food products, so they want to make sure that the food product stands a chance of appealing to consumers and selling well.

Task Tip:

Testing should form an important part of your work in both the Food Investigation task and the Food Preparation task. Sensory analysis techniques are a good way of testing your practical work. Try to use a range of tests.

There are a variety of ways in which sensory analysis tests can be carried out, some of which are shown on pages 251–253.

Key terms

Taste buds: special cells on the tongue that pick up flavours

Olfactory (smell) receptors: special cells in the nose that pick up aromas (smells)

Sensory analysis: a way of measuring the sensory qualities of food

Sensory descriptors: words used to describe the characteristics of a food

Preference tests

These tests are used to find out which food product people like the best.

There are two different preference tests that you could use.

1. Paired preference test

In this test, people are given two similar samples of food and they have to say which one they prefer, for example:

- two cheeses – one a mild Cheddar and one a mature Cheddar
- two soups – one made with tomatoes and chilli and one made with tomatoes and lentils
- two burgers – one made with beef and one made with lamb.

2. Hedonic rating test

In this test, people give their opinion of one or more food products by filling out a table that uses a scale of preference, as shown in the example below. Words, numbers or smiley faces can be used for the scale of preference, depending on the age or abilities of the people who are testing the food.

Please indicate, by ticking a box below, how much you liked the food product:

Sample – use random codes, e.g. 567, 897, 343, or XYZ, ZXY, etc.*	I liked it very much 1	I liked it a little bit 2	I didn't like or dislike it 3	I didn't like it much 4	I didn't like it at all 5
567					
897					
343					
291					

* Random numbers or letters are used to avoid any bias and ensure a fair test. If samples are labelled 1, 2, 3, the brain can automatically think that number 1 is the best or highest; the same relates to A, B, C. Using random letters and numbers avoids this, e.g. ZYY, 579.

Discriminatory tests

These tests are used to find out whether or not people can tell the difference between similar samples of food.

There are two different discriminatory tests that you could use.

1. Triangle test

In this test, people are given three samples of a food product to try. Two of the samples are identical. The third sample has had something changed. The testers have to say which one of the samples is **different** and the idea is to see if they can discriminate between the food samples when something has been changed in one of them, for example:

- bolognese sauce, where the salt content has been reduced in one sample
- lemon cheesecake, where the sugar content has been reduced in one sample
- chicken curry, where the fat content has been reduced in one sample.

2. A not A test

This test is opposite to the triangle test. People are given a sample of food to try (Sample A). They are then given two other samples to try, one of which is identical to Sample A and the other has had something changed. They have to identify which of the other two samples is the **same** as Sample A.

Grading tests

These tests are used to put in order a particular characteristic of a food product (e.g. sweetness/saltiness) or the order in which people like a set of food samples.

There are three types of test that you could use.

1. Ranking test

In this test, people are given some samples of food to taste, for example five samples arranged randomly. They are then asked to rank them in order for the characteristic of the food you are testing, e.g. spiciness, crispness, smoothness (1 = least, 5 = most).

Once all the people have completed the test, their rankings are placed on a chart and added up for each sample:

Tester	Samples					Rank sum
	XYZ	ZYX	XZY	YZX	ZXY	
1	1	4	5	3	2	15
2	2	3	5	4	1	15
3	1	3	4	5	2	15
4	2	4	5	3	1	15
5	2	4	3	5	1	15
6	3	4	5	2	1	15
7	2	3	5	4	1	15
8	1	4	5	3	2	15
Rank totals	14	29	37	29	11	120

The results in this example show that the samples are ranked like this:

Sample	Rank place
XYZ	4th
ZYX	= 2nd
XZY	1st
YZX	= 2nd
ZXY	5th

2. Rating test

In this test, testers try a food sample and are asked to rate it for a particular characteristic (e.g. taste, texture, appearance and aroma) or how much they like it, on a 5-point scale, as shown in the example table below:

	Taster 1	Taster 2	Taster 3	Taster 4	Total
Appearance	4	3	5	3	15
Texture	3	5	5	4	17
Taste	4	5	4	5	18
Aroma	3	4	3	3	13

Numbers, words or smiley faces can be used depending on the age or abilities of the people who are testing the food. The scale can go one way (as in scale examples 1 and 2 in the example chart below) or it can go from one extreme to another (as in scale examples 3 and 4 in the example chart below).

*Please indicate by using a tick in **one** box on the scale, how you rate the food sample:*

Examples of scales that can be used

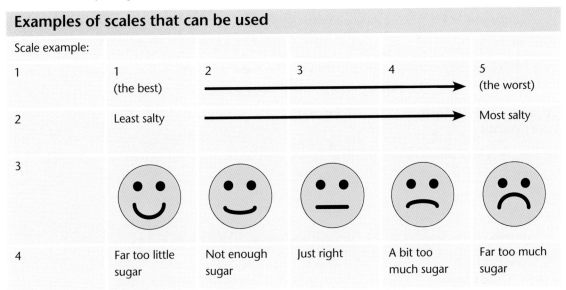

Scale example:

| 1 | 1 (the best) | 2 | 3 | 4 | 5 (the worst) |
| 2 | Least salty | | | | Most salty |

| 3 | Far too little sugar | Not enough sugar | Just right | A bit too much sugar | Far too much sugar |
| 4 | | | | | |

The number of ticks given in each of the 5 points of the scale are added up to give an indication of what people think about the food.

3. Profiling test

In this test, people are asked to rate the intensity from 1–5 (where 1 is the least and 5 is the most) of a set of **sensory descriptors** for a food product. A sensory descriptor is another term for the characteristics of a food (e.g. smoothness, sweetness, crunchiness).

Add up the answers and divide them by the number of people who tasted the food to get an average score for each sensory descriptor, as shown in the example below for a salsa recipe:

Sensory descriptor:	Tester ratings out of 5 (1 = the least, 5 = the most)						Average score
Spiciness	5	4	5	3	5	4	26 ÷ 6 = 4.3
Tomato flavour	3	2	2	3	2	1	13 ÷ 6 = 2.1
Texture – crunchiness	3	2	2	2	1	3	13 ÷ 6 = 2.1
Saltiness	4	5	5	5	4	5	28 ÷ 6 = 4.6

Plot the findings on a star diagram (sometimes called a spider or radar diagram) to give the product a visual profile.

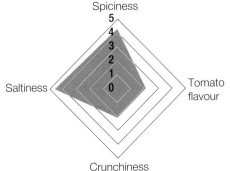

Profile test for salsa, which shows it is very salty and spicy, but not very crunchy and does not have a strong tomato flavour

How to set up a food tasting panel

When you are setting up a food tasting panel, there are some pieces of advice you need to follow to make the results as fair and as realistic as possible. These are shown in the table below, with reasons given.

The number of these that you will be able to follow will depend very much on how much time and the facilities you have for setting up a tasting panel.

Task Tip:

For your NEA tasks you need to explain what you have done to show that you have made every effort to carry out realistic and fair testing.

Advice for setting up and carrying out a sensory analysis tasting panel	Reasons
It should take place in a quiet area, away from where the food was prepared.	To avoid your food tasters being disturbed and influenced by other people.
Make sure you have enough food tasters taking part (e.g. between 5 and 10 people).	To ensure realistic results.
Carry out the test in hygienic conditions (e.g. separate spoons/samples for each taster).	To avoid contamination by micro-organisms.
Clear instructions should be given to food tasters.	So that they know exactly what they need to do.
Food tasters should be given charts to fill in as they taste the food or record the results using computer software.	So that you can keep an accurate record of the results of the panel.
Food tasters should be given water to drink or plain crackers to eat between each sample.	To clear their palate (tongue and taste buds) so they do not get confused between samples.
Food tasters should work on their own.	So that they are not influenced by other people's opinions.
Food samples should be coded randomly with numbers or letters. Only the person setting up and carrying out the tasting panel should know which code applies to which food sample.	So that food tasters do not know which sample is which, to ensure a fair test (called a blind test).
Small samples and same sized servings of food should be given.	To prevent food tasters filling up and not tasting all the samples properly.
Samples should be presented/served at the same temperature.	To prevent the flavours being affected and so that tasters can taste them comfortably.
Samples should be presented/served on the same coloured plates, usually black or white.	To prevent the taster's senses from being distracted or influenced by background colour and appearance of the food samples.
Controlled lighting in the tasting booths, e.g. red lighting.	This ensures all the samples look the same and it is often used when testing taste and texture to avoid the appearance of the food distracting from the flavour.

Practice questions

1. a) Explain how the senses of taste and smell work together to enable us to enjoy our food. *(3 marks)*

   b) Describe three ways of ensuring that the flavour of foods is retained during cooking. *(3 marks)*

2. a) Explain how the senses help us to enjoy our food. *(5 marks)*

   b) (i) Describe how you would set up a tasting panel to test the qualities of a dish you have recently made. *(5 marks)*

   (ii) Explain how you would ensure fair testing when carrying out sensory tests on food. *(5 marks)*

Chapter 10 Environmental impact and sustainability

5.1.1 Food sources

What will I learn?

In this section you will learn about:

- where and how ingredients are grown, gathered, reared and caught
- organic farming
- genetically modified foods (GM)
- seasonal food.

Introduction

This section of the book is about **food provenance** – *where* foods and the ingredients in them originally come from *before* they reach food manufacturers, retailers (supermarkets, etc.), the food service industry (e.g. restaurants) and our plates.

The production of food can have significant impacts on the environment. It is important for people to have an understanding of what these impacts are, in order for them to be able to make **informed** food choices.

In Chapter 8, you learned about some of the issues around food production that concern people and influence their food choices, such as:

- animal welfare
- intensive farming
- **pesticides** and fertilisers
- Fairtrade
- food miles
- organic food production.

In this section, you will learn more about how food is grown, gathered, reared and caught and how these issues are involved.

Where and how ingredients are grown, gathered, reared and caught

Over thousands of years, humans have grown, reared, gathered and caught their food to provide them with a varied diet. Today, many familiar foods and ingredients that we produce and eat were gradually introduced into the UK from other parts of the world, over many centuries. In modern Britain, many foods and ingredients that would not normally grow here, because our climate is not suitable, are imported, making our food choices very varied and multi-cultural.

There are four types of food provenance that you need to know and understand:

1. **Growing crops** (plants) for fruits, vegetables, herbs, cereals and nuts in fields, greenhouses, orchards and gardens.
2. **Rearing livestock** (animals) such as cattle, sheep, pigs, poultry (birds such as chicken and duck) for meat and their products (e.g. eggs, milk, dairy foods); and fish on farms.
3. **Gathering wild foods** such as herbs (e.g. wild garlic), edible fungi, berries (e.g. blackberries) and seaweed (e.g. kelp).
4. **Catching** (hunting) **wild** animals (e.g. boar, deer, rabbit), birds (e.g. ducks, grouse, pheasants), fish (e.g. salmon, trout) and shellfish (e.g. oysters, scallops).

Key terms

Food provenance: where foods and ingredients originally come from

Pesticides: chemicals sprayed onto plant crops to prevent insect and mould attack and weed growth, and produce strong plants

Grown ingredients: plants grown for food (herbs, fruits, vegetables, cereals)

Reared ingredients: animals, birds and fish specially bred in captivity and brought up to be ready to eat

Gathered ingredients: plant foods gathered from the wild for eating (e.g. herbs, edible fungi, berries, seaweed)

Caught ingredients: animals, birds, fish and shellfish hunted and caught from the wild for eating

Intensive farming: growing or rearing large numbers of the same type of plants or animals in one place

Organic farming: producing food using manure, compost and natural methods of weed, pest and disease control rather than chemicals

Genetic modification (GM): a scientific technique that enables a particular characteristic from one plant or animal to be inserted into the genes of another

1. Growing crops

Plant crops are an essential part of our food supply. They are usually grown by a method called **intensive farming**, where large numbers of the same crop are grown together.

A large number and variety of plant crops, particularly salad vegetables, tomatoes and herbs, are grown inside large glass houses or plastic poly-tunnels.

Poly-tunnels are long, curved plastic structures that plants are grown under to protect them from the effects of the weather, including wind, rain and extreme temperatures. They provide sheltered conditions and are large enough for people and machines to work inside. Some plant crops are grown in special troughs containing water (not soil), which has had nutrients added to it. This is called **hydroponic** production.

Harvesting a large crop of wheat

Growing peppers in a large plastic poly-tunnel

Growing oranges in large groves (orchards) in Florida, USA, with thousands of trees in each grove

A crop of lettuces being grown hydroponically

Points to consider about intensive farming of plant crops

Plant foods that are grown intensively on a large scale are susceptible to (likely to be affected by) attack from **pests** such as insects, animals and micro-organisms (e.g. moulds) or have to **compete** for space, light and soil nutrients with other wild plants (weeds).

In order for a crop not to fail because of pests or weeds, many farmers spray the plants several times as they grow with chemical pesticides in order to stop insect and mould attack, prevent weeds growing and encourage the crop to be strong.

Also, artificial **fertilisers** are often added to the soil because **intensive farming** removes lots of nutrients that need to be replaced quickly in order to grow another crop.

Many people object to the amount of pesticides and fertilisers that are used because they are concerned about the short- and long-term effects of these chemicals on:

- the health of themselves and their families
- the health of the soil and the wildlife in streams and rivers into which a lot of these chemicals leak
- the natural **ecology** of the environment (the natural life cycles of all the plants and animals that live, grow and depend on each other in an area).

Organic farming

Organic farming is a method of producing crops in which:

- artificial chemical fertilisers are not allowed to be used
- farmers develop healthy, fertile soil by adding **organic matter** (e.g. **manure** [animal waste] and **compost** [rotted down plant waste]) so that the plants receive plenty of naturally produced nutrients
- farmers **rotate** their crops (i.e. they grow something different each year on a particular piece of land) so that the soil does not have all the goodness taken out of it
- farmers leave a piece of land **fallow** (no crop growing in it) for a year to break the life cycle of pests and allow the soil to naturally become more fertile again
- pesticide use is severely restricted – farmers encourage wild, natural predators such as ladybirds and other insects to control pests.

Many people choose to buy organically produced food and, in the UK, the **Soil Association** is the organisation that oversees organic food production standards and awards its logo to foods that meet these standards.

2. Rearing livestock

Many types of animals, including birds and fish, are reared all over the world in large numbers for people to eat. As the world's population increases there is a demand for more meat to be produced.

There are many large **factory farms** where hundreds or thousands of animals, fish or birds (**livestock**) are **intensively farmed** in one place (often indoors), as shown in the pictures below:

Spraying a field crop of potato plants

Soil association logo, which indicates the food has been produced organically

Intensively farmed chickens (called broiler chickens) – produced for meat

Intensively produced eggs – usually called 'eggs from caged hens' (the old name was battery hens)

A fish farm, containing hundreds of thousands of salmon in cages submerged in the water

A fish farm in Thailand showing lots of fish in the tanks

Intensive milk production

The RSPCA Freedom Food symbol

The UK Red Tractor symbol

Intensive milk production. This is where the cows stay inside a large barn for most of the time but often have access to pasture outside for a few weeks when they are not lactating (producing milk). Inside the barns, many farmers provide the cows with access to areas where they can lie down, fans and water sprinklers to keep them comfortable, and cow grooming brushes. The cows are fed and milked regularly each day.

Points to consider about intensive farming of livestock

It costs less money to rear livestock and produce animal products (meat, fish, milk, eggs, etc.) by having large numbers together in one space than it does to have them in smaller numbers in lots of separate farms. This is because in intensive farming, less land is used (land is expensive to buy and maintain) and fewer people are needed to run an intensive farm (labour [paying people to work] costs a lot of money).

Intensive farming has significantly brought down the price of many foods over the last 40–50 years. For example, 50–60 years ago in the UK, chicken and fresh salmon were so expensive that most ordinary people would only eat them once or twice a year for a special occasion. Now, chicken and salmon are both mass produced on intensive farms and, as a result, are a lot cheaper and people have become used to paying low prices for intensively produced meat, poultry, fish, eggs and dairy products.

Farmers take a lot of risk when they rear livestock because they have to invest a lot of money, time and effort into feeding, housing and keeping the animals, birds and fish healthy. The outbreak of a disease can cause the loss of large numbers of livestock and seriously affect the livelihood of the farmer.

Having lots of livestock together in one space can lead to **animal welfare** concerns, including:

- the easy spread of diseases and pests (so livestock have to be given medicines or chemical sprays to prevent this)
- fighting and injury amongst animals, birds and fish who are naturally not used to living in such crowded conditions
- distress and trauma because of the noise of other animals, small living conditions and the threat of outside predators who will try to catch them (often a problem in fish farms).

People may choose to buy foods that are not intensively produced and where there are controls to ensure that the livestock are treated with the highest standards of animal welfare. These foods often have a symbol on their labels.

The UK Red Tractor symbol is a farm and food quality assurance scheme. The food industry introduced it to promote clearer food labelling and assure consumers that farms and food companies follow high standards of food safety and food hygiene, animal welfare and environmental protection.

As in crop production, livestock is also produced **organically** on some farms and there are rules about how this should be done:

- Livestock must be produced as naturally as possible, and be **free-range** (allowed to roam around outside, not in cages) so that they can express their natural behaviours. For example, hens like to peck and scratch the ground to find insects, cows like to graze on grass and pigs like to 'root' in the soil (dig it up with their snouts to look for things to eat).

- Drugs, antibiotics, growth promoters (to make the animals grow quickly) and other medicines are banned for livestock.

- Foods given to them to eat should be organically produced.

- Small herds and flocks of livestock are produced to control the spread of disease.

In the UK, organically produced livestock and the products from them are also labelled with the Soil Association logo (see page 257) so that consumers know what to look for when they are choosing their food.

Genetically modified food

Genetic modification (GM) of food plants and animals was developed to enable farmers to breed new types of animals or plants that have:

- better resistance to pests and diseases

- faster or stronger growth rates

- a different nutrient profile (e.g. Golden Rice project to increase vitamin A: http://www. goldenrice.org)

- a more intense flavour or colour.

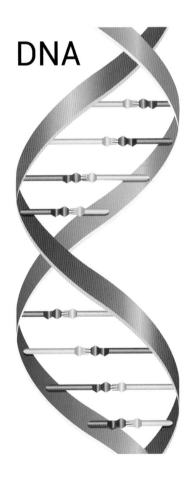

Most GM crops that have been developed are plants. In all plants and animals, **genes**, which are found in cells, control and make them have certain unique characteristics such as colour, shape, flavour and size. These characteristics are passed on to the next generation by the genes.

This happens because genes are made of **DNA** (which stands for deoxyribonucleic acid). DNA is made of two strands joined together and twisted into a double helix, like this:

The 'bridges' between the two strands of DNA are made of four different **amino acids** (protein building blocks). These are arranged in different sequences that create the code of instructions for each characteristic found in a plant or animal.

GM is a complex scientific technique where the code for a particular characteristic (e.g. a colour or the ability to grow bigger) in a gene is copied in a laboratory and inserted into a completely different plant or animal. This enables them to reproduce with that new characteristic in place.

Some people object to GM technology, because they have concerns about:

- the effects of GM crops on the natural ecology (plants and animals) and environment of an area where they are grown

- interfering with the natural process of plant and animal reproduction

- the possibility of some people being allergic to specific GM foods because a particular characteristic has been put in them

- the effects on farmers, especially in developing countries, who cannot save the seed from many GM crops to grow next year (the crops have been modified to prevent the seeds from developing into new plants). The farmers have to buy more seed from the GM company, which locks them into a contract from which it is hard to leave, and may affect their income if the GM company decides it no longer wants to grow that particular crop any more

- the fact that it is not possible to tell by looking whether a food has been genetically modified or not. If there are GM ingredients in a food product, it has to be stated on the label.

3. Gathering wild foods

Humans have gathered wild plant foods for many thousands of years. Once farming started, certain plants were selected for growing in large numbers in fields and orchards and the need to gather wild foods started to decline. Gathering is sometimes called 'foraging' for food.

Many people still gather wild plant foods, such as edible mushrooms, wild herbs, fruits and seaweed. You may have seen on the television celebrity chefs using ingredients they have gathered (e.g. mushrooms) in the dishes on their menus.

Sometimes wild foods are used in the production of a specialist item such as cheese, for example Cornish Yarg cheese.

Nettle leaves being gathered for use in the production of Cornish Yarg cheese

The nettle leaves are wrapped around the cheese and it is then left to ripen. An edible mould grows on the outside of the cheese

Gathering wild blackberries (brambles)

Gathering wild blackberries (brambles). These are usually available in the UK in September in hedgerows and around the edges of fields and woods. Traditionally, they are often cooked with apples, which are also in season in the UK at this time.

4. Catching (hunting) wild animals

Humans have hunted for wild animals, birds and fish to eat for thousands of years. As with plant foods, once farming started, certain species of animals and birds were selected for rearing in large numbers on farms, and the need to hunt for wild animals and birds started to decline, although it is still carried out in the UK and many other countries. Fish were not farmed until relatively recently, and a large amount of sea and river fish are still hunted and caught all over the world.

Animals, birds and fish that are hunted for food are often called 'wild game'. In the UK, they include:

Catching fish at sea in Thailand

- deer (to produce the meat called venison), rabbits, hare, wild boar (wild pig)

- pheasants, quail, guinea fowl, grouse

- salmon, brown trout, rainbow trout and seafood (shellfish, prawns, etc.).

Seasonal foods: plant crops

Plant crops all have a natural life cycle from the time they are a seed to when they mature and reproduce, as shown in the diagram below:

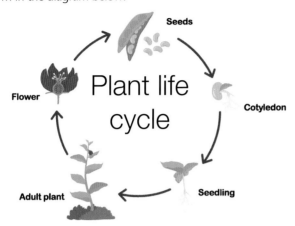

When plant foods are **in season**, this means that they are at the stage of their life cycle when they are ready to be harvested (picked/taken from the ground) and are at their best in terms of flavour, colour, texture and freshness. Also, because there will be a lot of them available at harvest time, they are usually cheaper to buy.

Here are some examples of when plant crops are in season in the UK:

Crop	JAN	FEB	MAR	APR	MAY	JUN	JUL	AUG	SEP	OCT	NOV	DEC
Apples	✓	✓							✓	✓	✓	✓
Asparagus					✓	✓						
Beetroot	✓						✓	✓	✓	✓	✓	✓
Blackcurrants						✓	✓					
Carrots						✓	✓	✓	✓			
Leeks	✓	✓	✓						✓	✓	✓	✓
New potatoes				✓	✓	✓	✓					
Pumpkins										✓	✓	✓
Spinach				✓	✓	✓	✓	✓	✓			
Strawberries						✓	✓	✓	✓			
Swede	✓	✓									✓	✓
Sweetcorn									✓			
Tomatoes						✓	✓	✓	✓	✓		

In the UK, we have become used to being able to buy many plant foods that are out of season (for the UK) all year round (e.g. strawberries, lettuces, asparagus, green beans, tomatoes and raspberries). We are able to do so because many plant crops are **imported** from other countries, such as Spain, Morocco, South Africa, the Netherlands (Holland) and Costa Rica, where they grow at different times of the year. More information on the environmental implications of importing foods out of season is given in Section 5.1.2 (Food and environment).

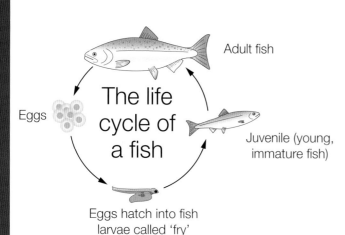

Adult fish

The life cycle of a fish

Eggs

Juvenile (young, immature fish)

Eggs hatch into fish larvae called 'fry'

Seasonal foods: animal foods

Just like plants, animals have a life cycle that can influence when certain animal foods are in season. This particularly applies to fish and seafood (shellfish, crustaceans such as prawns, etc.).

There are certain times of the year when there are more adult fish or seafood available to catch, so they are in season. At other times the fish or seafood should not be caught because they may be spawning (laying eggs) or may not have fully grown.

Here are some examples of when certain fish and seafood are in season in the UK:

Fish	JAN	FEB	MAR	APR	MAY	JUN	JUL	AUG	SEP	OCT	NOV	DEC
Cod	✓	✓	✓									
Dover sole	✓	✓	✓									
Haddock		✓	✓	✓	✓	✓						
Mackerel	✓	✓	✓			✓	✓	✓	✓	✓		
Mussel	✓	✓	✓	✓				✓	✓	✓	✓	✓
Plaice					✓	✓	✓	✓	✓	✓		
Salmon (wild)							✓	✓				
Sardine	✓	✓	✓	✓								

More information on the environmental implications of fishing is given in Section 5.1.2 (Food and environment). There are also seasons when game (wild) birds may and may not be hunted and caught for food.

Stretch and challenge question

GM food: research and then explain the advantages and disadvantages of genetically modified food production. Carry out a mini case study on one GM food and present it to your class.

Practice questions

1. a) Explain what intensive farming means. *(2 marks)*

    b) State two reasons why intensive farming has become a main method of food production. *(2 marks)*

    c) State two reasons why people may have concerns about intensive farming. *(2 marks)*

2. Explain what organic food production is and comment on why some people prefer to buy organically produced foods. *(8 marks)*

5.1.2   Food and environment

What will I learn?

In this section you will learn about:

- the environmental issues associated with food
- the carbon footprint of food
- the reasons for buying locally produced food
- food waste.

The environmental issues associated with food

Food production

Research shows that food production is responsible for having a major impact on **climate change**. Many **greenhouse gases** (e.g. carbon dioxide, methane, nitrous oxide) are released into the atmosphere from industry, transport, food production, etc. Greenhouse gases form an insulating layer around the earth's atmosphere, which traps heat and raises the earth's temperature. If there are too many greenhouse gases produced, some of the heat is prevented from escaping into space, and the earth heats up too much (**global warming**). This is called the '**greenhouse effect**', which results in climate change that can affect life on earth.

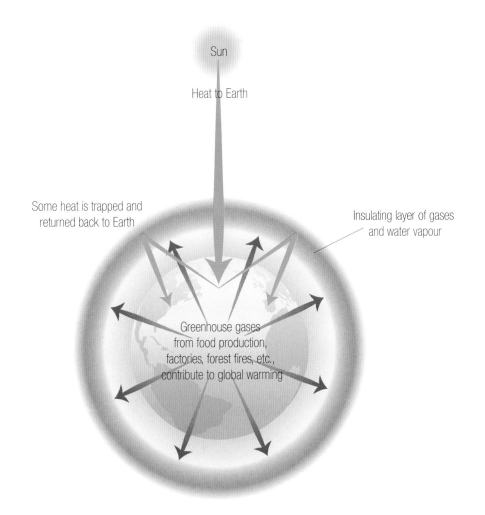

Sun

Heat to Earth

Some heat is trapped and returned back to Earth

Insulating layer of gases and water vapour

Greenhouse gases from food production, factories, forest fires, etc., contribute to global warming

Key terms

Climate change: changes in the earth's temperature that can lead to unusual and extreme weather conditions

Greenhouse gases: form an insulating layer around the earth's atmosphere, which traps heat and raises the earth's temperature

Non-renewable energy: energy produced from fossil fuels that cannot be renewed once they are used up

Fossil fuels: fuels such as coal, oil and gas that were created over millions of years by fossilised plants and animals

Climate change can cause **extreme weather conditions** to develop in different parts of the world, which can have negative effects on food production and people's lives.

Effects of climate change on the weather

Effects on food production

Effects on people and the local environment

Drought (lack of rainfall)

- Failed plant crops.
- Plant crops cannot be irrigated (watered).
- Dry streams and rivers.
- Dead fish and livestock.
- Dry soil blows away (soil erosion) and the land becomes like a desert.
- Forest and bush fires damage farmland and kill livestock.

- Hunger and starvation.
- Thirst.
- Higher food costs because food has to be imported.
- Air pollution from dust and fires.

Flooding

- Soil and soil nutrients washed away.
- Soil and farmland polluted by sewage, rubbish, silt and stones left behind from floods.
- Livestock drowned.
- Landslides destroy plant crops, livestock and farmland.

- Polluted water supply.
- Polluted living conditions.
- Hunger and starvation.
- Waterborne diseases.
- Homes and belongings lost.
- Higher food costs because food has to be imported.

Severe gales and hurricanes

- Damage to crops and livestock housing.
- Livestock killed.
- Transport affected.

- Food shortage.
- Damage to property and livelihoods.
- Higher food costs because food has to be imported.

Higher or lower than normal temperatures

- Growing season for plant crops changes.
- Plant pollination by insects does not happen at the right time, so plant crop may not produce fruits and seeds.
- Pests such as insects and moulds may grow in very large numbers and destroy plant crops.
- Native species of plants may die out and get replaced by others.
- Livestock may not survive.

- Traditional food supply changes.
- Food supply may be damaged or lost by invading species of plants and animals.

Extreme storms, such as dust, snow, thunder and lightning, cyclones (severe wind storms)

- Plant crops damaged.
- Livestock may die or become ill.
- Water and soil become polluted.

- Food supply affected.
- Air pollution affects health.
- Lack of clean drinking water.
- Damage to homes, belongings and livelihoods.

The production of meat and dairy foods

Globally, more and more people are consuming meat and dairy products, and this trend is set to continue. Research shows that meat and dairy food production already produces approximately 18% of all greenhouse gas emissions.

- Vast amounts of forests are cleared (the trees are often burned) to turn it into land for livestock to graze and also to grow livestock feed, such as cereal grains and soya beans. One-quarter of the landmass of the earth is used as pasture for livestock and, in the European Union (EU), three-quarters of agricultural land is used for growing livestock feed.
- Large quantities of artificial fertiliser are added to the land to grow livestock feed.
- The production and use of fertilisers can cause pollution on land, in the air and in water.
- Livestock animals produce large amounts of greenhouse gases by belching and releasing gas from their intestines and from the urine and manure (waste products) they produce.
- Intensive farming of livestock increases emissions of greenhouse gases.

There are several health and environmental campaigns that are trying to encourage people to eat less meat and dairy foods, and have more plant foods in their diets.

Deforestation to produce land for livestock

Food processing and manufacturing

When food and food products are processed and manufactured, large amounts of **non-renewable energy** from **fossil fuels** (coal, oil) are used.

- As fossil fuels are burnt to release the energy they contain, large quantities of **carbon dioxide (CO_2)** gas are produced. CO_2 is a greenhouse gas.
- The refrigeration of food products has increased greatly in recent years, especially as people's food choices have changed and they now consume lots of chilled foods (e.g. drinks and snacks), as well as increased amounts of meat and dairy foods that require refrigeration, because they are high-risk foods.
- Refrigeration causes the release of greenhouse gas emissions, and there is a big push to use more energy-efficient equipment in manufacturing and domestic refrigeration.

Food packaging

Most foods sold in shops have some form of packaging. Packaging is used for several reasons:

- To provide the consumer with information about the food product.
- To contain and protect the food product from damage and contamination by micro-organisms, dirt and chemicals during transportation and storage.
- To preserve and prolong the shelf-life of a food product.

A large proportion of household waste is food packaging. Some food packaging can be recycled but, if it is contaminated with food waste or formed of different layers of material, it can be difficult to recycle.

Spreading fertiliser on farmland

Household rubbish, including food packaging in a landfill site

Food packaging can cause a litter problem

Food packaging has a number of environmental issues:

- A lot of non-renewable energy from fossil fuels is used in its manufacture, especially for plastics.

- Production of packaging can lead to the emission of greenhouse gases.

- When food packaging is finished with, it has to be disposed of in landfill sites or by burning, although an increasing amount is being designed and produced so that it can be recycled.

- There are some plastics that are **biodegradable**. This means that over a period of time, they will break down by the action of micro-organisms, usually bacteria. Some of these are used for food packaging.

- Food packaging from take-away outlets and snack foods and drinks causes a significant litter problem in many places.

Transportation of food and food miles

Many foods and the ingredients in foods travel a long way – hundreds or thousands of miles – before they reach our shops in the UK.

The pie chart below shows which countries supply the UK with its food. Nearly half of all our food travels long distances from other countries and continents.

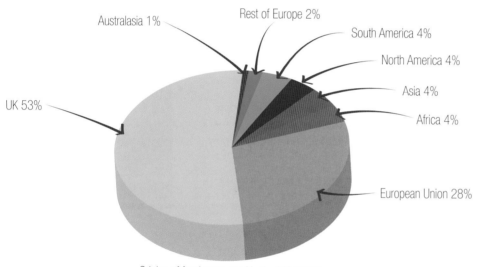

Origins of food consumed in the UK (2012)

Source: Defra (Government Department for the Environment, Food and Rural Affairs)

The distance that food is transported from the time it is produced until it is eaten by consumers is measured in what are called '**food miles**'.

There is concern about the environmental impact of food miles because of the enormous amounts of **non-renewable energy** used to transport foods by land, sea and air, and the pollution that is caused by these forms of transport.

One-quarter of all the miles that heavy-goods vehicles drive in the UK are for the transport of food, and approximately one in every ten car journeys by consumers is for food shopping.

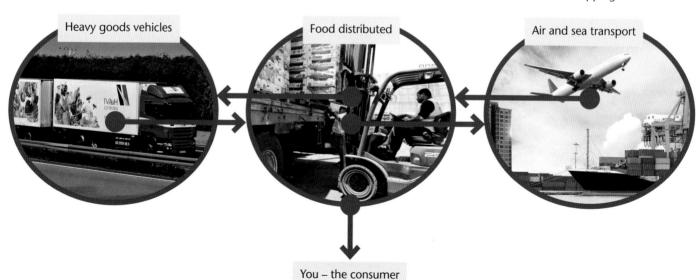

You – the consumer

Food miles have increased due to a number of factors, including:

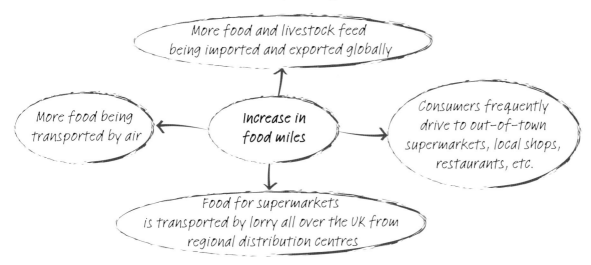

The reasons for buying locally produced food

Many people choose to buy foods that are **locally grown** to avoid the environmental impact of food miles. Locally grown foods are often fresher and cheaper to buy and help to support local farmers and producers. Locally grown food is sometimes sold in supermarkets, but it is also possible to buy it from other outlets in many places in the UK, including:

- local farmers' markets
- farm shops
- direct from a farm or producer
- local box delivery schemes.

Locally grown food is available in season, when it is at its most abundant and freshest. It is often sold loose and unpackaged. Many farms also offer 'pick your own' plant crops (e.g. fruit) where consumers go into the fields and orchards to collect as much as they want to buy.

The carbon footprint of food

The term **carbon footprint** is used as a measure of the amount of CO_2 gas that is released into the atmosphere from the activities of people, communities, industry, transport, etc. The **carbon footprint** of food measures how much CO_2 and other greenhouse gases is released throughout the whole process of producing and consuming food.

Key term

Carbon footprint: a measure of the contribution of something (e.g. food production) to the emission of greenhouse gases

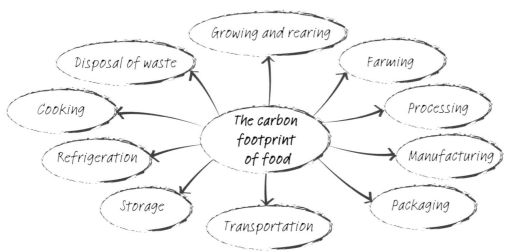

The production of meat, dairy foods and eggs has the highest carbon footprint.

The production of vegetables, fruits, nuts, beans and cereals has the lowest carbon footprint.

Throwing away food that is still edible

A pile of wasted, rotting apples from a farm

'Good looking' vegetables?

Food waste

Research by the charity WRAP has shown that in the UK, 7 million tonnes (Mt) of food is thrown away every year by consumer households, which is about one-fifth of what they buy (approximately £700 worth for an average household). More than 4.2 Mt of this wasted food is good enough to be eaten.

Consumers and households waste food for a number of reasons:

- Not planning meals properly – buying more food than is needed.
- Serving portions of food that are too large.
- Not storing food properly.
- Misunderstanding the use-by and best before dates on food packaging.
- Misunderstanding which left-over foods could be frozen for later use.
- Limited knowledge, confidence and cooking skills to make use of left-over foods.

The main groups of foods that are wasted are (in this order):

- fresh vegetables and salads (e.g. salads sold in plastic bags)
- bread and other bakery items
- milk, dairy foods and eggs
- home-cooked and take-away meals
- fresh fruit
- meat and fish.

Lots of food is also wasted every year in the UK by food manufacturers (3.9 Mt), retailers (0.2 Mt), the hospitality and food service (catering) industry (0.9 Mt) and farming (3.0 Mt).

The EU and supermarkets have been criticised for the demands they place on farmers and growers to only supply 'good looking' fruits and vegetables, i.e. those that meet a rigid set of criteria for shape, colour and size. It is estimated that between 20% and 40% of perfectly edible, nutritious fruits and vegetables have been wasted every year because they did not meet the criteria and were misshapen and had variable colours and sizes.

There have been recent campaigns by celebrity chefs Hugh Fearnley-Whittingstall and Jamie Oliver to highlight the issue of food wastage, and encourage supermarkets to sell misshapen fruits and vegetables and for consumers to buy them.

Some supermarkets and food retailers donate food that is just out-of-date, but still edible, safe and nutritious, to charities who support homeless and low-income families.

Scientists are developing 'smart' packaging that will change colour when the food inside starts to give off natural chemicals that indicate it is decomposing and definitely unsafe to eat. An example is a plastic milk carton that changes colour when milk begins to sour. The acid reacts with the plastic and changes colour. It is hoped that this type of technology will help to reduce food wastage.

Wasted food has a significant environmental effect because it is usually put into landfill sites where it produces large amounts of the **greenhouse gas**, methane, as it rots. There are some schemes being developed to collect the methane to produce energy for households to use as electricity, but these schemes are expensive to build and run.

1. a) State one reason why it may be better for the environment to buy locally grown foods *(1 mark)*

   b) State two ways in which consumers can cut down on food wastage in the home. *(2 marks)*

2. a) Explain why the production of meat and dairy foods has a higher carbon footprint than the production of fruit and vegetables. *(4 marks)*

   b) Explain three ways in which climate change can affect food production. *(3 marks)*

In the fruit and vegetable section of a supermarket, single bananas are being sold in individual polystyrene food trays, covered in cling film with a sticky label giving the price and nutritional information.

Investigate and explain in detail, the environmental implications of packaging and selling bananas in this way.

[5.1.3] Sustainability of food

What will I learn?

In this section you will learn about:

- food security
- sustainability of food production
- Fairtrade.

Key terms

Food security: the ability of people to buy sufficient safe, nutritious and affordable food

Sustainability: producing food in a way that can be maintained over a long period of time and protects the environment

Fairtrade: a foundation set up to ensure that food producers in developing countries get paid fair prices for their crops and have decent working and living conditions

Food security

The aim of **food security** is to make sure that all people, at all times, have the ability to buy enough **safe, nutritious and affordable high-quality food** to meet their dietary needs for an active and healthy life.

The world is facing problems with **food security.** In 2011–2013, approximately 842 million people were suffering from continuous hunger. The world's population is forecast to exceed nine billion (9,000,000,000) people by the year 2050, which means that the demand for food is constantly increasing and more food must be produced with:

- less land available
- fewer resources available, such as water, energy and fertile soil
- the effects of climate change
- environmental damage from pollution, extreme weather and human activities.

Food security is put at risk by:

- extreme weather causing droughts, flooding, storms, etc.

- disruption to the production, transport and distribution of food caused by fuel shortages, severe weather, wars and civil unrest

- economic problems in a country, for example when people are unemployed or do not get paid enough to be able to afford to feed themselves well

- crop failures caused by pests, diseases, shortage of pollinating insects (e.g. bees), poor weather and lack of fresh water for irrigation (watering plants).

The sustainability of food production

In order for there to be food security, food production needs to be **sustainable**. This means that food production should:

- enable communities in the UK and other countries who produce food to earn enough to enable them to live well and continue their work

- protect plant and animal diversity (different varieties and species), so that food production does not just depend on only a few types, which could become diseased and have nothing to replace them

- protect the welfare of farmed and wild species of plants and animals

- avoid damaging or wasting natural resources such as land, the water supply, the ecology of the sea and the countryside

- avoid contributing to climate change through the emission of greenhouse gases

- give social benefits to everyone, e.g. safe, healthy and good-quality food, educational opportunities, employment and stable communities

- reduce food waste and food packaging.

Dried river bed

Crop failure due to drought

Sustainable fishing

For thousands of years, humans have caught wild fish from the sea and rivers to provide them with protein. Today, fish and seafood (shellfish such as mussels, scallops; crustaceans such as prawns and crabs, etc.) provide over three billion people with their main source of protein. Fisheries (places where caught fish are brought in on boats) are very important for local communities as they provide employment and bring in money, but there are pressures on fishing to become more sustainable.

Modern fishing boats are large trawlers (sometimes called factory ships). They drag (trawl) large fishing nets through the water and sometimes across the sea bed to catch fish. The fish are pulled onto the ship and then processed: sorted into type, gutted (cut open to remove their digestive systems and other organs) and chilled to keep them safe to eat for when they are brought ashore and sold in a market.

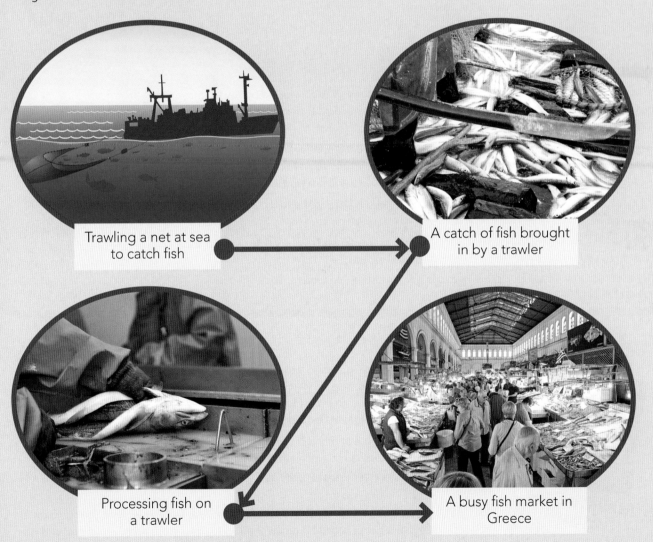

Trawling a net at sea to catch fish

A catch of fish brought in by a trawler

Processing fish on a trawler

A busy fish market in Greece

Environmental concerns about fishing

Over the years, large-scale, commercial sea fishing has become big business, which has caused problems for fish stocks (the numbers of fish available to catch) and the marine environment (the sea, seabed and all the other plants and animals that live in the sea). Fishing has become unsustainable because of:

- **Damage to habitats and ecology.** When trawlers drag their nets across the seabed, they remove everything (plants, animals and fish of all sizes) and can damage habitats (where animals and plants live and breed) and the natural ecology, which can take years to recover. This severely reduces the food available for any remaining fish.

- **By-catch.** Many of the fish that are caught are too young and too small to be eaten and are discarded (thrown back dead into the sea) – this breaks the natural life-cycle of the fish and reduces the number that will go on to become adults to lay eggs for the next generation of fish. Not all the species of fish that are caught are wanted because they cannot be sold, so they are discarded. Sometimes other marine life (e.g. dolphins, sharks, sea turtles, corals, starfish, etc.) get caught up in the nets and cannot escape. This upsets the natural life-cycles of these species, causes pollution as they decompose and reduces the **biodiversity** (the varieties of marine life) in the sea.

- **Overfishing.** This means that more of particular species of fish (e.g. cod) are caught than is sustainable, because they cannot be replaced quickly enough due to the length of the life-cycle of the fish. In 2009, it was estimated that more than half of the world's fish stocks were overfished (Food and Agricultural Organization).

Overfishing also affects the **food chain** because it removes species of fish that are eaten by other species of marine life.

The marine food chain

Making fishing more sustainable

- The numbers of fish (fish stocks) in the sea need to be **conserved** (protected by law from overfishing) so that their natural life-cycle can go on and increase their numbers, which will take a long time for some species of fish.

- To reduce overfishing, fish quotas (the number of fish of certain species and size that are allowed to be caught by law) have been set for EU countries and fishing boats. If fewer fish are caught, there is more chance that remaining ones will breed and help the fish stocks recover.

- The size of the holes in fishing nets have been increased by law, so that only larger, mature fish can be caught, and smaller, immature fish have a greater chance of escaping the net.

- Fish need to be caught using methods that do not cause damage to natural ecosystems and habitats, and limit the amount of by-catch (e.g. line caught).

It is possible to buy fish products that have come from sustainable sources. They often have a logo on the packaging to indicate this.

MSC on this logo means 'Marine Stewardship Council' – an organisation that promotes sustainable fishing practices

Fairtrade

Much of the food we eat is grown in large amounts in other countries, often by people in developing countries, who have very little money and poor living and working conditions. They often grow crops that they can export to make some money (called 'cash crops') and therefore do not have enough space, time or resources to grow enough food for themselves.

There is also the problem that many of the crops they grow (e.g. coffee beans, fresh tea leaves and cocoa beans) are processed into highly priced products in countries such as the UK, yet the farmers who produce the raw ingredients are paid very little. If their crop fails for any reason, they will receive no payment.

The **Fairtrade** foundation was established to help make sure that farmers and their workers in developing countries get paid better and fairer prices for their crops and their labour, and have decent working and living conditions. Sustainable food production is also encouraged and promoted by the foundation to improve the local environment in which the food is grown. Over 1.4 million farmers and workers in 1,140 producer organisations are in the Fairtrade system, and many Fairtrade products are available to buy in the UK.

Fairtrade products have a logo, so people know which ones to buy.

Carry out a piece of research on Fairtrade ingredients. Use the internet or visit a supermarket and find out which ingredients are available that are Fairtrade.

Task:
Design a recipe card for a supermarket that encourages the use of Fairtrade ingredients. The recipe must include **at least three** Fairtrade ingredients. Include on the recipe card information to consumers explaining the benefits of using Fairtrade ingredients.

Producing your meals sustainably

There are various ways in which you can produce your meals sustainably. Use some or all of the following suggestions to prepare a two-course cooked dinner for two people (either a starter and main course **or** a main course and dessert).

Choosing your food:

- Read food labels carefully to find out where and how the food was produced, so that you can make informed choices.
- Buy locally produced foods where possible.

Saving energy to cut greenhouse gas emissions:

- Choose to eat more raw foods that do not need cooking.
- Use the cooker hob whenever possible, rather than heating the whole oven. A lot of heat (and therefore energy) is lost when an oven is heated.
- Use the oven efficiently by not pre-heating it for too long, cooking several foods at the same time, turning it off early so that the food finishes cooking in the residual (remaining) heat.
- Microwave ovens use approximately 50% less energy than ovens.
- Use an electric kettle to boil water for cooking or drinking, rather than heating up water in a pan on the hob.

1. a) Explain what the term 'food security' means'. *(2 marks)*

   b) Explain what 'sustainable food production' means. *(2 marks)*

   c) Illustrate or suggest ways that the Fairtrade foundation helps food producers. *(2 marks)*

2. Summarise, giving reasons and examples, why the sustainability of food production is important for the future of global food security. *(10 marks)*

Chapter 11 Processing and production

5.2.1 Food production

What will I learn?

In this section you will learn about:

- the primary stages of food processing and production
- the secondary stages of food processing and production
- how processing affects the sensory and nutritional properties of ingredients.

Key terms

Primary food processing: when foods are processed straight after harvest or slaughter, to get them ready to be eaten or ready to be used in other food products, such as wheat grain (seeds) turned into flour

Secondary food processing: when primary processed foods are either used on their own or mixed with other foods and turned into other food products, such as wheat flour turned into bread or pasta

Milling: breaking cereal grains (seeds) down and separating the layers, turning the grain into flour

Introduction

Before food reaches our plates, various things (processes) are done to it to prepare it for consumption (eating). 'Processing' means making changes to foods to ensure that they are:

- safe, appetising and nice (palatable) to eat
- able to be transported to shops and ready to be displayed for sale
- convenient and easy to buy, store and use
- appealing and attractive to consumers
- ready for consumers to prepare, cook and serve.

Many foods that we buy have been processed. Modern processing techniques have enabled the food industry to develop a wide range and variety of food products that can be produced to the same quality, standard, colour, flavour, shape and size every time. This encourages consumers to buy products again and again, because they know what to expect.

There are two main stages to food processing:

Primary processing: in this stage, foods are processed straight after harvest or slaughter (when livestock are killed), to get them ready to be eaten or ready to be used in other food products, such as wheat grain (seeds) turned into flour.

Secondary processing: in this stage, primary processed foods are either used on their own or mixed with other foods and turned into other food products, such as wheat flour turned into bread or pasta.

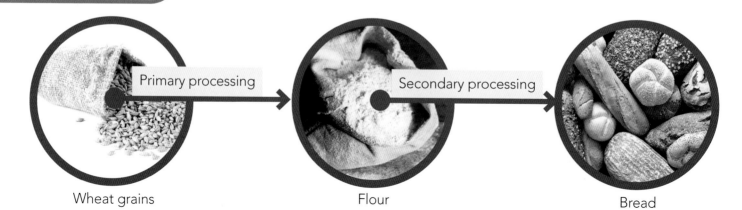

Wheat grains → Primary processing → Flour → Secondary processing → Bread

The primary stages of food processing and production

The table below shows different ways in which **plant foods** are processed straight after **harvest**.

Sorting and grading tomatoes by size

Harvesting and trimming cauliflowers

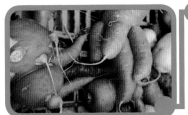

Misshapen vegetables

Potatoes being washed

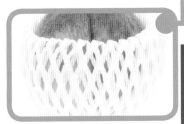

Peaches are often transported in protective plastic nets

Identification stickers on apples

Plant crops

Primary processing	Examples/what happens
Sorting (grading) into different sizes	Potatoes, oranges, apples, tomatoes **Notes:** Minimum sizes for fruits and vegetables that can be sold are often set by the EU – this can lead to wastage of perfectly good crops because they are too small.
Trimming off leaves, shoots and roots	Carrots, leeks, cabbages, lettuces **Notes:** This is very time consuming and requires lots of people to do it. Some machines have been developed for trimming some crops.
Discarding (throwing away) any that are misshapen or damaged	Often potatoes, carrots, parsnips, apples, tomatoes, peppers, etc. **Notes:** Campaigners are trying to reduce food waste by encouraging retailers to sell and consumers to buy misshapen plant crops.
Washing to remove soil/dirt, stones, twigs, insects, chemical sprays	Root vegetables (e.g. potatoes, parsnips and carrots) **Notes:** A large amount of water is used for washing crops, which has implications for the environment and the availability of natural resources. Not all chemical sprays can easily be washed off.
Wrapping delicate fruits in tissue paper or other material such as plastic to protect it during transport	Exotic fruits such as mangoes, melons, lychees, peaches, berries, etc. **Notes:** Food packaging has environmental implications because of the use of non-renewable energy sources to make it and its disposal afterwards.
Adding identification stickers and labels for use in retail shops and markets	Fruits such as apples; exotic fruits such as melons, pineapples, mangoes **Notes:** Use of labels has the same environmental implications as food packaging, and they are not always easy to remove without leaving a sticky residue.
Storing fruits, vegetables and cereal grains (seeds) at a suitable temperature and humidity (moisture level) ready for transport. May be stored in an atmosphere of CO_2 or other safe gases to slow down the ripening process and make the crop last longer	All plant crops **Notes:** Environmental implications because of the use of energy to cool/heat/de-humidify/add moisture or gases to the storage area.

Stacks of fruit crates at a cold storage warehouse

How wheat is turned into flour

Primary processing	What happens
Stage 1: harvest	When the wheat plants are mature, the wheat grains (seeds) ripen. **Combine harvesters** are used to cut the wheat plants and a revolving **thresher** inside them separates the wheat grains from the rest of the plant (which is turned into straw bales).
Stage 2: cleaning and storage	The harvested wheat grains (seeds) are cleaned then stored until they are ready to be **milled**. They must be kept dry to prevent moulds growing on them.
Stage 3: milling the grain to produce flour	Cereal grains are made up of layers. The **aleurone** and **bran layers** on the outside contain lots of dietary fibre. Many of the vitamins in the grain are found just below these two layers. The **endosperm** contains mostly starch, and some protein. The **germ** contains the genetic information and nutrients that would turn the seed into a new plant if it germinated (started to grow) in the soil.

Milling breaks the grains down and separates the layers, turning the seeds into **flour**. There are different types of flour produced depending on how the milled grains are processed:

- **Wholemeal or wholegrain flour** contains all (100%) of the layers in the wheat grains.
- **Wheatmeal (brown) flour** contains 85% of the grain, because some of the bran and aleurone layers are removed during milling.

The outside layers and the germ can be removed by **sieving** the flour. This produces **white flour**, which contains approximately 70% of the wheat grain – mostly the endosperm.

The milling process

In modern factory flour production, wheat grain is passed through a series of steel rollers, set close together, which rotate (turn) at different speeds. As the wheat seeds pass between them, they are crushed, as shown in the diagram on the left.

Milling diagram (left column)

Cleaned wheat (seeds) put into a hopper (container with a hole in the base)

↓

Hopper

Wheat seeds drop down between the rollers and are crushed

Break rolls (up to 4)

↓

Sieves

Flour is sieved to remove outside layers of seeds (bran)

Reducing rolls (up to 12)
Rollers gradually reduce the flour in size until it becomes very fine

↓

Sieves

↓ (outputs)

- White flour
- Wheatgerm separated from the white flour
- Wheatmeal (brown) flour
- Wholemeal flour

Wheat grains (seeds) growing on wheat plants

The wheat grain is collected in in the trailer of a tractor travelling alongside the combine harvester

Wheat seeds

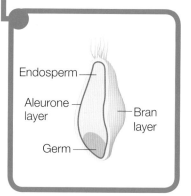
Endosperm

Aleurone layer

Bran layer

Germ

Under a microscope you can see the structure of wheat grain, showing the different layers

Task Tip:

As part of Task 1: Food Investigation, it may be necessary as part of the research to find out how food is processed.

The primary stages of food processing and production

The table below shows different ways in which **animal foods** are processed straight after **slaughter**.

Animal foods	
Primary processing	**What happens**
Animals	The blood from animals such as pigs, cattle and sheep is allowed to drain away.
	The skin and hide (leather) are removed.
	The carcase is split open lengthways and the internal organs (e.g. intestines, etc.) are removed.
	The **offal** (edible internal organs such as the heart, liver and kidneys) are also removed.
	Beef carcases are split in half completely as they are so big.
	Pig, sheep and lamb carcases are often, but not always, kept whole.
	How does processing affect the sensory and nutritional properties?
	Meat carcases are hung for a few hours or days at 1°C.
	Hanging the meat is important to develop its flavour and texture. This is because before slaughter, animals store the carbohydrate **glycogen** (see page 17) in their muscles. After slaughter, the glycogen is broken down to **lactic acid**, which helps to preserve the meat. Hanging the meat allows the natural **enzymes** in it enough time to start to tenderise the protein and develop its particular flavour.
Poultry (birds)	The blood is allowed to drain away.
	The head and feet are usually removed.
	The feathers and internal organs are removed.
	The carcase is **trussed**, which means the legs and wings are tied neatly together, ready for sale.
Fish	The internal organs are removed (gutted).
	The fish may be left whole or filleted to remove the bones.
	Sometimes just one part of the fish is used, for example the tail of a monkfish.

Pig carcases hanging in a cold store

A trussed chicken

Fish on sale in a supermarket

Task Tip:

Filleting fish is a complex practical skill. This skill could be demonstrated as part of the Food Preparation task.

Primary processing example: preparing milk ready for sale

Primary processing	What happens
Skimming milk to remove the fat (cream)	The fat (cream) can be removed from fresh milk by a process called **skimming**. The fresh milk is placed in a large tank and cooled. The fat naturally rises to the surface of the milk and is skimmed off with special equipment. Depending on how much fat is removed, different milks are produced. **Whole milk** contains all of the fat that is naturally produced (e.g. whole cow's milk has approximately 3.9% fat) Semi-skimmed milk contains approximately half the amount of fat naturally produced (e.g. semi-skimmed cow's milk has 1.5–2% fat). **Skimmed milk** contains virtually no fat (e.g. skimmed cow's milk has approximately 0.5–0.9% fat). **1% fat cow's milk** is also available.
Heat treatment of milk	Fresh milk is **heat treated** to kill pathogenic bacteria and make the milk safe to drink for several days if it is stored between 0°C and below 5°C. Milk is usually **homogenised** during heat treatment. This means processing it to prevent the cream from rising to the surface of the milk, which gives it a consistent texture and flavour. When fresh milk is left to stand, the natural fat in it will separate from the rest of the liquid and rise to the surface. **Homogenisation** forces the milk, under **pressure**, through thousands of tiny holes, which breaks up the fat and prevents it from separating out. There are different types of heat treatment.
Pasteurisation (often called High Temperature Short Time [HTST] Pasteurisation)	The milk is heated very quickly in a **heat exchanger** to a temperature of **72°C for 15 seconds**, then very rapidly cooled to below 10°C (usually to 4°C). **How does processing affect the sensory and nutritional properties of the milk?** Pasteurisation does not significantly affect the flavour or colour of the milk, and has little effect on the nutrients in the milk.
Ultra Heat Treatment (UHT)	The milk is heated very quickly in a **heat exchanger** to a temperature of **132°C for 1 second**, then rapidly cooled and packed inside special multi-layered storage packs. These are completely sealed so the milk can be stored un-opened and at ambient (room) temperature for several months (it is often called **long-life milk**). Once it is opened, it becomes high-risk and must be stored in a refrigerator and consumed within a few days. **How does processing affect the sensory and nutritional properties of the milk?** The UHT method has a minimal effect on the flavour of the milk or its nutrients. However, after about 6 months in storage, up to 60% of the vitamin B12 in the milk may be lost.

A cream separator

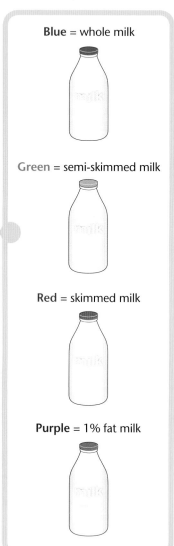

Blue = whole milk

Green = semi-skimmed milk

Red = skimmed milk

Purple = 1% fat milk

The four main types of milk

Milk pasteurisation tank and pipes

Primary processing	What happens
Sterilisation	Milk can be sterilised, which means putting it into special sealed bottles, often made from glass, then heating it to **110°C for 30 minutes**. It can be stored un-opened, at ambient (room) temperature for several months. Once it is opened, it becomes high-risk and must be stored in a refrigerator and consumed within a few days. **How does processing affect the sensory and nutritional properties of the milk?** Sterilisation causes the milk to darken in colour and change flavour due to the effects of the heat on the natural sugar (lactose) and proteins in the milk. Some of the proteins (including the natural enzymes) in the milk are denatured and 35% of the vitamin B1 and 90% of the vitamin B12 are lost.
Micro-filtered milk	In ordinary pasteurised milk the pathogenic bacteria are destroyed, but bacteria that naturally cause the milk to go sour, by producing lactic acid, are left behind. In micro-filtered milk, the souring bacteria are also removed, so that virtually all the bacteria found in the milk are removed. The milk is forced, under pressure, through very fine **filtration membranes** to remove the bacteria. It is then homogenised and pasteurised as usual. Micro-filtered whole, semi-skimmed and skimmed milk is available. Micro-filtration increases the shelf-life of the milk, providing it is stored between 0°C and below 5°C. **How does processing affect the sensory and nutritional properties of the milk?** The flavour and nutritional content of micro-filtered milk are not significantly affected.

The secondary stages of food processing and production

The secondary processing of food turns primary processed foods into other food products by mixing and processing them with different ingredients.

Three examples of this are:

- turning wheat flour into pasta
- turning milk into yogurt
- turning fresh fruit into jam.

Secondary processing: turning wheat flour into pasta

- Pasta is made from a special type of wheat called **durum wheat**, which produces pasta flour called **00 grade durum wheat flour**. This has a very high gluten (protein) content.
- When the durum wheat is milled, **semolina** and **flour** are both produced and blended together to produce pasta.
- Pasta dough is made by adding eggs and sometimes water to the flour and semolina and mixing thoroughly to form a smooth dough.
- Other ingredients can be added to produce a variety of flavours and colours, for example:
  - tomato and carrot puree produces red/orange coloured pasta
  - beetroot produces purple pasta
  - spinach produces green pasta (pasta Verdi)
  - squid ink produces a black coloured pasta
  - wholegrain flour produces a light brown pasta
  - celery, salt, garlic, herbs add flavour.

00 grade durum wheat flour for pasta making

Section 5: Food provenance

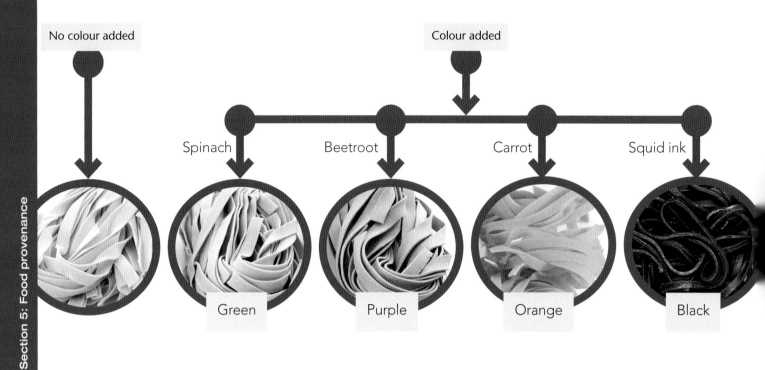

No colour added

Colour added

Spinach — Green

Beetroot — Purple

Carrot — Orange

Squid ink — Black

Wholegrain pasta

- To make flat shaped pasta such as lasagne and tagliatelle, the dough is rolled several times through a pasta machine to make it thinner and smoother.

- To make pasta shapes, the dough is forced, under high pressure, through a metal **die**. A die is part of a piece of machinery called a **press**. The dough is squeezed (extruded) by the press through the die. The way the die is designed, cut and shaped will decide which shape pasta is produced.

- Behind the die is a part of the machinery that folds, twists or cuts the pasta to produce the final shape.

- Pasta can be sold fresh and must be stored in the refrigerator and consumed within a few days.

- A large amount of pasta is sold dried. This is done after the pasta shapes have been formed, using warm air in special driers to dry the shapes as they come out of the die so that they do not stick to each other.

A hand-operated pasta machine

Industrial sized ravioli pasta making machine

Die for making pasta shapes

Secondary processing: turning milk into yogurt

In Chapter 5 on pages 165–167, you learnt how milk is turned into cheese as a secondary processing technique.

Milk is also turned into yogurt.

↓

Yogurt is a fermented milk product and can be made from any type of milk.

↓

The milk is homogenised, then pasteurised at a temperature between 85°C and 95°C to destroy micro-organisms.

↓

The milk is then cooled to between 40°C and 43°C.

↓

A special, non-pathogenic **bacteria** culture is added to the milk.

↓

The mixture is **incubated** (kept warm) at between 37°C and 44°C for 4–6 hours.

↓

The bacteria in the culture **ferment** the milk by turning the **lactose** in the milk to lactic acid, which denatures and coagulates the milk proteins and makes the yogurt set.

↓

When the acidity level reaches 0.8–1.8%, the bacteria become inactive, but they are still alive.

↓

The yogurt is cooled to 4.5°C to stop the bacteria growing.

↓

The yogurt can be pasteurised at this stage to kill the bacteria.

↓

'Live' yogurt is not pasteurised at this stage and contains bacteria that are **dormant** (alive but inactive).

↓

The yogurt is packed into cartons and sealed.

↓

Yogurt can have fruit, sugar, other flavours such as coconut and vanilla, thickeners and stabilisers added to it to change its flavour and texture.

Inside a yogurt-making factory

Finished yogurt sealed into cartons

Activity: making your own yogurt

Here is a recipe for making your own yogurt. Remember to keep everything clean and hygienic when you are making it.

Recipe for natural yogurt (makes 1 litre)

Ingredients:

1 litre whole milk
1 heaped tbsp powdered milk
60g natural, full-fat 'live' yogurt (check that the label says 'live')

Method:

1. Wash and sterilise a 1 litre jar or a few smaller ones.
2. Place the milk in a saucepan and heat it gently until a thermometer or food probe reads 80°C – do not let it boil.
3. Take the milk off the heat and stir in the milk powder.
4. When the temperature of the milk drops to 45°C, stir in the yogurt. Mix well.
5. Pour into the jar and seal it with the lid. Place the jar somewhere slightly warm for 4–6 hours – the longer the yogurt is allowed to ferment, the more acidic the yogurt will taste.
6. The yogurt should have set after this time.
7. Store it in the refrigerator between 0°C and below 5°C and consume within 4–5 days.

Think about which different ingredients you could use to flavour the yogurt.

Secondary processing: turning fruit into jam

- Jam making is a traditional method of **food preservation**, which uses **sugar** to prevent the growth of micro-organisms and enable the jam to set into a **gel**.

- Jams are often called **preserves**. Other preserves include lemon curd, pickles, chutney, cranberry or mint jelly, and mint sauce.

- To enable a gel to form in the jam, there needs to be enough **pectin**, **acid** and **sugar** in the jam recipe.

- **Pectin** is a polysaccharide (see page 18). It is found in fruits, especially stone fruits, such as plums and greengages, as well as apples, blackcurrants and gooseberries.

- If the fruit is slightly under-ripe, it will contain more pectin than if it is over-ripe.

- The fruit should be in good condition – not mouldy, soft or damaged.

- When boiled with sugar, water and acid (from the fruit), pectin will form a three-dimensional gel that sets as the jam cools.

- When jam is made, the fruit is firstly stewed for a while with some water to extract the pectin.

- Sugar is then added, stirred until it dissolves, then the mixture is boiled quickly until the jam reaches 105°C, which is the **setting point** of the jam.

- The hot jam is poured into clean, dry, hot, sterile jars (heated in the oven to destroy micro-organisms and to prevent the glass from breaking when the hot jam is poured in), and sealed to prevent micro-organisms from getting in to the jam.

- The jars of jam are left to go cold, in which time the gel will form and trap the fruit, sugar and water.

Making home-made jam

Stretch and challenge activity

Research and make another preserve that uses fruit and/or vegetables.

Here is a recipe for making home-made jam, which you might like to try.

- **Caution**: jam making involves using high temperatures to enable the jam to set.

- Boiling sugar is very dangerous, because if it goes onto your skin, it will stick and burn you badly.

- You need to make sure that you use a big enough pan so the boiling jam mixture does not boil over. Stir the jam occasionally and very carefully.

- Handle the hot jars carefully – place them on a wooden board or heat-proof surface when they come out of the oven. They may crack if placed on a cold surface.

- This recipe will make two 454g jars of jam.

Jam

Ingredients:
450g plums, apricots or greengages (slightly under-ripe if possible)
450g preserving (jam) sugar
150ml water

You also need:
2 × 454g clean jam jars
A few jam pot covers, wax discs and rubber bands (available from supermarkets and kitchen shops)

Method:
1. Heat the clean jars in the oven for at least 20 minutes at 100°C/Gas 2 to sterilise them.
2. Wash the fruit, removing any bruised or over-ripe pieces.
3. Dry the fruit.
4. Slit the plums, apricots or greengages to loosen the stones, but leave the stones in (they have pectin attached to them).

5. Place the fruit and water in a large, heavy-based pan and stew the fruit gently on the hob, until very tender – this is an important process to extract the pectin from the fruit and takes about 30 minutes.
6. Add the sugar and stir until dissolved over a gentle heat.
7. Bring the mixture to the boil, **stirring only occasionally**, and boil rapidly to a setting point of 105°C using a sugar thermometer or a food probe.
8. You can also test to see if the jam has set by doing the 'wrinkle test'. Remove the jam from the heat while you do this to avoid over-cooking it. Place a teaspoon of the jam onto a cold plate (keep it in the refrigerator). After a few minutes, touch the jam with your finger. If the surface wrinkles, it means it is at setting point. If not, re-boil it for 5 minutes and try again.
9. Carefully pour the hot jam into the hot, sterilised jars, seal and cool until set.
10. To seal the jam: place a waxed circle, waxed side down onto the hot jam.
    - The edible wax will melt, then set again when the jam cools, forming a seal.
    - Then carefully dip one side of the transparent cellophane circle into a little water, turn it over and place the **dry side** onto the top of the jam jar.
    - Place a rubber band over it to hold it in place.
    - The cellophane will gradually shrink and go tight onto the jam jar, forming a good seal. When it has cooled, place a jam jar lid over the jam to keep it clean.

1. a) State two reasons why foods are processed. *(2 marks)*

   b) Define and describe primary food processing and secondary food processing, giving examples in your answer. *(2 marks)*

2. Choose one of the following foods and explain in detail how it is processed and turned into other food products:

   - Milk.

   - Wheat. *(15 marks)*

3. Research and explain how plant oils are made into vegetable fat spreads that are used in cooking. *(12 marks)*

5.2.2 # Technological developments associated with better health and food production

What will I learn?

In this section you will learn about:

- why and how some foods are nutritionally modified
- why and how some foods are fortified
- the use of additives in food products.

Key terms

Nutritional modification: changing the nutritional profile of a food product so that it meets current dietary guidelines or helps provide a health benefit

Fortification: adding extra nutrients to a food product during its manufacture

Food additives: natural or synthetic (man-made) chemical substances that are added to foods during manufacturing or processing to improve the quality, flavour, colour, texture or stability

Nutritional modification

Through developments in food technology and food processing, food manufacturers are able to **modify** the **nutritional profile** of some foods to make them meet the requirements of current dietary guidelines (e.g. increasing dietary fibre intake, reducing sugar content), or to help provide a health benefit (e.g. reducing the risks associated with diet-related health concerns, such as high blood cholesterol levels – see page 72).

Fortification

- Foods can also be **fortified** with nutrients.

- **Fortification** means adding extra nutrients to a food, either to increase the amounts of those nutrients naturally present in the food or add other nutrients to the food that are not naturally present in the food.

- Some foods (e.g. vegetable fat spreads) are fortified by law.

- Some foods (e.g. breakfast cereals, baby foods) are fortified voluntarily by food manufacturers.

- Fortification of food is strictly controlled by law.

- Food manufacturers are not allowed to say or suggest that their nutritionally modified or fortified food products can prevent, treat or cure a disease, but they can say that the products can provide a health benefit, such as maintaining healthy bones.

Vitamins A and D, vegetable fat spreads, low-fat spreads

Iron, wheat flour (except wholemeal flour)

Sterols/stanols, cholesterol-lowering vegetable fat spreads, yogurts and yogurt drinks

Fortification

Calcium, all types of wheat flour (except wholemeal and SR flour)

B group vitamins (folic acid, thiamine, niacin), wheat flour, breakfast cereals, soya products

The table below shows some examples of the types of foods that are nutritionally modified/fortified.

Fat spreads/dairy foods

Type of food product	How it has been nutritionally modified/ fortified	Has it been modified or fortified by law or voluntarily by the food manufacturer?	How does it work/why is it done/who might it benefit?
Vegetable fat spreads	Vitamins A and D are added to the product during manufacture	By law	These spreads are often used instead of butter, which contains vitamins A and D naturally, so they provide an important amount to the diet.
Cholesterol lowering vegetable fat spreads, yogurts and yogurt drinks	Natural substances called sterols and stanols that are found in plants are added to these food products during manufacture	Voluntarily	The sterols and stanols help to prevent the absorption of cholesterol that is formed in the body from saturated fat so it cannot go into the bloodstream. Only people with known high blood cholesterol levels will benefit from eating these foods.
Low-fat spreads	Vitamins A and D are added to the product during manufacture	Voluntarily	These spreads are often used instead of butter and vegetable fat spreads that contain vitamins A and D naturally or by law, so they provide an important amount to the diet.

Cereals and cereal products

Type of food product	How it has been nutritionally modified/ fortified	Has it been modified or fortified by law or voluntarily by the food manufacturer?	How does it work/why is it done/who might it benefit?
All types of wheat flour (except wholemeal flour)	Iron, thiamine (vitamin B1) and niacin (vitamin B3) added during the milling process	By law	There are concerns that some people in the population have low intakes of these nutrients.
All types of wheat flour (except wholemeal and some self-raising flours)	Calcium added during the milling process	By law	There is concern about low intakes of calcium in some groups of the population.
Wheat flour	Folic acid (vitamin B9) added during the milling process	By law – but still under discussion	There is concern about pregnant women not having enough folate (Vitamin B9) in their diet. Research has shown that having enough folate can significantly reduce the risk of an unborn baby developing spinal column defects such as spina bifida, if taken as a supplement of folic acid (folate is called folic acid when it is added to foods and used in supplements), or provided by food in the early stages of pregnancy.
Some breakfast cereals	B group vitamins, (including folic acid – vitamin B9) iron, vitamin D added to the product during manufacture	Voluntarily	These contribute significant amounts of these nutrients to many people in the population.

Soya products

Type of food product	How it has been nutritionally modified/ fortified	Has it been modified or fortified by law or voluntarily by the food manufacturer?	How does it work/why is it done/who might it benefit?
Soya products (e.g. fat spreads, milks, drinks, yogurts)	Vitamin B12 and calcium added to the product during manufacture	Voluntarily	These products are targeted at vegetarians and vegans and people who may not eat dairy foods because of allergies or choice. Plant foods contain virtually no natural vitamin B12, which can be a problem for vegans.

Activity

Conduct a survey, either in a supermarket or on an online supermarket site, of a range of food products to find out how many are nutritionally modified or fortified.

- Who are the target groups for the food products?
- What health benefits do the food manufacturers say their products provide?
- How do manufacturers try to persuade consumers to buy their products?

The use of additives in food products

- **Food additives** are natural or synthetic (man-made) chemical substances that are added to foods during manufacturing or processing to improve their quality, flavour, colour, texture or stability. Most processed foods have additives put in them.
- There are about 6,000 food additives available to use, most of which are flavourings.

Additives are used for a variety of reasons:

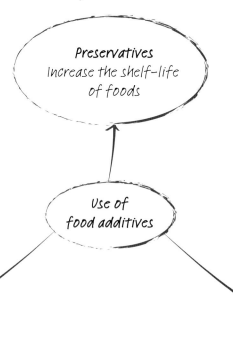

Preservatives
Increase the shelf-life of foods

Use of food additives

Emulsifiers/stabilisers
Improve the structure and texture of foods

Flavourings, sweeteners, colourings
Improve the sensory qualities of foods

If people eat mainly processed foods, it is likely that they will be consuming a wide variety of additives.

- There is concern about the use of additives, as some have been shown to cause side effects such as poor behaviour in children, headaches and other health problems.

- The use of food additives is regulated and controlled by law.

- The EU requires food manufacturers to clearly label additives in the list of ingredients on a food label, describing what they are added for (their function) and giving either the additive name or its **E number**.

- **E numbers** are given to food additives that have passed various safety tests and have been approved for use in food. Some examples of E numbers are given in the following table.

Type of food additive	Why they are used (their function in food)	Name and E number	Possible side effects/ problems
Colourings	To enhance (improve) or intensify the colour of a food to attract consumers. Sometimes natural food colours are affected by processing, so the colour is restored by using additives.	Tartrazine E102 Allura red AC E129 Green S E142 Annatto E160b	There have been cases of babies and young children becoming hyperactive (unable to concentrate, very agitated, temper tantrums, unable to sleep properly) because of the effects of some food colourings on their brains.
Flavourings	To improve or modify (change) the natural flavour and odour of foods.	Flavourings are not given E numbers. There are thousands in use.	Some flavourings are very intense (e.g. those used to flavour fried snack foods such as crisps and corn snacks). Often large amounts of salt (sodium) are used, which can affect health (see pages 33, 57 and 71). People become used to this intense flavour, which can deter them from eating more natural foods.
Sweeteners	To use as a substitute sweetener to sugar, in order to reduce sugar intake and prevent high blood sugar levels.	Sorbitol E420 Aspartame E951 Sucralose E955 Saccharin E954	Recent research suggests that using sweeteners instead of sugar does not lower blood sugar levels as much as was once thought. Some sweeteners can cause digestive upsets (diarrhoea).

Type of food additive	Why they are used (their function in food)	Name and E number	Possible side effects/ problems
Preservatives	To prevent the food from becoming spoiled by micro-organisms and to increase its shelf-life so that it is edible for a longer period of time.	Potassium sorbate E202 Sodium metabisulphite E223 Sodium nitrate E251 Sodium propionate E281 Sodium benzoate E211	Some people are allergic to some preservatives and need to avoid those foods that contain them.
Emulsifiers, stabilisers	To develop certain textures in foods so that the food does not change (is stable) while it is being stored or used. Emulsifiers are used to prevent oil and water from separating out in products such as salad dressings.	Lecithins (emulsifiers) 322 Carrageenan E407 Guar gum E412	Side effects are not common with these types of additives.

There are other groups of additives that you may see listed on food labels and you should be aware of, including:

- acidity regulators
- anti-caking agents (stop dry ingredients sticking together)
- antioxidants
- thickeners
- gelling agents
- flavour enhancers (intensify flavours)
- modified starches (help thicken food products)
- packaging gases.

Stretch and challenge activity

Research the advantages and disadvantages of food additives.

Write an article for a magazine, giving a balanced point of view about the use of additives in food production.

Practice questions

1. a) Explain why some foods are fortified by food manufacturers. *(3 marks)*

    b) Identify an example of a food that is fortified by law and one that is fortified voluntarily by food manufacturers. *(2 marks)*

2. Explain why soya products, such as soya milk and yogurt, are fortified with calcium and vitamin B12. *(4 marks)*

3. a) Identify **four** reasons why additives are used in food products. *(4 marks)*

    b) Identify how a consumer can find out from a food label which additives are in a food product. *(2 marks)*

Chapter 12 Non-Exam Assessment

12.1.1 Introduction

Study tip

The Non-Exam Assessment makes up 50% of the GCSE grade so it is very important that you produce your best possible work.

The Non-Exam Assessment will be worth 50% of the final GCSE grade. The Non-Exam Assessment is made up of two distinct tasks:

1. The **Food Investigation task** which is worth 15% of the GCSE grade.

2. The **Food Preparation task** which is worth 35% of the GCSE grade.

The tasks will allow you to show your knowledge and understanding of nutrition, food science, food safety, food choice and food provenance. At the heart of the Non-Exam Assessment is the opportunity for you to showcase your practical cooking skills and your knowledge and understanding of ingredients, cooking and processes.

Both projects must be produced in the final year of the GCSE course. A range of titles will be provided, by AQA, for both the Food Investigation and the Food Preparation tasks. These titles will change each year.

The table includes the key details about both tasks.

	Food Investigation task	Food Preparation task
Time allowed for the task	The investigation and writing of the report must not exceed **10 hours**.	The practical work and portfolio must not exceed **20 hours**. This includes a 3-hour practical session to make the three final dishes.
Length of the task	A written or electronic report which will be **1500–2000 words**. This will be approximately **6–8 sides** of A4 or A3 equivalent. This includes all charts, annotation, practical results, etc.	A written or electronic portfolio including photographic evidence. Photographic evidence of the three final dishes must be included. The report will be no more than **20 sides** of A4 or A3 equivalent.
Release date of the task	The Food Investigation tasks will be released in **September** of the final year of assessment.	The Food Preparation tasks will be released in **November** of the final year of assessment.
Assessment details	The Food Investigation task is marked out of **30** and this will be **15%** of the final GCSE grade.	The Food Preparation task is marked out of **70** and this will be **35%** of the final GCSE grade.
Assessment breakdown	Your teacher will be marking against the following three criteria: • Section A: Research: 6 marks • Section B: Investigation: 15 marks • Section C: Analysis and evaluation: 9 marks. Total: 30 marks.	Your teacher will be marking against the following five criteria: • Section A: Researching the task: 6 marks • Section B: Demonstrating technical skills: 18 marks • Section C: Planning for the final menu: 8 marks • Section D: Making the final dishes: 30 marks • Section E: Analysis and evaluation: 8 marks. Total: 70 marks.
Assessing the work	The completed tasks will then be assessed by your teacher. A sample of students' work will be sent to AQA to be moderated.	
Assessment criteria	The assessment criteria your teacher will be using can be seen on the AQA website http://www.aqa.org.uk/subjects/food-preparation-and-nutrition/gcse/food-preparation-and-nutrition-8585.	

Top tips for Non-Exam Assessment

You need to plan your work carefully.

It is good practice to include aims and conclusions to relevant pages.

Research must be focused, relevant and analysed.

Keep all research concise. Do not copy from books and websites – summarise the information you find out.

Explain and justify decisions at each stage of both tasks, this will help your teacher and the moderator understand your thought process.

The quality of your practical dishes needs to be very good. You need to showcase your best making skills.

The dishes you make need to look appetising and attractive but also taste very good.

Explain the working properties of ingredients to show that you understand how ingredients work and why.

Testing should form an important part of all your work. Try to use a range of tests.

Understanding and application of nutritional knowledge must be evident throughout your work. Nutritional analysis of your final dishes for the Food Preparation task will be required.

Subject specific terminology/ technical language should be used when recording and evaluating your work.

Add the sources of information used through an appendix containing a bibliography, or through footnotes.

Presenting your work

- Make the best use of the space available on each page.
- Write concisely.
- Use appropriate size font (e.g. size 12).
- Label and annotate photographs and diagrams.
- Proofread all work to avoid errors.
- Check spelling, punctuation and grammar.
- Include headings and separate paragraphs to make your written work easier to read.
- Photographs of all your practical work must include your name and candidate number.
- Keep within the word limit for the Food Investigation task: 1500–2000 words.
- Do not exceed 20 single sided A4 pages or A3 equivalent for the Food Preparation task.
- Include a front cover that includes the title of the task, your name, candidate number and centre number.

The following chapter will help you to focus on what you need to do for each task.

Plan your work carefully

12.1.2 Food Investigation task

Section 6: Assessment

What will I learn?

In this section you will learn:

- how to **research**, **plan** and **carry out** an investigation into the working characteristics, functional and chemical properties of ingredients
- how to **record** the investigation findings
- how to **analyse** and **evaluate** your results
- how to **present** the Food Investigation task.

Key terms

Analyse: to break down a task or question explaining the key words and what is required

Hypothesis: an idea, prediction or explanation that you then test through investigation and experimentation

Control: a standard of comparison for checking or verifying the results of an experiment

The Food Investigation task

The purpose/objective of this task

As you cook and prepare food, scientific changes take place between ingredients. The Food Investigation task involves investigating and understanding how ingredients work and why. This will be done through practical experimentation and investigation evaluating the working characteristics, functional and chemical properties of ingredients.

The experiments and investigations you carry out will help in the understanding of what happens when food is prepared and cooked. The Food Investigation task allows you to expand on this learning through practical investigations.

As part of your GCSE course, you will have already studied the science behind how and why ingredients react in particular ways when we prepare and cook with them. In Section 2 of this book (pages 105–157), you will have studied the functional and chemical properties of:

- Proteins
- Fats
- Carbohydrates
- Raising agents.

You will hopefully now be able to answer some of the questions below:

- Why is yeast used in bread making?
- Why do baked dishes rise?
- Why are certain microbes used in food preparation?
- Why do some foods change colour when they are cooked?
- Why do apples go brown when left in the air?
- Why do different pastries have different textures?
- Why does a sauce thicken when heated?
- Why does bread turn golden brown when toasted?
- Why do onions caramelise when heated?
- Why do foods change in appearance, texture and flavour when they are cut, chilled, frozen, cooked or mixed with other foods?
- Why do some foods have many different uses in food preparation and cooking?
- Why do we need to whisk egg whites to make meringue?

The Food Investigation task will allow you to carry out a detailed practical investigation. Examples of Food Investigation tasks can be seen below.

Examples of Food Investigation tasks

1. Investigate the ingredients used for bread making.
2. Investigate the use of raising agents in baked products.
3. Investigate the use of ingredients used to thicken sauces and soups.

How the task will be assessed

Breakdown of assessment	
Choose and analyse task	
Section A: Research	6 marks
Section B: Investigation	15 marks
Section C: Analysis and evaluation	9 marks
Total	**30 marks**

What will I need to do to complete the task?

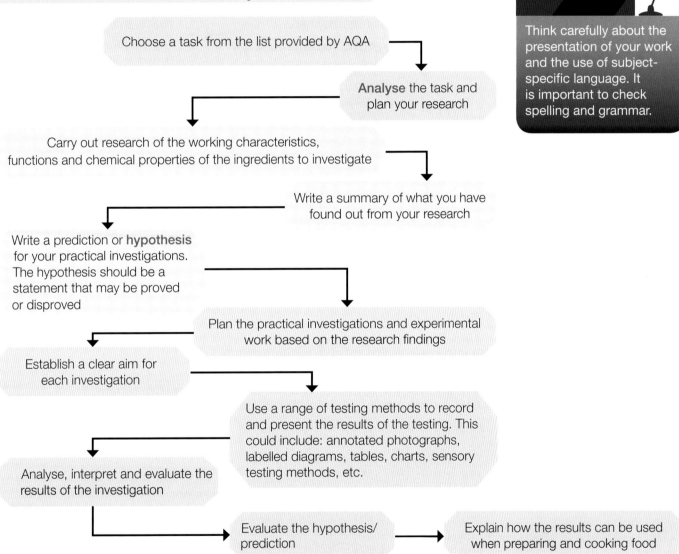

Choose a task from the list provided by AQA

Analyse the task and plan your research

Carry out research of the working characteristics, functions and chemical properties of the ingredients to investigate

Write a summary of what you have found out from your research

Write a prediction or **hypothesis** for your practical investigations. The hypothesis should be a statement that may be proved or disproved

Plan the practical investigations and experimental work based on the research findings

Establish a clear aim for each investigation

Use a range of testing methods to record and present the results of the testing. This could include: annotated photographs, labelled diagrams, tables, charts, sensory testing methods, etc.

Analyse, interpret and evaluate the results of the investigation

Evaluate the hypothesis/prediction

Explain how the results can be used when preparing and cooking food

Planning the investigation

The Food Investigation task will be fun, engaging and you will learn a lot from researching the task and the practical investigations that will be carried out. You will be able to use the information you learn from carrying out the investigation when preparing and cooking food in the future. Throughout the chapter, there are pieces of work based on the task: Investigate the ingredients used for bread making. These pieces of work are included to simply show how information could be presented. Remember the word limit for the Food Investigation task is 1500–2000 words.

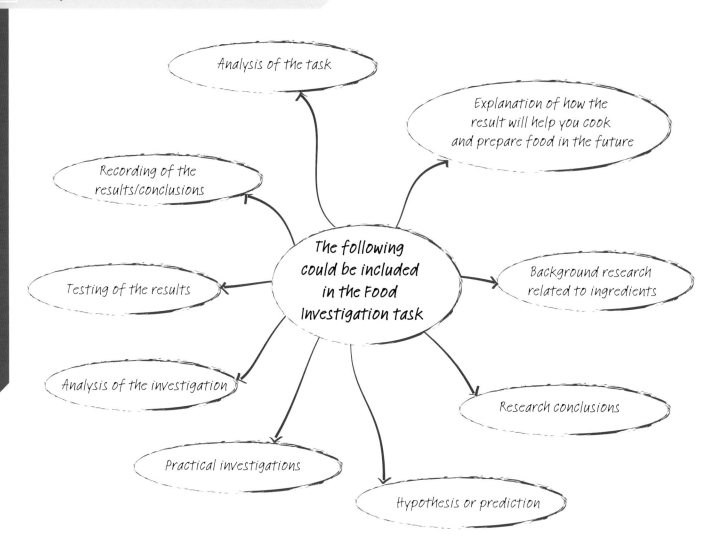

Section A: Research (6 marks)

Stage 1: Analysing the task

When you are presented with the Food Investigation task you need to start thinking about what you have been asked to do. A good starting point could be to focus on the key words within the task.

This will help you to understand what is being asked. As with all new tasks, questions and projects, a good starting point is to produce a mind map of all your ideas. This can then be used to plan your work.

Study tip

When starting a new project it is always a good idea to produce an initial plan. This will help you to understand the requirements of the task and keep you focused and on track. Remember you only have 10 hours to complete this task which includes the practical investigation and writing the report.

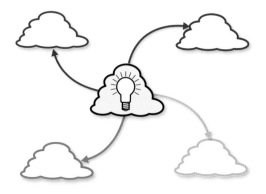

Stage 2: Carrying out the research

After analysing the task a good starting point could be to list or mind map the research you need to carry out before starting the practical investigation work. An example of this can be seen below.

You may wish to carry out some background research for the task which focuses on the ingredients and processes you are investigating. Think carefully about how you will carry out any background research and the sources of information you will use. The diagram below illustrates one potential approach.

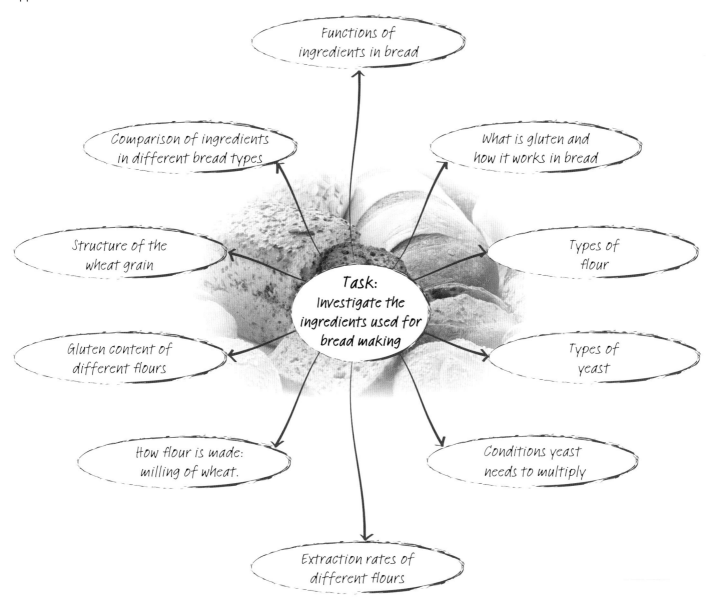

Functions of ingredients in bread

Comparison of ingredients in different bread types

What is gluten and how it works in bread

Structure of the wheat grain

Types of flour

Task: Investigate the ingredients used for bread making

Gluten content of different flours

Types of yeast

How flour is made: milling of wheat.

Conditions yeast needs to multiply

Extraction rates of different flours

Example of research mind map

Activity

Carry out a mind map to show the research that would be required for the task below.

Task: Investigate the use of ingredients used to thicken sauces and soups.

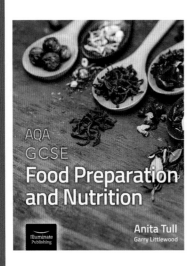

AQA GCSE
Food Preparation and Nutrition

Anita Tull
Garry Littlewood

Illuminate Publishing

Research methods

Research can be both primary and secondary.

> **Primary research** involves gathering data/information that has not been collected by other people and that you have designed and carried out yourself. For example, surveys, interviews and questionnaires.
>
> **Secondary research** involves gathering existing data/information that has already been produced, for example, researching the Internet, using text books or newspapers. Don't forget to say where you gathered the information from by giving a reference to it, e.g. Tull, A. and Littlewood, G. (2016) *Food Preparation and Nutrition*, Illuminate Publishing.
>
> British Nutrition Foundation: www.nutrition.org.uk

Examples of secondary sources of research include:

Text books: There are many food-related text books. You may wish to use some of the information from Chapter 4: the functional and chemical properties of ingredients. It is important that you do not copy information from books; you need to edit and analyse what you find out. You must understand what you have written because you will be using this information later in your project.

Websites: There are many excellent websites containing useful information. When using websites you need to use reliable sources and check (validate) that the work is accurate. This can be done by comparing the information with other sources (e.g. textbooks and other websites). It is important not to copy and paste information from websites.

Multimedia: There are many good film clips/ graphics related to ingredients that you may wish to use when finding out how ingredients work and why. There are animations and films clips to watch in the digital book.

Using prior knowledge: This means using the knowledge you already have without the need to find out. You will already have done lots of work as part of your GCSE Food Preparation and Nutrition course and may wish to analyse some of this to include in the investigation. Think about the learning that has taken place in other areas of the curriculum, such as Science, Geography, etc.

Study tip

- Set clear aims for each piece of research. What are you trying to find out?
- The background research must relate to the task and be relevant and focused and should be presented concisely.
- Add the sources of information used through an appendix containing a bibliography, or alternatively through footnotes.

The example below shows one possible way of approaching research when investigating the ingredients used for bread making.

Research

Aim: to find out what gluten is and why it is essential for bread making

Research

Two proteins present in flour (gliadin and glutenin) form gluten when mixed with water. Gluten is essential for bread making and influences the mixing, kneading and baking properties of dough. Stirring and kneading increases gluten formation. The gluten catches the carbon dioxide produced by the yeast and stretches, resulting in millions of tiny bubbles.

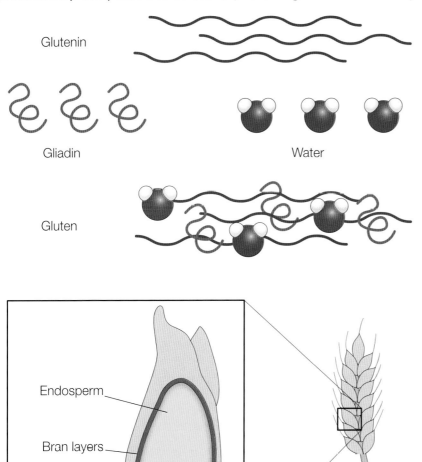

Glutenin

Gliadin   Water

Gluten

Endosperm

Bran layers

Germ

Strong plain flour creates the best results for bread as it is high in gluten. The gluten content in the flour can hold the carbon dioxide gas which is produced during the dough fermentation. This creates a good crumb texture which is most suitable for bread. The extraction rate of strong plain flour is 70%. Strong white flour contains 70% of the original grain, with most of the bran, germ, fat and minerals removed.

Activity

Explain how this example has been researched and presented:

a) How well do you think the research has been written?

b) How well has the science associated with gluten been explained?

c) Do you think there is anything missing from this research?

Stage 3: Analysing the research and planning the practical investigations

- When you have completed the research it is important to summarise what you have found out.
- The research analysis should be used to help you to decide what practical investigations you intend to carry out. You may wish to discuss this with your teacher.
- It is good practice to set a hypothesis for your project – this is an idea, prediction or explanation that you then test through investigation and experimentation.

Activity

Explain how this example has been analysed and a hypothesis produced:

a) What do you think about the way in which the analysis and conclusion of the research have been written?

b) Is there anything else that could be included in the analysis and conclusion?

c) Do you think the hypothesis is relevant and suitable?

d) Do you think the chosen investigations to prove the hypothesis are relevant and suitable?

e) Can you suggest any other investigations that would be suitable?

This is one possible way in which the research can be analysed and a hypothesis written

Research conclusions

From the research that has been carried out, the flour that creates the best results for bread is strong plain flour, as it has a high gluten content that contributes towards the texture of the bread. It also creates the most appropriate framework for the bread when it coagulates once heated. As part of the investigation I also intend to find out the most suitable conditions for the fermentation of yeast which is required during the bread-making process.

Hypothesis:
The hypothesis that I am intending to test is: That strong plain flour will be the most successful flour to be used when making bread.

Investigations:
To prove this hypothesis I will carry out these three investigations:

Investigation 1: Experiment with making bread rolls with different types of flour: wholemeal flour, plain flour, strong plain flour and granary flour.

Investigation 2: Gluten balls experiment: make ×4 dough mixtures with different flours and remove the starch from the dough.

Investigation 3: The conditions for the fermentation of yeast when making bread rolls.

Section B: Investigation (15 marks)

When the practical investigation has been planned it will be necessary to carry out the experimental and investigation work to prove or disprove your hypothesis or prediction.

Stage 4: Carrying out practical investigations

- Plan the practical investigation carefully. Have a clear **aim**: what are you trying to find out? For example – Aim: To experiment making bread rolls with different types of flours (wholemeal flour, plain flour, strong plain flour and granary flour) to find which flour creates an elastic texture and the effects on taste and appearance.
- Have a clear **method** of how to carry out the investigation. Think carefully about the **controls** you will need to apply to make this a fair test.
- Here are some possible ideas of methods that could be used to record the results. A chart/table should be prepared before you start the investigation. It could be a sensory chart (e.g. rating table) or a viscosity chart if testing sauces, etc. (see page 301).

Experiment making bread rolls with different types of flour: wholemeal, plain, strong plain flour, gluten free.

Investigate the comparison of kneading by hand and using electrical equipment.

Investigation: gluten balls experiment. Make ×4 dough mixtures with different flours washing away the starch from the dough.

Task:
Investigate the ingredients used for bread making

Investigate the kneading time of bread dough to achieve the ideal bread rolls.

Investigate the ideal conditions for the fermentation of yeast (e.g. balloon and test tube experiment).

Investigate the ideal volume of water to make the perfect bread dough.

Investigate the effect of adding sugar in a bread recipe.

Investigate the effect of adding ascorbic acid to breads.

Examples of different practical investigations that could be included for a bread making task

Controls when carrying out practical investigations

When carrying out investigations controlled testing ensures the results are accurate.

Examples of controls to ensure a fair test
Weigh ingredients accurately, if possible, use digital scales.
Use cutters and templates to ensure a consistent size.
Cook at the same temperature and for the same amount of time.
When testing use random codes (e.g. XZY) to avoid any bias.
Serve samples at the correct and same temperature.
Make sure testers know how to fill in the charts.

Activity

Comment on how these examples have been presented:

a) What do you think the test tube and balloon photographs are about and what do they show?

b) What else should be included in photographs to prove that it is your work?

Examples of controls when carrying out a Food Investigation task

Controls:

1. Each bread sample weighed to the exact weight (50g with a 1g tolerance).

2. The bread is cooked at the same temperature (220°C).

3. The bread samples are cooked for the same amount of time (10 minutes).

4. Random codes (XYX) used to avoid bias.

5. A chart included for the taster to record the results.

  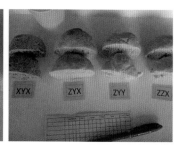

Controls:

1. Equal quantities of yeast in the test tubes.

2. The timing is controlled, each test tube left for 60 minutes.

3. Equal amounts of liquid in each test tube.

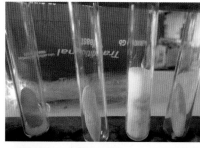 

Section C: Analysis and evaluation (9 marks)

Stage 5: Analysis and evaluation of the results

When the practical investigations are completed record the outcome of the investigations. When analysing your findings you could demonstrate your understanding of how the ingredients reacted and worked in your investigations.

Recording practical investigations

You could use different methods to record the results of the practical investigations. Some of these include:

- Annotated photographs/images/diagrams.
- Sensory testing methods (e.g. ranking and rating tests).
- Charts and graphs (e.g. viscosity testing charts for sauces).

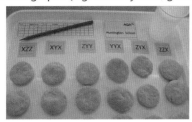

Photographic evidence showing the results of an investigation testing different fats to make shortcrust pastry

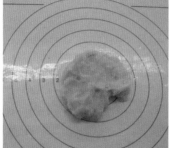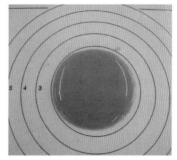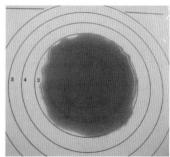

Photographic evidence showing the results of an investigation testing the viscosity of sauces

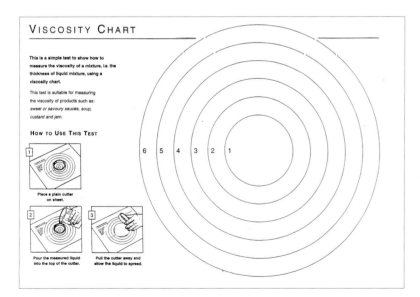

Example of a viscosity testing chart

See Chapter 9 for other methods to record sensory testing.

Sample	Appearance				Total	Texture				Total	Taste				Total	Aroma				Total	Total
XYZ																					
ZYX																					
ZYY																					
ZZX																					

Sensory chart

Section 6: Assessment

Recording an investigation

Activity

Comment on how these examples have been presented:

a) How does annotating a photograph help to show your understanding?

b) What should also be added to the photograph to prove it is your work?

This is a possible way in which the evidence for a practical investigation can be recorded and presented

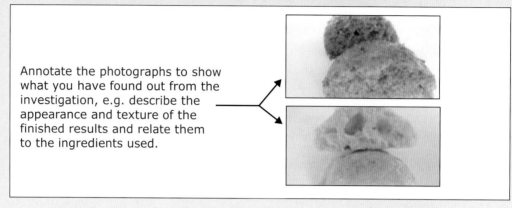

Annotate the photographs to show what you have found out from the investigation, e.g. describe the appearance and texture of the finished results and relate them to the ingredients used.

Recording the investigation results

Recording and analysing a practical investigation

- When writing the results of the investigation the following structure is one possible way the results could be recorded.

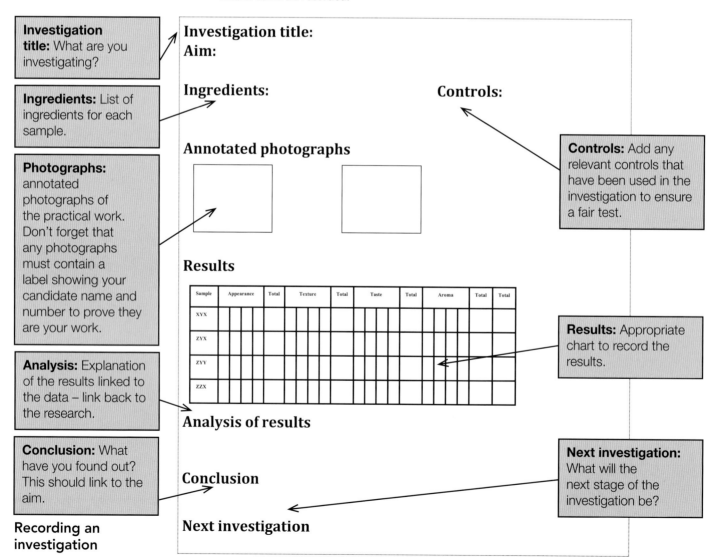

Investigation title: What are you investigating?

Ingredients: List of ingredients for each sample.

Photographs: annotated photographs of the practical work. Don't forget that any photographs must contain a label showing your candidate name and number to prove they are your work.

Analysis: Explanation of the results linked to the data – link back to the research.

Conclusion: What have you found out? This should link to the aim.

Recording an investigation

Investigation title:
Aim:

Ingredients: **Controls:**

Annotated photographs

Results

Sample	Appearance	Total	Texture	Total	Taste	Total	Aroma	Total	Total
XYX									
ZYX									
ZYY									
ZZX									

Analysis of results

Conclusion

Next investigation

Controls: Add any relevant controls that have been used in the investigation to ensure a fair test.

Results: Appropriate chart to record the results.

Next investigation: What will the next stage of the investigation be?

- **Analyse and interpret the results of the investigations.** This will involve linking the results to the background research.

Recording practical investigations

Investigation 2:

Aim: To test the amount of gluten in the different types of flour by removing the starch from the dough.

Investigation:
An investigation was carried to see the amount of gluten that is in each different type of flour; testing strong plain flour, wholemeal flour, granary flour and plain flour. The gluten content is important in bread as it influences the characteristics of bread. Each sample of dough was made and the starch was removed from each one using cold water.

Controls:
- Each bread dough sample was made using the same quantities of flour weighed using digital scales for accuracy.
- The four samples were baked at the same temperature and for the same amount of time.

Results:

Sample	Appearance				Total	Texture				Total	Taste				Total	Aroma				Total	Final Total
XYX Plain	3	3	3	3	12	3	3	4	4	14	3	3	3	3	12	3	3	3	3	12	50
ZYX Granary	2	1	1	1	4	1	1	1	1	4	2	2	2	2	8	2	2	2	2	8	24
ZYY Strong	5	4	4	5	18	5	5	5	5	20	4	4	3	3	14	4	4	4	4	16	68
ZZX Wholemeal	4	4	4	4	16	4	4	4	4	16	4	4	4	4	16	4	4	4	4	16	64

These results show that the sample that had the most gluten was ZYY which scored 68/80; this was the gluten content from strong plain flour. This amount of gluten helps to create the perfect elasticity for the bread dough in order to create the most suitable bread. The lowest scoring sample was ZYX which scored 24/80. This particular sample lacked gluten as it was made using granary flour.

Conclusion: The results collected from this investigation show that the strong plain flour has the highest amount of gluten content within the flour to create the most suitable bread as it creates the best characteristics for the bread. To help create the best characteristics it is important the conditions in which the yeast needs to multiply. The final investigation tests the ideal conditions for the fermentation of yeast.

Activity

Explain how this practical investigation has been carried out and recorded:

a) What do you think about the way in which the aim of the investigation has been written?

b) What controls have been applied to ensure fair testing?

c) Do you think the chosen investigation to prove the hypothesis is relevant and suitable? Give reasons.

d) Can you think of anything else that could be done to improve the investigation and presentation of the work?

Stage 6: Analysis and evaluation of the results

Final evaluation

- Explain and justify your conclusion. The conclusion may show what you have learned as a result of carrying out each of the practical investigations. The final evaluation will summarise the main points of the investigation and relate to the hypothesis/prediction.

- Finally, explain how the results might be applied in practical food preparation and cooking.

Activity

Comment on how well the analysis and evaluation of the project have been written:

a) Explain what is good about the example.

b) Suggest some improvements that could be made.

Shown below is one possible approach to the conclusion of the task

Analysis and evaluation

The investigations carried out have created a clear understanding of the working chemical properties of the most suitable ingredients for bread making. The results of the first investigation prove that strong plain flour is the ingredient to make the most suitable sensory characteristics for bread: the soft fluffy texture, the subtle taste, the light appearance of the bread. The strong plain flour also consists of a sufficient amount of gluten; as discovered in my research, gluten is essential for bread making and influences aspects such as the kneading and baking properties of the dough. The condition for yeast to ferment is important to create the most suitable bread. Yeast needs food, warmth, moisture and time to ferment and release carbon dioxide. The final investigation showed that the test tube that consisted of yeast, warm water, sugar and was left at room temperature created the most ideal conditions for the yeast to ferment as it released the most carbon dioxide when the bread was left to prove before baking in the oven. The research conclusion and hypothesis has been proven and strong plain flour is the most successful flour to be used in bread making. When making sweet and savoury dough and using yeast, I now know that strong plain flour must always be used. Wholemeal flour worked successfully but to further enhance the stretch and open texture, a mixture of wholemeal and strong plain flour can achieve successful results.

Gliadin   Glutenin

Gluten
(Gliadin + Glutenin)

Food Investigation checklist

- [✓] Is the research well explained and related to the task?
- [✓] Is the investigation thoroughly planned with clear aims and conclusions throughout?
- [✓] Does the task include appropriate, relevant and well planned practical investigations?
- [✓] Have the practical experiments been carried out under controlled conditions to ensure fair and accurate results?
- [✓] Has a wide range of testing been carried out?
- [✓] Are the results of the investigations clearly recorded?
- [✓] Are the findings of the investigations linked to the background research?
- [✓] Does the work show evidence of very good understanding of how ingredients work and why?
- [✓] Do the conclusions explain what has been found out?
- [✓] Is there explanation of how the findings of the investigation could be used when preparing and cooking in the future?
- [✓] Is the work original and not copied from other sources?
- [✓] Does the work use subject-specific terminology?

12.1.3 Food Preparation task

What will I learn?

In this section you will learn:

- how to **plan**, **prepare**, cook and present three dishes in three hours
- how to **showcase** your food preparation/technical skills
- how to **produce** a time plan
- how to **analyse** and **evaluate** your work.

The Food Preparation task

The purpose/objective of the task

The Food Preparation task will be the final assessment of the GCSE Food Preparation and Nutrition course and will be an opportunity for you to put into practice all that you have learnt throughout the course. The task will be mainly practically based and will allow you to showcase a range of food preparation and technical skills. The final assessment will involve planning, preparing, cooking and presenting three dishes in a 3-hour session.

You will produce a concise portfolio of no more than 20 sides of A4 or A3/electronic equivalent. Use appropriate size font (e.g. size 12). The portfolio will show:

- Evidence of researching the task.
- Evidence of practical skills, including demonstrations of different technical skills. The outcomes of demonstrating technical skills will be used to justify the choices of dishes for the final menu.
- Evidence of planning, preparing, cooking and presenting three dishes within a single period of no more than 3 hours.
- Analysis and evaluation of the nutritional profile, cost and sensory properties of the three final dishes.

How the task will be assessed

Breakdown of assessment	
Section A: Researching the task	6 marks
Section B: Demonstrating technical skills	18 marks
Section C: Planning for the final menu	8 marks
Section D: Making the final dishes	30 marks
Section E: Analysis and evaluation	8 marks
Total	**70 marks**

Key term

Menu: a selection of dishes. For the Non-Exam Assessment three dishes will be produced to meet the chosen task. These may be a selection of three individual dishes or three dishes that make up a meal

Study tip

The Food Preparation task makes up 35% of the total marks for the GCSE grade so it is very important that you produce the best possible work.

Examples of Food Preparation tasks

1. Plan, prepare, cook and present a range of dishes, using a variety of skills, which would be suitable for vegetarians. Present three final dishes.
2. Plan, prepare, cook and present a range of dishes, using a variety of skills, which are a good source of fibre and would appeal to teenagers. Present three final dishes.
3. Plan, prepare, cook and present a range of dishes, using a variety of skills, from the Mediterranean culinary tradition. Present three final dishes.

Understanding and application of nutritional knowledge will be a requirement of all tasks.

Section 6: Assessment

What will I need to do to complete the task?

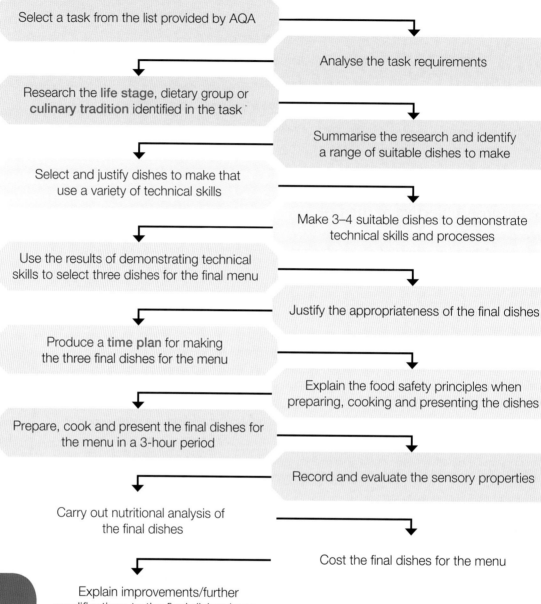

Select a task from the list provided by AQA

Analyse the task requirements

Research the **life stage**, dietary group or **culinary tradition** identified in the task

Summarise the research and identify a range of suitable dishes to make

Select and justify dishes to make that use a variety of technical skills

Make 3–4 suitable dishes to demonstrate technical skills and processes

Use the results of demonstrating technical skills to select three dishes for the final menu

Justify the appropriateness of the final dishes

Produce a **time plan** for making the three final dishes for the menu

Explain the food safety principles when preparing, cooking and presenting the dishes

Prepare, cook and present the final dishes for the menu in a 3-hour period

Record and evaluate the sensory properties

Carry out nutritional analysis of the final dishes

Cost the final dishes for the menu

Explain improvements/further modifications to the final dishes/menu

Key terms

Life stage: phases of development that people go through during their life, such as infancy, childhood, adolescence (teenagers), adulthood and the elderly

Culinary tradition: ingredients or foods that are associated with a particular country or region, e.g. pasta is a traditional Italian food

Time plan: a step-by-step plan to follow when making the final dishes

Study tip

There is no word limit for the Food Preparation task. The project must not exceed 20 sides of A4 or 10 sides of A3/electronic equivalent. The practical work and portfolio must not exceed **20 hours**. This includes a 3-hour practical session to make the three final dishes.

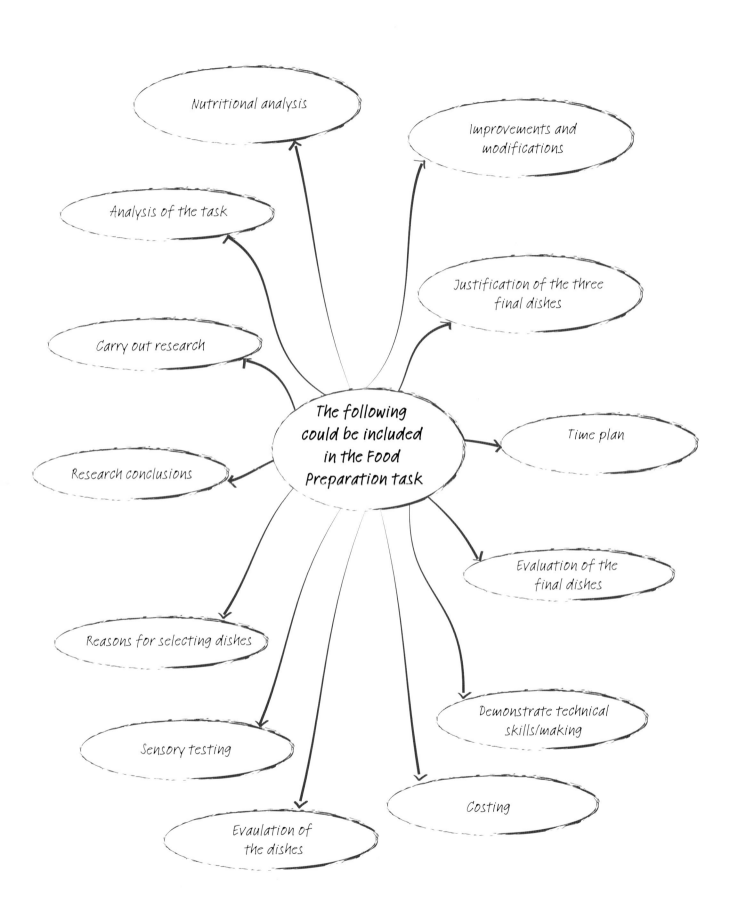

Nutritional analysis

Improvements and modifications

Analysis of the task

Justification of the three final dishes

Carry out research

The following could be included in the Food Preparation task

Time plan

Research conclusions

Reasons for selecting dishes

Evaluation of the final dishes

Sensory testing

Demonstrate technical skills/making

Evauation of the dishes

Costing

Section A: Researching the task (6 marks)

Choosing the right task will be very important. When selecting a task think carefully about:

- The research you could carry out to answer the task.
- Possible practical dishes that you could make to answer the task.
- The target group the dishes will be aimed at.

Stage 1: Research

The first stage will be to analyse the task and consider the research you will need to carry out.

The research will be focused on either a:

- **Life stage** (young children, teenagers, adults, elderly).
- Dietary group (vegetarians, vegans, coeliacs, lactose intolerant and high fibre diets).
- **Culinary tradition** (Mediterranean, Middle Eastern, British, Asian etc.).

The type of research will depend on the chosen task. For the Food Preparation task it may be appropriate to collect the information using primary as well as secondary sources. Primary sources could include:

- **Questionnaire/interviews:** a useful method of finding out information from a group of people such as a target group (e.g. teenagers).
- **Ingredients investigation:** you may want to carry out some sensory analysis of different ingredients.
- **Market research:** similar to a questionnaire but you observe and record the information yourself, for example analyse the range of Mediterranean foods available in a supermarket or the food available in a school canteen. This allows you to compare different dishes.
- **Menu analysis:** you could analyse a menu you have collected from a restaurant or school canteen.
- **Product testing:** you could look at existing dishes e.g. dishes from another country, that are sold in shops. You could carry out some sensory testing.

Examples of research for different tasks

Task	Possible types of research to select from
Plan, prepare, cook and present a range of dishes, using a variety of skills, from the **Mediterranean culinary tradition.** Present three final dishes.	• Find out the traditional foods/ingredients/recipes from different Mediterranean countries. • Investigate herbs and spices used to flavour foods. • Nutritional research into Mediterranean diets. See the Exemplar on page 309. • Find out how a particular ingredient is made (e.g. pasta). • Investigate different cooking techniques and methods. • Analyse a Mediterranean menu.
 Plan, prepare, cook and present a range of dishes, using a variety of skills, which would be suitable for **vegetarians.** Present three final dishes.	• Different types of vegetarians. • Alternative proteins to replace meat and fish. • Nutritional guidelines for vegetarians. • Health benefits of a vegetarian diet. • Advantages and disadvantages of vegetarian diets. • Interview or carry out a questionnaire of vegetarian food choices. • Shop survey of vegetarian dishes/ingredients. • Experimental work based on alternative proteins.

The example below shows one possible way of researching a range of dishes from the Mediterranean culinary tradition.

Research

Aim: To find out why Mediterranean diets are balanced and healthy

The same as poultry, it suggests fish to be consumed at least twice a week. To cook them healthily, you should grill, bake, or boil, and most definitely avoid frying in butter and batter. Avoid also breaded and fried fish.

Poultry is recommended to be consumed at least twice a week, due to the low-fat yet high-protein content. Examples of poultry are chicken, turkey, duck, goose, guinea fowl, pheasant and ostrich.

In the case of meats, the Mediterranean Food Authorities recommend eating red meats no more than a few times a month. They say to substitute red meats in your diets for fish. However, when eating the meat, make sure the piece of meat is no bigger than a deck of cards. They also tend to avoid sausages, bacon, and other high-fat, processed meats.

In the Mediterranean diet, olive oils play a big part in replacing unhealthy fats, such as butter. The native people eat primarily plant-based foods, such as fruits, vegetables, whole grains and nuts. Spices and herbs are an extremely important aspect of the diet because they provide flavourings instead of salt. This is a healthier alternative, hence why many Mediterranean dishes use such a wide variety of fragrant herbs and spices.

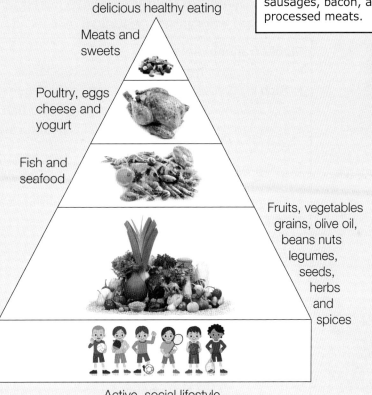

Mediterranean diet pyramid
delicious healthy eating

Meats and sweets

Poultry, eggs cheese and yogurt

Fish and seafood

Fruits, vegetables grains, olive oil, beans nuts legumes, seeds, herbs and spices

Active, social lifestyle

Activity

Explain how this example has been researched and presented:

a) How well do you think the research has been written?

b) What are the good points of this piece of research?

c) Do you think there is anything missing from this research?

Analysis of the Mediterranean diet pyramid: The Mediterranean countries base their healthy eating model on a pyramid not the Eatwell Guide. The triangle is saying similar messages: Eat fruit and vegetables, and switch to wholegrain produce, such as wholegrain bread or wholegrain cereals. Include fruits and vegetables in every meal, and eat them as snacks as well. Brown rice and pasta are healthier alternatives. Nuts and seeds are also good sources of fibre, protein and healthy fats. Almonds, cashews, pistachios and walnuts are great for snacking rather than sugary products. Olive oil is a healthier alternative to butter or soft spread. Instead of smothering vegetables or potatoes in butter, drizzle them in olive oil which offers the same texture and less saturated fat. Using spices and herbs livens up dishes rather than salt. Salt is used in dishes to enhance flavours, but spices and herbs provide flavours, which is fantastic for creating new flavour. Red meats should not be eaten often; a few times a month will suffice. Fish is a major part of the Mediterranean diet and I will therefore include some in the dishes I make.

Activity

Carry out a mind map of the research that could be carried out for the task below.

Plan, prepare, cook and present a range of dishes, using a variety of skills, which are a good source of fibre and would appeal to teenagers. Present three final dishes.

Summarising the research

When you have completed all the research it is important to summarise what you have found out. This can be presented as bullet points or in paragraphs. The research analysis should be used to help you to decide on a selection of dishes to demonstrate technical skills.

Activity

Comment on how well the research findings have been summarised:

a) Is the research relevant to the task title?

b) How well has the analysis been written?

c) How does the analysis focus on the task topic?

d) How will the analysis help in the selection of recipes for the practical work?

Shown below is one possible approach to summarising the research

Analysis of research: key points to consider before selecting the dishes to demonstrate technical skills

---

Mediterranean diets

- Include lots of **fresh** fruit, salad and vegetables.
- **Rich** in vegetables, fruit, peas and beans (legumes) and grains.
- Includes moderate amounts of **chicken** and **fish**.
- There is little red meat and most fat is **unsaturated** and comes from olive oil and nuts.
- Pasta is commonly mixed with fresh vegetables and fish to produce **balanced meals**.
- Beans and pulses are included in many dishes because they are a **cheaper** source of protein.
- Nuts and seeds are also good **sources** of fibre, protein and healthy fats.
- **Olive oil** is a healthier alternative to butter or soft spreads.
- Spices and herbs provide **flavours** in many dishes.
- Fish is a major part of the Mediterranean diet including both white and **oily fish**.
- Reliance on local and **freshly sourced** ingredients.

Making pasta

- Fresh pasta is a **simple** and cheap dish and can be quickly made and then mixed with fresh vegetables, meats and fish to produce balanced meals.
- Fresh pasta can be **flavoured** with tomato, spinach, etc. and made into different shapes to add variety to dishes (e.g. penne, shells, spaghetti).
- Pasta can be filled with different fillings and served as ravioli, tortellini, etc.
- To make fresh pasta start with the flour and egg and mix well. **Knead** it, let it rest and then make the pasta in the pasta maker.

Herbs and spices

- For thousands of years, herbs and spices have been incorporated into Mediterranean dishes to add **flavour**.
- Herbs and spices boost flavour without adding a significant amount of **calories**, sodium or fat.
- Herbs and spices have nutritional advantages. They contain a range of nutrients and **antioxidants** and offer various health benefits.
- **Common** herbs and spices include oregano, rosemary, basil, marjoram, coriander and thyme.

Section B: Demonstrating technical skills (18 marks)

Stage 2: Selecting dishes

At this stage of your project you will be able to experiment with new technical skills, develop and refine existing skills, and make and modify different dishes. The dishes you select must reflect the research findings. This is an excellent opportunity to experiment and be creative and showcase your making/technical skills. Remember there are 18 marks for this section.

One possible approach is to start this section by mind mapping possible ideas of recipes to make, always thinking about the technical skills within each dish and how relevant these dishes are to the research analysis.

Mind map of possible dishes to demonstrate technical skills

Activity

Comment on how well the choice of dishes has been researched:

a) How many different skills have been covered by the dishes chosen?

b) How well do the choices of dishes match the Mediterranean cuisine?

*Plan, prepare, cook and present a range of dishes, using a variety of skills, from the **Mediterranean culinary tradition**. Present three final dishes.*

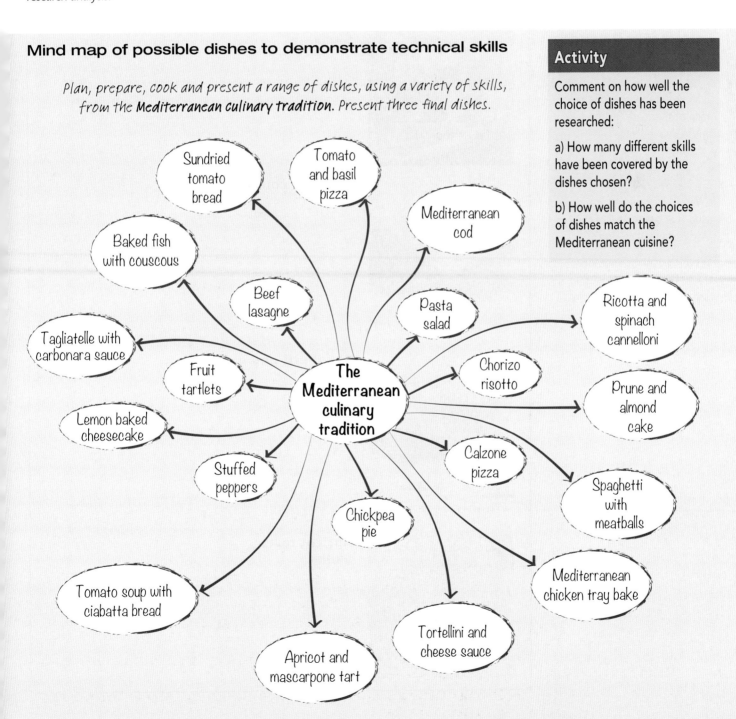

After mind mapping the possible dishes you can refine your choices, rejecting recipes that may not demonstrate your technical skills, for example you may not have made fresh pasta before and want to make a recipe to demonstrate this skill.

The following show some ideas for practical work. When recording the ideas you might annotate:

- the technical skills you will be using;
- the cooking techniques you will use.

Examples of possible ideas for practical work

Activity

Comment on the four example choices for the practical work shown here:

a) How suitable do you think each of them are for the task title? Give reasons.

b) Which practical skills are used in each dish?

c) Which ingredients are used that are typical of the Mediterranean cuisine?

d) Which cooking methods would be used to make the dishes?

Mediterranean-style pizza
Skills:

Fish and couscous
Skills:

Spaghetti and meatballs
Skills:

Apricot tarts
Skills:

Stage 3: Selecting and making dishes to demonstrate technical skills

The dishes you will make must demonstrate your technical skills. When selecting the dishes consider the following:

- ✓ *Are the dishes a suitable choice for my chosen task and do they reflect the findings of the earlier research?*
- ✓ *Am I demonstrating a range of technical skills (e.g. vegetable preparation, sauce making, producing dough, filleting fish)?*
- ✓ *Have I considered the nutritional guidelines?*
- ✓ *Can I present the dishes to a high standard?*
- ✓ *Will I be using different processes and cooking methods (e.g. whisking method, roux method)?*
- ✓ *Have I considered the source (where ingredients come from) and cost of ingredients?*

Possible ideas for dishes/skills chosen when demonstrating technical skills

The table below shows two examples of dishes chosen for two different tasks. The technical skills within each dish have been listed.

Task	Demonstrating technical skills
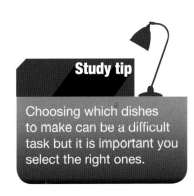 Plan, prepare, cook and present a range of dishes, using a variety of skills, from the **Mediterranean culinary tradition**. Present three final dishes.	**Roasted vegetable lasagne** *Skills:* making fresh pasta/tomato-based sauce/Béchamel sauce/vegetable preparation **Pizza** *Skills:* bread making/reduced tomato sauce/vegetable preparation **Mediterranean cod with couscous** *Skills:* filleting fish/vegetable preparation **Apricot tarts** *Skills:* shortcrust pastry, blended sauce – custard, fruit preparation, decoration

> **Study tip**
>
> Choosing which dishes to make can be a difficult task but it is important you select the right ones.

Example of dishes for a different task

Task	Demonstrating technical skills
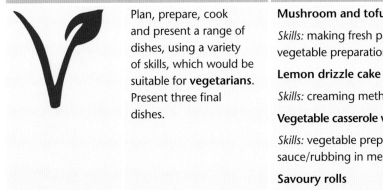 Plan, prepare, cook and present a range of dishes, using a variety of skills, which would be suitable for **vegetarians**. Present three final dishes.	**Mushroom and tofu tagliatelle** *Skills:* making fresh pasta/roux sauce/vegetable preparation **Lemon drizzle cake** *Skills:* creaming method/lemon sauce **Vegetable casserole with crumble topping** *Skills:* vegetable preparation/tomato sauce/rubbing in method **Savoury rolls** *Skills:* rough puff pastry/shaping/forming

Food preparation/technical skills

Different dishes/recipes include different levels of skill. Throughout your GCSE course you will have practised many different skills in your cooking. You will have discovered that some skills are more difficult (complex) than others. For example, when making a fish pie, filleting and removing the skin off the fish would be complex, compared to using fish that has already been prepared.

For the Food Preparation task, you are trying to showcase your practical skills and you should avoid, where possible, using ready-made ingredients, e.g. ready-made pastry. The table below shows another example of different skill levels related to making pasta.

Skill 10: Making a dough

Complex	Medium demand	Basic
Make pasta dough, roll to the required thickness, add a filling and shape the pasta accurately eg tortellini/ravioli and cook accurately.	Make pasta dough, roll to the required thickness and make pasta sheets for a pasta dish.	Use ready-made pasta in the making of a dish but demonstrate other processes in the dish eg slicing meat.

Making pasta	Fruit and vegetable preparation	Sauce making
Meat and fish preparation	Pastry making	Decoration

Some complex preparation skills

Film clips can be seen on all these techniques via the digital resources.

Recording the dishes produced when demonstrating technical skills

One possible approach when recording the dishes to demonstrate technical skills is shown below. You may wish to include:

- Name of the recipe.
- Reasons for choice.
- A photograph of each dish must be included in the portfolio. The candidate number and name must be clearly visible.
- Technical skills in the dish.
- Ingredient list.
- Sensory testing results (see Recording a dish, page 315).

One possible approach to recording a dish is shown below:

Recipe 1: Roasted vegetable lasagne

Reasons for choice: I chose to make this product because it is possible to showcase my sauce-making skills. The sauce also requires a lot of stirring, and understanding of gelatinisation, in order to prevent lumps forming. This is a typical Mediterranean dish.

Ingredients: Filling 400g peppers/aubergine, courgettes and red onion, 75g mushrooms, can tomatoes, 1 pepper, 10g fresh basis. **Pasta** 140g flour, 2 medium eggs. **Sauce** 50g plain flour, 50g soft spread, 500ml milk, 100g cheese.

Skills: Making pasta is a complex skill: making the dough, rolling the dough out to the correct thickness, cooking the pasta. For a roux sauce I need to ensure the sauce is at the correct consistency. Vegetable preparation: chopping and slicing.

Sensory evaluation:

	Taster 1	Taster 2	Taster 3	Taster 4	Total
Appearance	4	5	1	4	15
Texture	4	4	4	5	17
Taste	4	4	3	5	16
Aroma	3	2	4	3	13

The appearance scored 15/20. The tasting panel liked the crisp golden brown cheese topping and the contrast with the red peppers. The purpose of this skills test was to test how to make pasta as this is something I have not done before. The texture scored 17 out of 20. The tasting panel liked the texture and commented that it was cooked correctly. I hope to use fresh pasta as part of my final menu. The taste scored only 16 out of 20. The panel thought the pasta was a little bland and could have more flavouring such as basil to give a more appetising overall flavour.

Activity

Comment on how this practical investigation has been carried out and recorded:

a) What do you think about the way in which the recording of the dish has been written?

b) What do you think about the way in which the reasons for choice have been written?

c) What do you think about the way in which the sensory evaluation has been carried out and recorded?

d) Can you think of anything else that could be done to improve the presentation of the work?

Assessment

When assessing this section your teacher will be looking to see that you can:

- [✓] Make recipes with a variety of technical skills
- [✓] Select dishes relevant to the task
- [✓] Work accurately and confidently
- [✓] Show a very good understanding of the ingredients and processes you are using
- [✓] Work independently
- [✓] Use equipment skilfully and accurately
- [✓] Work safely and hygienically at all times

Section C: Planning for the final menu (8 marks)

Stage 4: Selecting the final dishes

After demonstrating a range of technical skills you need to decide on three dishes to make for the final assessment. The final dishes will relate to the task, research and the technical skills you have demonstrated. The final dishes will not have been made previously.

Examples:

- **Initial dish 1:** Make a fish pie to experiment with filleting fish and making a Béchamel sauce.

Final dish: Fish cakes with parsley sauce.

- **Initial dish 2:** Make a meat lasagne to investigate pasta making.

Final dish: Cannelloni with homemade pasta.

- **Initial dish 3:** Make a traditional quiche with shortcrust pastry making.

Final dish: Roasted vegetable quiche with reduced fat ingredients to improve the nutritional properties.

- **Initial dish:** Make flavoured bread rolls.

Not used in the making of the final dishes.

Possible ideas for demonstrating technical skills and final dishes for the Mediterranean culinary tradition task

Example of initial dishes and the final three dishes for two different tasks

Task	Demonstrating technical skills	Final dishes for the menu
Plan, prepare, cook and present a range of dishes, using a variety of skills, from the **Mediterranean culinary tradition**. Present three final dishes.	**Pizza** *Skills:* bread making/reduced tomato sauce/ vegetable preparation	**Minestrone soup with chilli and basil bread** – using bread-making skills
	Roasted vegetable lasagne *Skills:* making fresh pasta/tomato-based sauce/Béchamel sauce/vegetable preparation	**Tortellini with a salmon, spinach and ricotta filling** – using pasta-making skills
	Mediterranean cod with couscous *Skills:* filleting fish/vegetable preparation	
	Apricot tarts *Skills:* shortcrust pastry, blended sauce – custard, fruit preparation, decoration	**Caramelised fig and honey tarts:** using shortcrust pastry

Example of dishes and final three dishes for a different task

Task	Demonstrating technical skills	Final dishes for the menu
Plan, prepare, cook and present a range of dishes, using a variety of skills, which would be suitable for **vegetarians**. Present three final dishes.	**Mushroom and tofu tagliatelle** *Skills:* making fresh pasta/roux sauce/ vegetable preparation	**Roasted vegetable lasagne:** using fresh pasta/roux sauce/vegetable preparation
	Vegetable casserole with crumble topping *Skills:* vegetable preparation/tomato sauce/ rubbing in method	**Spicy bean casserole with sundried tomato bread** *Skills:* vegetable preparation/tomato sauce/bread making
	Savoury rolls *Skills:* rough puff pastry/shaping/forming	
	Lemon drizzle cake *Skills:* creaming method/lemon sauce	**Banana bread with lemon icing** *Skills:* creaming method/lemon glacé icing

Reasons for choice

When you have selected the final three dishes you will need to give reasons for choosing the dishes. You may wish to think about some of the following when considering your reasons for choice:

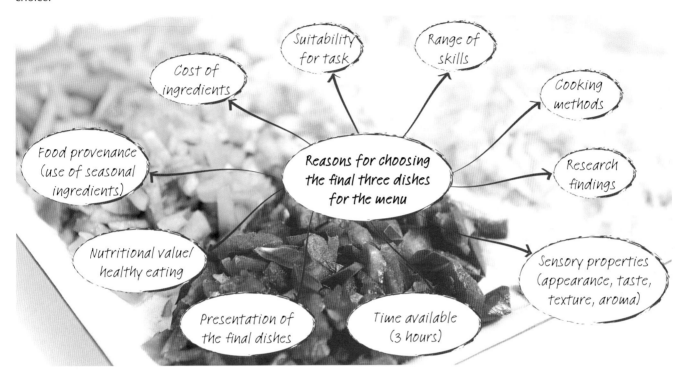

Cost of ingredients

Suitability for task

Range of skills

Cooking methods

Food provenance (use of seasonal ingredients)

Reasons for choosing the final three dishes for the menu

Research findings

Nutritional value/ healthy eating

Sensory properties (appearance, taste, texture, aroma)

Presentation of the final dishes

Time available (3 hours)

Assessment for learning

A student has selected three dishes to make in the 3 hour assessment. Reasons for choice are given on page 318.

1. Using the mark scheme below: how many marks could be awarded for reasons for choice?

2. What has the student done well when giving their reasons for choice?

3. How could this work be improved?

Assessment Criteria: Planning for the final menu	
Mark range	**Description**
7–8	Detailed review and justification of the choice and appropriateness of the final three dishes related to the task and research, e.g. nutrition, ingredients, cooking methods.
5–6	Reviews and explains the choice and appropriateness of the final dishes related to the task and research, e.g. nutrition, ingredients, cooking methods.
3–4	Limited reasons for choice of the final dishes, e.g. nutrition, ingredients, cooking methods.
1–2	The justification for the choice of the final dishes is not clear.
0	Nothing worthy of credit.

Examples of reasons for selecting the final dishes

Tortellini: I have chosen to make tortellini because it requires the skills to make pasta which I practised when making lasagne. I will use an extrusion machine for my pasta to create thin sheets, which I can then form into pasta parcels with a filling of salmon, spinach and ricotta. I will be making the sauce by the roux method. The spinach and ricotta are both ingredients that originate from the Mediterranean so meet the task.

Minestrone soup with chilli and basil bread: the soup I will be making is minestrone. The vegetables need to be consistent sizes. I will be using locally sourced vegetables to reduce food miles. I will be making chilli and basil bread which is very Mediterranean. I made bread at the skills trial stage and will be using the bread making process for the dough. For consistency, the chillies and basil leaves will need to be evenly distributed when incorporated into the bread.

Fig tarts: the fig is a very traditional Mediterranean fruit which is grown in hot climates. The tart will have a shortcrust sweet pastry case. The apricot tarts were good but the custard layer was not popular. I will replace this with a sponge layer. I will make four mini tarts. The skill involved is making sure the pastry cases are not too thick, but also not too thin and the base is cooked so not to have a soggy bottom. I have thought carefully about all three dishes and will be able to make them in the time available.

Producing a time plan

When you have decided on the final dishes to make in the 3-hour assessment you will need to write a time plan. You will use the time plan to ensure you are organised and complete the work on time.

A time plan will include:

- all the stages of making in the correct order
- timings for each stage
- food safety principles when storing, preparing, cooking and presenting the final dishes.

Writing a time plan

- You will need the recipes for all the dishes you are cooking.
- Work through each recipe and highlight when you will need to carry out each task. You will need to **dovetail** the tasks. For example, you will probably not make a complete dish and then move on to the next dish. You may start a dish (e.g. make bread dough for a pizza and leave it to prove) and then start to prepare vegetables.
- When producing a time plan think about which dishes:
  - need to be chilled before the next stage of preparation (e.g. setting a mousse)
  - need to be cooked the longest (e.g. a beef casserole)
  - need time to cool before decorating/garnishing (e.g. biscuits).
- When you have annotated/highlighted the copies of the recipes decide on the order of work and produce a plan.

Key term

Dovetail: to fit together a variety of different stages into a plan (e.g. different stages of making different recipes)

Time	Order of work	Health and safety considerations (personal hygiene/ food safety/kitchen safety)/special points

- The first row could include your *mise en place*. This is a catering term and means all your preparation before starting to cook.
- On your time plan you may wish to include any key food safety points and times and temperatures.
- It may help when following the plan to colour code each dish.

The example below shows one possible approach to producing a time plan.

Example of a time plan for dishes for the Mediterranean task

Dish 1: Minestrone soup with chilli and basil bread rolls

Dish 2: Tortellini with salmon, spinach and ricotta

Dish 3: Caramelised fig and honey tarts

Time	Order of work	Health and safety/special points
10:00	**Mise en place:** Collect equipment, utensils. Wash all vegetables. Weigh ingredients for pastry, bread and tart filling. Grease the tart tins. **Soup:** Peel and chop carrot, shred the cabbage, chop garlic, chop parsley, slice the green beans. Chop chilli and basil for the bread. **Figs:** Cut across halfway down gently squeeze to open the fig out like a flower. Segment an orange.	**Personal hygiene:** Key personal hygiene rules could be added to the time plan. **Food safety:** Clean surfaces with antibacterial spray. Check all equipment is clean. Check use by and best before dates. Use a brown chopping board for vegetables. **Refrigerate:** high risk ingredients (between 0°C and below 5°C). **Oven:** Pre heat oven to 200°C/Gas 6. **Cooking temperatures:** Temperatures recorded for the cooking of each dish to allow for oven management.
10:15	**Bread:** Mix flour and salt. Measure the warm water, add yeast, sugar and stir until dissolved. Add to the flour and mix to soft dough with a knife. Turn onto a floured table and knead well. Add the chopped chilli and basil.	Use warm water so not to kill the yeast. Cover with oiled cling-film and leave to prove in a warm area.
10:20	Wash up and clean work surfaces.	
10:25	**Pastry:** Place the flour, butter and icing sugar into a food processor and pulse until the mixture resembles breadcrumbs. Add half of the beaten egg and pulse until the mixture forms a dough. Turn out onto floured work surface and knead briefly until smooth.	The food processor is sharp, so care must be taken when handling the blade. Wrap the dough in cling film and chill for 20 minutes until firm.
10:35	**Pasta:** Add flour to a bowl and make a well. Crack the eggs into the well and gradually mix with a blunt knife. Incorporate the flour. Knead until well blended and the dough is soft and flexible. Place the salmon fillet in foil and bake in the oven for 15 minutes.	Use flour dredger to stop the dough sticking. Cover and leave pasta to rest for at least 20 minutes. Oven bake the salmon at 180°C for 15 minutes.
10:40	Wash up and clean work surfaces – care with food processor blade.	
10:50	Remove bread from proving oven and knock back. Divide into six and shape.	Cover with cling film and leave to prove for 10 minutes.
10:55	Roll out chilled pastry onto lightly floured work surface line six loose bottomed tart tins. Line with greaseproof paper and fill with baking beans. Remove salmon fillet from oven.	Bake at 200°C for 15 minutes.

Mise en place: explanation of preparation required before cooking.

Food safety: key temperatures could be included related to the storage of ingredients.

Equipment: the use of equipment could be recorded on the time plan.

Processes: knowledge of different process and techniques could be added.

Activity

Look through the example time plan and comment on the following:

a) How well has the *mis en place* been done?

b) How well has knowledge of food safety and hygiene been demonstrated in the time plan?

c) How well has knowledge of food preparation processes been demonstrated in the time plan?

d) How well has the use of the hob and oven been demonstrated in the time plan?

e) How well has the time plan been set out and how easy is it to follow?

f) How well have the different processes been dovetailed in the time plan?

g) How well has the clearing up been incorporated into the time plan?

h) How well has the presentation of the finished dishes been considered?

Timings: clear timings could be recorded at key stages.

Kitchen safety points could be listed to avoid any accidents.

Presentation: explanation of how each dish will be finished could be included.

11:05	Pasta filling: Remove the skin from the salmon and flake with a fork. Mix the salmon, spinach, ricotta, parmesan and nutmeg well, and season with salt and freshly ground black pepper.	Cover and refrigerate.
11:10	Remove the pastry cases from the oven. Remove the baking beans and paper, prick the tart base and brush with beaten egg.	Use oven gloves. Return to the oven for another 10 minutes, or until the tarts are crisp and lightly golden. Set aside to cool.
11:15	Soup: Gently fry the leeks, softening them. Add the garlic, rest of the vegetables, dried herbs and tomato puree and stir for a minute. Add the tinned tomatoes and stock and bring to the boil.	Add the pasta and beans and cook for 8 minutes.
11:25	Remove bread from proving, reshape if needed, and remove cling film and place in oven for 10 minutes until golden brown.	Remove pastry cases. Check bread has doubled in size. Glaze with egg wash for a golden brown appearance. Bake at 220°C for 15 minutes.
	Wash up and clean work surfaces.	
11:35	Divide the fresh pasta into four and roll out the pasta into a long, wide strip about 1mm in thickness, using a machine. Cut the strip in half.	Keep three portions under a bowl. This prevents the pasta from drying out. Check bread.
11:45	Place teaspoons of the filling in a line down the centre of one of the strips about 5cm apart. Place the other strip directly on top. Press the air out from around the filling by pushing down the pasta around them sealing them in. With a 7cm cutter cut circles out of the pasta around each mould of filling.	Remove bread rolls and leave to cool. Fill a saucepan with water and boil.
12:05	Sprinkle the base of each tart with ground almonds and then arrange one fig in the centre of each case. Place the honey, butter and orange juice into a small pan and gently melt. Remove from heat and using a pastry brush, brush the mixture over the figs.	Return the tarts to the oven. Bake at 200°C for 15 minutes until the figs are tender.
12:10	Wash and clean work surfaces.	
12:15	Check the soup. Season the soup and add any necessary herbs or flavours.	Leave until the pasta and carrots are soft enough to eat.
12:20	Remove tarts from the oven. Brush over the remaining honey, butter and orange mixture to glaze.	Use oven gloves.
12:25	Add pasta to boil water in batches. Sauce: toast the pine nuts, put the pine nuts, sage leaves and butter in a frying pan and melt the butter. Add about a tablespoon of the pasta water and stir together to emulsify the sauce. Remove from the heat.	Cook the pasta in boiling water for 3 minutes maximum or until al dente. Pine nuts cook quickly. Use a pan stand when removing off the heat.
12.45	To serve: Drizzle the sauce over the pasta and add grated parmesan. Put the soup in a bowl finish with basil and serve with bread roll. Serve the tarts with a segmented orange.	Garnish all dishes.
12.50	Wash and clean work surfaces.	

Section D: Making the final dishes (30 marks)

Stage 5: Making the final dishes

All the planning and preparation will now be completed and you will be ready for the practical assessment.

Before the assessed practical:

- Check you have all your recipes and the time plan.
- Read through the time plan the night before so you will be ready for the assessment.
- Check you have all the ingredients you will need.
- Have you checked with your teacher the equipment is available?
- Have you considered how you will present the dishes?

Assessment on the day

During the practical assessment your teacher will be assessing:

- [✓] Use of a range of technical skills
- [✓] Accurate and confident working
- [✓] Organisation and the use of the time plan
- [✓] Independent working
- [✓] Use of equipment
- [✓] Good personal hygiene and food safety
- [✓] Knowledge of ingredients and processes
- [✓] Presentation of the final dishes

Presenting the dishes

Presentation of the final dishes is important. When planning your assessment think carefully about:

- garnishes
- decorations
- portion size
- how to present your dishes with a high level of finish and decoration.

The photographs below show three different dishes that have been made for the Mediterranean task. The quality of finish has been considered and different finishes and garnishes used to present the final dishes.

> **Study tip**
>
> You must be well prepared for the assessment because you will only have one chance to make your dishes.

The following photographs show how you might choose to present practical work

Section 6: Assessment

Activity

Comment on how well you think these dishes have been garnished and presented:

a) Suggest some other ideas for garnishing and presenting these dishes.

Section E: Analysis and evaluation (8 marks)

Stage 6: Evaluating the practical work

When you have completed the practical work you need to:

- Carry out sensory evaluation (appearance, taste, texture and aroma) of the results. This can be achieved by setting up testing panels. You can use a variety of sensory analysis methods including ranking, rating and profiling tests (see Chapter 9).

- Cost the final dishes (see Chapter 2).

- Carry out nutritional analysis of the three final dishes (see Chapter 2). This can be done using a nutritional analysis program or using food tables. Think carefully about the target group the dishes are aimed (e.g. teenagers). You could compare against the Dietary Reference Values (DRVs) for the group.

- Identify improvements for the final dishes.

Possible ideas for presenting the evaluation, nutritional analysis and cost of dish

Evaluation and analysis: Tortellini with salmon, spinach and ricotta

For an aesthetically pleasing finish, I presented my pasta with a butter, sage and pine nut sauce and parsley in a white dish with a side of salad leaves and tomatoes. The skills used in the process of making this dish include: pasta making, shaping and making a sauce. I practised pasta making as part of the demonstrating technical skills which helped me to produce good pasta for the final assessment.

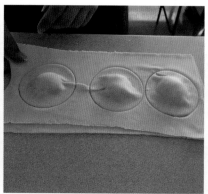

Candidate No 1343

Sensory evaluation

	Taster 1	Taster 2	Taster 3	Taster 4	Total
Appearance	4	3	5	3	15
Texture	3	5	5	4	17
Taste	4	5	4	5	18
Aroma	3	4	3	3	13

From my results table the most popular feature of the tortellini dish was the taste scoring 18/20. I included many different Mediterranean flavourings such as ricotta and spinach to make my pasta tortellini have a more interesting flavour. The sauce had parmesan cheese another Italian cheese to fit the theme of the task. The least popular was the aroma 13/20 as the dish did not have much of a scent. Texture scored 17/20, the pasta was al dente and this contrasted well to the moist filling. I could work at developing the appearance to include more vibrant colours, e.g. making a tomato sauce.

Nutritional analysis

This dish was quite balanced and scored no red traffic light warnings. There was 14g of saturated fat per portion (33%). This will be as a result of the butter in the sauce, and the ricotta and parmesan cheese in the filling and topping. To reduce the saturated fat I could develop a tomato-based sauce. The salt was low with 7% of the RI. However, the dish is low in sugar which is a healthy benefit of the dish and nearly one-third of the RI for protein which is needed for growth and repair. The fibre could be increased from 9% by using wholemeal flour.

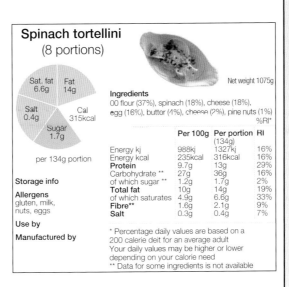

Spinach tortellini
(8 portions)

Sat. fat 6.6g Fat 14g
Salt 0.4g   Cal 315kcal
Sugar 1.7g

per 134g portion

Storage info

Allergens
gluten, milk, nuts, eggs

Use by

Manufactured by

Ingredients
00 flour (37%), spinach (18%), cheese (18%), egg (16%), butter (4%), cheese (2%), pine nuts (1%)

	Per 100g	Per portion (134g)	RI %RI*
Energy kj	988kj	1327kj	16%
Energy kcal	235kcal	316kcal	16%
Protein	9.7g	13g	29%
Carbohydrate **	27g	36g	16%
of which sugar **	1.2g	1.7g	2%
Total fat	10g	14g	19%
of which saturates	4.9g	6.6g	33%
Fibre**	1.6g	2.1g	9%
Salt	0.3g	0.4g	7%

* Percentage daily values are based on a 200 calerie deit for an average adult
Your daily values may be higher or lower depending on your calorie need
** Data for some ingredients is not available

Net weight 1075g

Costing

Cost for recipe: £4.86

Cost for each portion: £0.61

I was pleased with the overall cost of the dish. The recipe made a lot of pasta which could be used in another recipe (e.g. lasagne).

Cost analysis

Name	Amount used	Cost for 100g	Recipe cost	Portion cost
00 flour	400g	£0.19	£0.76	£0.10
Butter	50g	£0.44	£0.22	£0.03
Pine nuts	15g	£3.33	£0.50	£0.06
Cheese (Parmesan)	30g	£1.60	£0.48	£0.06
Cheese (ricotta)	200g	£0.40	£0.80	£0.10
Spinach (raw)	200g	£0.60	£1.20	£0.15
Egg	180g	£0.50	£0.90	£0.11
Totals			**£4.86**	**£0.61**

Activity

Comment on how the evaluation, sensory evaluation and nutritional analysis have been presented:

a) What do you think about the way in which the evaluation of the dish has been written?

b) What do you think about the way in which the sensory evaluation has been carried out and recorded?

c) What do you think about the way in which the nutritional analysis has been recorded and commented on?

d) What do you think about the way in which the costing has been carried out and recorded?

e) Can you think of anything else that could be done to improve the presentation of the work?

Final evaluation

At the end of the project you need to produce a final evaluation to identify any improvements.

When identifying improvements consider and explain:

- How suitable the final dishes were related to the task.
- The improvements you would make and why. The improvements could relate to:
  - sensory testing results
  - the cost analysis
  - food provenance
  - nutritional aspects
  - technical skills and techniques
  - quality and finish of the final menu.

Study tip

When evaluating concentrate on the dishes you have made. It is not necessary to evaluate how you have carried out the project.

Food Preparation task checklist

- ✓ Is the research well explained and related to the task?
- ✓ Is there evidence of a range of technical skills when making?
- ✓ Was the practical assessment well planned and the time plan used?
- ✓ Was the level of organisation/food safety in practical lessons good?
- ✓ Were the dishes finished to a high standard?
- ✓ Is the practical work independently produced?
- ✓ Is there good evidence of analysis and evaluation when carrying out sensory analysis?
- ✓ Is there good understanding of nutrition and costing?

Chapter 13 Written examination

What will I learn?

In this section you will learn about:

- how the written examination is organised
- how to be well prepared for the written examination
- the types of questions that will be asked in the written examination.

How the written examination is organised

At the end of the GCSE Food Preparation and Nutrition course you will take a written examination that lasts for **1 hour and 45 minutes**. It is designed to give you the opportunity to:

- demonstrate your knowledge and understanding of nutrition, food, cooking and preparation
- apply your knowledge and understanding of nutrition, food, cooking and preparation
- analyse and evaluate different aspects of nutrition, food, cooking and preparation including food you and others have made.

The examination is divided into two sections:

- **Section A:** This is worth 20 marks. It consists of 20 multiple-choice questions from different sections of the course.
- **Section B:** This is worth 80 marks. It consists of 5 questions of different styles from different sections of the course.

All of the examination questions must be answered.

How to prepare for the written examination

The most successful students in written examinations are the ones who are well prepared.

There are several ways of making sure that you are well prepared for your written examination, as shown in the table below.

Key terms

Command words: the way in which examination questions are asked

Close-ended (closed) questions: questions that need short and factual answers/responses

Open-ended (open) questions: questions that need detailed answers to show your knowledge and understanding

What to do	How and why this helps
During the course	
• Organise your written notes about different topics so they are tidy and in order	It means you are unlikely to lose important information.
• Keep the notes together in topic sections	It saves you time when you come to start your revision for the examination.
• Make your own brief revision notes/mind maps/revision cards about each topic	Making your own notes helps to reinforce the information in your brain so it is easier to remember and quicker to use when you revise.
• If you are unsure about a topic, ask your teacher to explain it to you again	Asking for help reduces any stress you might feel about something you do not understand at first.
For several weeks before the examination is due to take place	
• Plan a revision timetable	A timetable helps ensure that you have covered all your subjects and topics equally.

What to do	How and why this helps
• Start to read through your notes regularly	The more you read about a topic, the more familiar it will become and easier to remember, but don't just read your notes and highlight text.
• Concentrate on learning topics that you find more challenging to understand so that you will be better prepared and more able to answer questions on them	Evidence shows that re-writing notes, producing diagrams and flash cards help embed the learning in your long-term memory.
• It is better to revise for examinations in up to 45-minute blocks of time, with a short break (10–15 minutes) between each revision session	Here are some other strategies to help you to remember the information you revise: 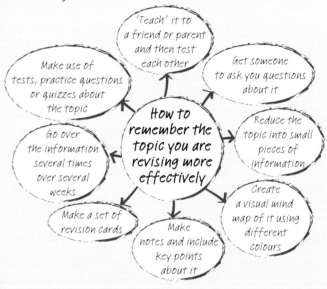
• Don't revise late into the evening or at night	Research shows that most people concentrate well for up to 45 minutes, then they need a break.
	If you are tired and your body is telling you to get some sleep, your capacity to absorb information is reduced and you are less likely to revise effectively or retain the information at this time of the day.
• Practise answering revision questions	Look on the AQA website for past exam papers. There are mark schemes available so you can test yourself.
	Answering questions makes you recall information and write it down, which reinforces what you have learnt.

During revision and when the examinations start

• Get plenty of sleep at night	Your brain and body need to rest properly so that you are alert and ready to start the next day.
	Research shows that your ability to recall information is better after you have had a good night's sleep.
• Get some fresh air and exercise during the day and at weekends	Fresh air and exercise will oxygenate your body and brain so that you are working at your most efficient levels and can concentrate well.
• Drink plenty of water	Water is important to help the body stay hydrated and avoid headaches.

What to do	How and why this helps
• Eat well – including plenty of fresh fruit and vegetables	A well-balanced diet will provide you with all the nutrients your body needs to be able to cope with the stress of examinations and to make sure your concentration and memory are at their best.
• Eat a well-balanced, filling breakfast every day	A good breakfast will enable you to concentrate and recall information because your blood sugar levels will be steady and your brain will be working well.

When you start your examination

• Read the instructions on the front page of the examination paper carefully	This will ensure that you know exactly what you must do and do not miss any vital detail (e.g. your candidate number or how to fill out the answers for the multiple-choice questions).
• Spend a few minutes at the start of the examination looking through the question paper and familiarise yourself with the types of questions it is asking	This will help you to stay calm, prepare yourself and focus on what you are being asked to do.
• Before you start to write anything, read each question once, then again to make sure you understand what you are being asked to do. Pay particular attention to the command words in each question (see the table on page 328)	This helps you to avoid just looking quickly at a question without really taking it all in, which could make you run the risk of misunderstanding what you have been asked to do and lose marks for leaving out information or not following the command words.
• Underline any key words to help you focus on answering the question well	Visual marks, highlights and signposts help to make you stay focused on the question.
• Check how many marks the question is worth	Many examination questions are separated into different parts. Checking what each is worth will help you know how many responses or facts you have to provide in your answer. Knowing how much each part of the question is worth will help you avoid giving too much detail in one part of your answer and not enough in another.
• Leave time at the end to read through your paper to check your answers. Check your quality of written communication.	Adding some additional points may well improve your answer.

Exam command words

Make sure you understand what command words are asking you to do.

AQA command word and definition	What it means	Example questions
Analyse: separate information into components and identify their characteristics	**Analyse:** to break up information about a topic into its different parts and put them in order, so that you can write about them in detail	An experiment is carried out to see the effects of different conditions on the activity of yeast. Five test tubes with balloons attached to the tops are prepared and left for 15 minutes as follows:
		<table><tr><th>Test tube and what it contains</th><th>Result</th></tr><tr><td>1 Yeast + warm water + sugar</td><td>Balloon has inflated well</td></tr><tr><td>2 Yeast + warm water + salt</td><td>Balloon has not inflated</td></tr><tr><td>3 Yeast + boiling water + sugar</td><td>Balloon has not inflated</td></tr><tr><td>4 Yeast + cold water + sugar</td><td>Balloon has only inflated a little bit</td></tr><tr><td>5 Yeast + warm water</td><td>Balloon has not inflated</td></tr></table> **Analyse** and explain the result of each test tube. Explain how this information will help you to understand how to make bread.
Comment: present an informed opinion	**Comment:** to write about a topic and make your own judgement about it, based on what you have learned and understood	Each year in the UK, millions of tonnes of food are wasted and end up in landfill sites. **Comment** on the effects of this on people and the environment and what could be done to try to reduce the amount of food wastage.
Compare: to identify similarities and/or differences	**Compare:** to write about the similarities and differences between two topics (usually two) and reach a conclusion about them	Here are the contents of two lunch boxes belonging to 10-year-old children: **Lunch box A:** cheese and salad sandwiches made with wholemeal bread; some carrot and cucumber sticks; a small slice of fruit cake; an orange and a banana; water to drink. **Lunch box B:** a packet of cheese and onion potato crisps; two caramel and chocolate bars; a satsuma; a carton of blackcurrant squash drink. **Compare** the nutritional values of the lunchboxes and their suitability for 10-year-old children.
Consider: review and respond to given information	**Consider:** to survey information, think carefully about it and then write about it, giving your views and opinions	Over the past 20 years, Fairtrade food products such as bananas, coffee, tea, chocolate, fresh vegetables and sugar have been available to buy in many supermarkets, restaurants, cafés and other outlets in the UK. **Consider** the reasons for the popularity of these products and the impact of buying Fairtrade foods from a consumer and producer's point of view.
Contrast: identify differences	**Contrast:** to consider and write about the differences between topics, actions, items or people (usually two), and then make a judgement about them (e.g. which one you think is better than the other)	Here are the ingredients lists for two breakfast cereal products: **Cereal A:** refined puffed wheat grains, sugar, almonds, honey, maltodextrin, palm oil, salt, flavourings, colour, iron, calcium, vitamins B1, B2, B3. **Cereal B:** 100% wholegrain wheat flakes, dried cranberries, pecan nuts. **Contrast** the ingredients lists for both products and justify which of the two cereals has the best nutritional profile.
Define: specify meaning	**Define:** to write down a clear and correct meaning of a word, term or phrase	**Define** the terms conduction, convection and radiation in terms of cooking food.

AQA command word and definition	What it means	Example questions
Describe: set out characteristics	**Describe:** to write in detail about the features and characteristics of a topic, activity, item or person	Self-raising flour, caster sugar, eggs and butter/vegetable fat spread are the main ingredients in cakes. **Describe** what happens to each ingredient when preparing and cooking an all-in-one cake mixture.
Discuss: present key points about different ideas or the strengths and weaknesses of an idea	**Discuss:** to write about a topic in a way that provides a balanced argument and gives unbiased reasons both for and against	According to recent statistics for the UK, the number of children who are developing obesity is increasing. In 2014, 9.5% of 4–5 year olds and 19.1% of 10–11 year olds were classified as obese. **Discuss** the reasons why obesity statistics are increasing and suggest ways to reduce obesity levels in children today.
Evaluate: judge from available evidence	**Evaluate:** to write about and assess the importance, quality or value of a topic, activity or item	**Evaluate** the importance of the following when preparing and cooking food: a) personal hygiene b) correct storage of foods and ingredients c) cooking foods thoroughly. Include examples in your answer.
Examine: investigate closely	**Examine:** to investigate something thoroughly and write in detail about what you have found out	**Examine** the photos below of some bananas. Write in detail, giving scientific facts, about what is happening in each of the photos:
Explain: set out purposes or reasons	**Explain:** to write about something in a very clear way, giving examples to illustrate your answer, to show that you understand what you are writing about	**Explain** why someone with coeliac disease cannot eat bread or other products made from wheat, and what would happen to them if they did.
Identify: name or otherwise characterise	**Identify:** to show that you know and understand something by being able to give its key features and characteristics	**Identify** different ways in which air can be incorporated into baked mixtures such as cakes, pastries and desserts. Give examples in your answer.
Illustrate: present clarifying examples	**Illustrate:** to show that you know about and understand a topic you are writing about by being able to give relevant and suitable examples	Explain why eggs are such a versatile ingredient in cooking. **Illustrate** your answer by giving examples.
Justify: support a case with evidence	**Justify:** to give reasons why you think something is better than something else, and to support those reasons with some evidence	Contrast the intensive production of vegetables with organic production. **Justify** which method of vegetable production is better for environmental sustainability.

AQA command word and definition	What it means	Example questions
Outline: set out main characteristics	**Outline:** to be able to write about and explain the main features of a topic	**Outline** the stages of: a) coagulation in a boiled egg b) gelatinisation of a Béchamel sauce c) plasticity of fat in the preparation of puff pastry d) caramelisation of sugar in cakes.
State: express clearly and briefly	**State:** to give a short, accurate and clear list	**State** the functions in the body of the following vitamins and minerals: a) vitamin A b) vitamin C c) iron d) iodine.
Suggest: present a possible case/solution	**Suggest:** to give a list of suitable and relevant ideas to solve a problem	Discuss the reasons why tooth decay statistics are increasing and **suggest** ways to reduce tooth decay levels in children today.
Summarise: present principal points without detail	**Summarise:** to give a brief account of the main points about a topic, activity or item	**Summarise** the use of the following micro-organisms in food production: • yeast • moulds • bacteria.

In multiple-choice questions, there is always one correct answer and usually three 'distractors' or incorrect answers. Some of these may be very close to the correct answer so you must read the choices very carefully! For example: Which one of the following groups are **all** high-risk foods?
A) Gravy, dried pasta, cold roasted beef, raw chicken
B) Fresh pasta, cold roasted beef, raw chicken, dried gravy powder
C) Raw chicken, cold roasted beef, gravy, fresh pasta
D) Dried pasta, dried gravy powder, raw chicken, gravy
(Answer: C)

Section A

Section A uses **close-ended (closed) questions** in the form of **multiple-choice questions**. These questions limit the amount of information you are asked to give, so they are quick to answer. Do not assume multiple-choice questions are easy. They can be very challenging and you must read the questions very carefully so you know exactly what they are focusing on and what they want to know. They test how well you can recall information from the different sections of the specification by giving you facts and asking questions using a variety of styles, such as:

- 'Which one of the following is correct …?'
- 'Identify one from the following …'
- 'Complete the sentence from one of the following …'
- 'True or false – select the answer that is true or false'
- 'Matching items – match a series of statements to a list of answers.'

There may be a table or picture given, with some multiple-choice questions about the information it shows.

There are some multiple choice questions on page 182 (*Food Safety section of book*) that you can practise answering.

Section B

Section B uses mainly **open-ended (open) questions**. The styles of these questions vary and they will use a range of command words. Open-ended questions cannot be answered with just a 'yes' or 'no' or a one-word answer. They require you to show your knowledge and understanding about the topic of the question by giving relevant information in your answer, often with examples, explanations, opinions, judgements and definitions to support it.

You must attempt all questions in this section. There will be a range of questions, with different degrees of difficulty, including some extended questions worth more marks. The questions do not get harder as you go through Section B.

The table on pages 331–334 gives some examples of different types of open-ended questions.

Data response question

Definition	Example questions

Definition

A piece of data is given and you are asked specific questions about it, often with some extra questions around the topic that the data is about.

Example questions

Typical values	Per 45g serving with 125ml semi-skimmed milk	Per 100g (cereal only)
Energy	918kJ	1442kJ
	217kcal	340kcal
Protein	9.6g	11.6g
Carbohydrate	37.5g	67.8g
of which: sugars	6.3g	0.9g
Fat	3.2g	2.5g
of which: saturates	1.4g	0.5g
Fibre	5.3g	11.8g
Salt	0.2g	Trace

Look at the table of nutritional information about a whole wheat breakfast cereal:

a) How many kcal will 50g of cereal only provide? _____ kcal   (1 mark)

b) What % of protein does the cereal only provide? _____ %   (1 mark)

c) How many g of fat will a serving of the cereal with milk provide?
_____ g   (1 mark)

d) Why is there more sugar in the 45g serving of cereal with milk than in 100g of the cereal only?   (2 marks)

e) Suggest two other foods that could be served with the cereal and milk to increase its nutritional value?   (2 marks)

Structured question

Definition	Example questions

Definition

Some information is given, such as a recipe, diagram or photograph, and specific questions are asked about it.

Mostly these are all fairly short, requiring a list of responses.

Spaces are provided for your answers and the number of marks each part of the question is worth are given.

Example questions

Food labels often have symbols or logos on them, such as the ones below:

A   B   C   D

a) State what each of the logos above means:

A _____   (1 mark)

B _____   (1 mark)

C _____   (1 mark)

D _____   (1 mark)

b) Explain three ways in which symbols and logos on food labels help the consumer when they are choosing their food.   (3 marks)

c) State five pieces of information that are mandatory (have to appear by law) on a food label.   (5 marks)

d) Identify the meanings of the following:

Use-by dates _____   (1 mark)

Best-before dates _____   (1 mark)

Examples of structured questions

Example A:

Definition	Example questions
Specific, factual information is required. This means that, in the example question given, you have to provide technical terms for the functions of eggs in your answer, and then show that you understand the terms by applying your knowledge and understanding of food science in describing what the eggs do in each dish.	The table below shows dishes that use eggs as an ingredient. For each of the two dishes, identify and describe **one** function of the eggs. An example has been completed for you. Do not repeat the function or description used in the example.

Dish	Identify and describe one function of the eggs used in the dish
Hollandaise sauce	Function: *Emulsification* Description: *Lecithin in the egg yolk prevents the separation of the oil (butter) and the water in the lemon juice*
Cheese and egg flan	Function: Description: *(3 marks)*
Swiss roll	Function: Description: *(3 marks)*

Example B:

Definition	Example questions
In the example question given, you have been given a specific topic and life stage to focus on. In your answer, you would need to show that you understand what iron deficiency is, what causes it, how it affects people and what is needed to prevent it. In the reasons for your answer, you would need to demonstrate your knowledge of how micronutrients work together – in this case vitamin C is needed to enable the body to absorb iron (so your main meal menu will have to include foods that contain both of these micronutrients), as well as how it is balanced in other ways.	Health professionals have expressed concern that many people, particularly teenage girls, suffer from iron deficiency anaemia. Describe a main meal that you could give a teenage girl that would supply all the micronutrients she needs to help prevent iron deficiency anaemia. Give reasons for your answer. *(6 marks)*

Example C:

Definition	Example questions
In the example question given, you are asked to judge how and why each of the storage situations is important for keeping food safe to eat. You have to show that you know and understand which foods have to be stored in different places and at certain temperatures, and how and why foods can become unsafe to eat.	Evaluate the importance of the following when storing foods: i) the correct temperature in a refrigerator. *(2 marks)* ii) a cool, well-ventilated cupboard for dry foods. *(2 marks)* iii) using older stocks of food before newer ones. *(2 marks)*

Free response question

Definition	Example question
A question is given about a specific topic and it is up to you to plan how you are going to answer it. The command words that are typically used for this type of question include 'explain', 'describe', 'discuss', 'comment', 'consider', 'analyse' or 'evaluate'.	Tooth decay is a serious problem, especially for children. Discuss the causes and consequences of this diet-related disease and what can be done to prevent it. *(12 marks)*

Answering a free response, open-ended question

Free response questions are often worth quite a lot of marks, so it is important that you plan your answer carefully and don't wander off the topic or keep repeating the information you give.

Marks for examination questions are awarded using a **mark scheme**, at three different levels of response (how well the student answers the question):

- **high** level of response
- **intermediate** (middle/average) level of response
- **low** level of response.

Below you will find example answers for the tooth decay question given above. Take a look at AQA's mark scheme and see how marks are awarded. Decide which of the following you think is the best answer and why.

Response A:

Response A	Comments
The teeth are part of the skeleton. They are needed to break food down so that it can be swallowed and digested properly. Teeth are made from an outer, hard protective layer called enamel, an inner, softer layer called dentine and a central part called the pulp cavity that contains nerves and blood vessels. The enamel can become damaged by acids, which make it dissolve and let bacteria from the mouth into the tooth. This causes tooth decay, which affects many children and is painful and makes the structure of the teeth break down and go black in colour. If they are damaged they will not be able to chew food properly. Sometimes the teeth will fall out. The bacteria that get into the tooth will cause an infection, which can go into the bloodstream and cause problems in other parts of the body.	• The answer is well set out with an introduction, main section and conclusion at the end.
The acids that cause tooth decay are formed by bacteria. There are thousands of bacteria in the mouth. Any food that gets stuck to the teeth, particularly foods with sugar and starch in them, will form a sticky substance all over the teeth, called plaque. The bacteria will break down the sugars and starches in the plaque and form acids. The acids stay on the teeth for about 45 minutes before the saliva in the mouth starts to neutralise them and stops them doing any more damage. If the child is allowed to eat lots of sugary snack foods and drinks in and between their meals, their mouth does not get a chance to neutralise the acids, so more decay will keep happening.	• The student has shown detailed knowledge and recall about teeth: what they are used for, how they are formed, how diet and eating habits affect their growth and health. • The student has applied this knowledge and accurately explained and described in detail how the structure of the teeth becomes damaged and the effects of this on the body. The student has correctly used specialist terminology throughout (e.g. plaque, decay, bacteria, neutralise).
Acids are also found in fruit juices (especially concentrated ones) and fizzy drinks, so if a child eats a lot of sugary foods and drinks a lot of fruit juices and fizzy drinks, they are more likely to develop tooth decay. Children start to get their adult teeth coming through when they are around 5 or 6 years old. If their first set of teeth have been affected by tooth decay, there is a chance that their second teeth will have been affected too, even though they have not yet come through.	• The student has demonstrated knowledge of foods that cause tooth decay and has made appropriate and relevant recommendations about how childhood tooth decay can be prevented by diet, specific nutrients and personal hygiene.
Tooth decay can be prevented by making sure that a very young child's diet does not contain many sugary foods and giving them water or milk to drink – not sweetened drinks. In this way, they will not develop a taste for sweet drinks. They also need to be encouraged to eat foods that will strengthen their teeth, such as those that contain calcium (e.g. milk, dairy foods and vegetables) and fluoride (e.g. fish and seafood). Children should also be encouraged and taught to clean their teeth regularly and properly to keep the numbers of bacteria in the mouth down and clean the plaque off the teeth. Children should also have regular check-ups at the dentist to make sure that their teeth stay healthy.	• How do you rate this response? How could it be improved?

Response B:

Response B	Comments
Teeth have an outside layer called enamel, and in the middle they have nerves and blood vessels. The enamel can be damaged by acids, which make holes in it and bacteria get in. This causes tooth decay and the teeth go black and may fall out. When we eat, food gets stuck to our teeth in a sticky layer called plaque. The bacteria in the mouth eat any sugar or starch in the plaque and turn them into acids. The acids stay on the teeth for quite a while before the saliva in the mouth stops them doing any more damage. Acids are also found in other foods and drinks such as fruit juices and fizzy drinks, so if a child eats a lot of sugary foods and drinks a lot of fruit juices and fizzy drinks all day, they are more likely to develop tooth decay. Tooth decay can be prevented by not giving children sugary foods and sweetened drinks very often, but mostly giving them water or milk to drink so they don't get into bad habits and want to have lots of sweets. They should be encouraged to eat foods that will make their teeth strong and have lots of calcium. They should also clean their teeth twice a day and have regular visits to the dentist to make sure that their teeth stay healthy.	• The answer is quite well set out with an introduction, main section and conclusion at the end. • The student has shown some good knowledge and recall about teeth: how they are formed, and how diet and eating habits affect their health. • The student has applied this knowledge and explained and described quite well how the structure of the teeth becomes damaged. The student has correctly used some specialist terminology (e.g. plaque, decay, bacteria). • The student has demonstrated knowledge of foods that cause tooth decay and has made some appropriate and relevant recommendations about how childhood tooth decay can be prevented by diet and personal hygiene. • How do you rate this response? How could it be improved?

Response C:

Response C	Activity
Teeth are white on the outside, but they can go bad and go black. They can go bad if you don't look after them. A lot of children get tooth decay. People who eat a lot of sugar and sweets can have bad teeth because it makes holes in their teeth. If you give children lots of sweets and fizzy drinks and they don't clean their teeth they will get tooth decay. Fruit juice can also make teeth go bad if you drink too much of it. They should drink water instead and clean their teeth properly.	Read Response C, then discuss and answer the following questions as a class, giving reasons: • Is this answer well structured? • What knowledge has the student shown about teeth? • How could the answer be improved?

Weights, measures and other useful information for practical food preparation

Definitions of abbreviations that are often used in recipes

Abbreviation	Definition
tsp	Teaspoon
tbsp	Tablespoon
dsp	Dessertspoon
ml	Millilitre
l	Litre
g	Gram
kg	Kilogram
mins	Minutes
SR	Self-raising (flour)

Oven temperature conversions

NB – this is a guide that is in general use. All types of ovens can vary slightly in the temperatures they reach, depending on how they are constructed, how good their oven door seal is and how well they are insulated to stop heat escaping.

Gas Regulo number ('Regulo' is the trademark name for a type of thermostatic control used on gas ovens)	Electric ovens (standard, non-fan oven) °C	Electric fan ovens (always set at a lower temperature because they are usually faster) °C	Description
¼	110	100	Very cool/slow
½	120	110	Very cool/slow
1	140	130	Cool/slow
2	150	140	Cool/slow
3	170	160	Moderate
4	180	170	Moderate
5	190	180	Fairly/moderately hot
6	200	190	Fairly/moderately hot
7	220	200	Hot
8	230	220	Very hot
9	240	230	Very hot

Weights/volume conversions (metric/imperial)

Weights

Metric	Imperial practical conversion (sometimes used in recipes)
25g	1oz (oz = ounce)
50g	2
75g	3
100g	4 (¼lb = pound)
150g	5
170g	6
200g	7
225g	8 (½lb)
250g	9
275g	10
300g	11
350g	12 (¾lb)
375g	13
400g	14
425g	15
450g	16 (1lb)
500g/½kg	
1,000g/1kg	

Volume

Metric	Imperial practical conversion (sometimes used in recipes)
25ml	1 fl oz (fl oz = fluid ounce)
50ml	2
75ml	3
100ml	4
150ml	5 (¼ pint)
275ml	10 (½ pint)
425ml	15 (¾ pint)
575ml	20 (1 pint)
500ml/½ litre	
1,000ml/1 litre	

Measuring spoons

Spoon size	Metric measurement (level)
⅛ tsp	0.6ml/0.6g
¼ tsp	1.25ml/1.25g
½ tsp	2.5ml/2.5g
1 tsp	5ml/5g
1 dsp	10ml/10g
1 tbsp	15ml/10g

American cup measurements for different ingredients (cup measurements from other countries vary in size)

Ingredient	¼ cup	⅓ cup	½ cup	⅔ cup	¾ cup	1 cup
Almonds – chopped	40g	50g	75g	100g	110g	150g
Almonds – ground	30g	40g	60g	80g	90g	120g
Brown sugar	45g	60g	90g	120g	135g	180g
Butter	60g	80g	120g	160g	180g	240g
Caster sugar	55g	75g	110g	150g	165g	225g
Cornflour	30g	40g	60g	80g	90g	120g
Dried fruit – sultanas	50g	65g	100g	130g	150g	200g
Flour	30g	40g	60g	80g	90g	120g
Golden syrup	85g	95g	170g	190g	255g	340g
Granulated sugar	50g	65g	100g	130g	150g	200g
Icing sugar	25g	35g	50g	70g	80g	100g
Porridge oats (dry)	20g	25g	40g	50g	60g	80g
Uncooked rice	45g	60g	90g	120g	135g	180g
Vegetable fat spread	50g	65g	100g	130g	150g	200g

Critical temperatures in food handling and safety

Food handling stage	Safe temperatures
Food storage:	
Refrigerator	0°C to below 5°C
Freezer	–18°C or below
Cooking food:	
Core temperature	Minimum 75°C for 2 minutes
Keeping food hot	Minimum core temperature of 63°C
Cooling down cooked food to store in refrigerator	Core temperature must reach 5°C or cooler within 1½–2 hours
Reheating cooked food	Reheat only ONCE to minimum core temperature of 75°C for 2 minutes
Keeping food cold	0°C to below 5°C
Thawing frozen food	0°C to below 5°C

Acknowledgements

Alamy: © MBI p203; © Alex Segre p231; © Alistair Heap p232; © Andy Selinger p272, p331; © ASP Food p275; © Carolyn Jenkins p221; © Cliff Hide News p287; © Clynt Garnham Food & Drink p217; © Dash p190, p197; © Edward Westmacott p221; © Erik Tham p223; © FoodPhotography p204; © Ian Francis p224; © incamerastock p285; © Jeff Morgan p232; © Jeff Morgan p232; © Kevin Wheal p221; © Libby Welch p258, p331; © Mediablitzimages p221, p285; © Newscast Online p221, p233; © Peter Titmuss p258, p272; © Simon Dack p186; © Steven May p186, p257, p331; © studiomode p218, p286; © Tim Hill p260; © travellight p40; © urbanbuzz p285; **Others:** © www.plastic-surgeon.co.uk p86; **Shutterstock:** 5 second Studio p177; abimages p227, p233; AdamEdwards p86; Adrian Petrean p124; aekikuis p261; Africa Studio p18, p33, p43, p56, p59, p155, p177, p188, p194, p274, p285, p322; Air Images p167; akiyoko p275; al1962 p225; Albina Glisic p56; Alessia Pierdomenico p181; aletermi p280; Alex Helin p240; Alexander Raths p66, p176, p180, p183, p194; Alexey Lysenko p59; Alexeysun p91, p94; alexmillos p216; Alhovik p232; Alila Medical Media p31; alisafarov p83; AllAnd p144; Amayra p213; Analia Valeria Urani p107, p155; Anastasia Petrova p181; Anatoly Tiplyashin p241; ANCH pvi, p12; Andrea Skjold Mink p152; Andrey_Kuzmin p17, p172; Andrey_Popov p203; Angela Aladro melia p164; Angela Waye p210; AnjelikaGr p123; ankomando p309; Anna Hoychuk p3, p78, p249; Antonio Guillem p327; antoniodiaz p60, p327; ARENA Creative p247; Arina P Habich p209; Artem Zhushman p64; Artit Fongfung p93, p99; AS Food studio p81, p249, p315; Aumsama p216; Axel Bueckert p159; B and E Dudzinscy p312; Baloncici p271, p278; Barbro Bergfeldt p5; Benoit Daoust p276; Bernd Juergens p92, p98; betto rodrigues p213; bikeriderlondon p61; bitt24 p5; Blan-k p232; Blend Images p205; Bloomua p296; BlueSkyImage p48; Bochkarev Photography p100; Bochkarev Photography p312; bonchan pvii, p3, p4, p240; branislavpudar p275; Brent Hofacker p12, p46, p52, p81, p169, p176; Burlingham p266; BW Folsom p97; AFANASEV IVAN p296; Canadapanda p156; Candus Camera p206; Carlos Rondon p84; Catalin Petolea p81, p93, p100; Celig p205; ChameleonsEye p214, p219, p266; Chanclos p83; CHAPLIA YAROSLAV p272; Charlotte Lake p200; charnsitr p244; ChiccoDodiFC p166; chinahbzyg p257; Christian Bertrand p60; Christian Delbert p177; Christian Jung p172; Christine Langer-Pueschel pvii, p64; Christopher Elwell p79, p134; Claire Fraser Photography p123, p157; cobraphotography p84; Constantine Pankin p127; ConstantinosZ p127, p157; Corepics VOF p185; Creativa Images p204; Cylonphoto p166; D7INAMI7S p277; D and S Photographic Services p54; Daimond Shutter p264; Dan Kosmayer p122; Dani Vincek p322; danm12 p245; Darren K. Fisher p96; daseaford p132; DavidEwingPhotography p270; David Peter Robinson p268; Daxiao Productions piv, p178, p248; De Repente p173; denio109 p5; Dereje p215; Designua p32; Destinyweddingstudio p280; Diana Taliun p11; Dionisvera p82; Ditty_about_summer p181, p220, p222; Dmitry Kalinovsky p205; donatas1205 p188; Dotshock p60; Douglas Freer p173, p200; draconus p279; Dragon Images piv; Dream79 p249; Drozhzhina Elena p11, p82; ducu59us p56; DUSAN ZIDAR p177; Edler von Rabenstein p249; Eldred Lim p179, p195; Elena Schweitzer p3, p23, p117; Elena Shashkina p11; Elena Veselova p247; elenabsl p70; Elenadesign p242; ElenaGaak p168; Elzbieta Sekowska p245, p264; emran p242; EQRoy p268, p275; Eskymaks p4; espies p213; eugena-klykova p84; eurobanks p216; Ev Thomas p137; Evan Lorne p228; Everything p81, p123; Evgeny Karandaev p296; Family Business p23; Fanfo p240; farbled p11; Fedorov Oleksiy p265; Feng Yu p195; ffolas p143, p249; Fleckstone p123; Foodpictures p17, p188; FotograFFF p277; Fotoluminate LLC p65; Francesco83 p120; Franck Boston p222; FuzzBones p170; g-stockstudio p248; Garsya p11; Gayvoronskaya_Yana p84, p212; gcpics p227; Gelpi JM p18; Gertjan Hooijer p163; Gigira p265; Giuseppe Parisi p242; Giuseppe_R p232; givaga p33, p196; greatstockimages p58; Grezova Olga p245; HandmadePictures p82; heliopix p216; highviews p213; hlphoto p91, p95, p96; homydesign p188; Horst Lieber p167; Hriana p72; humbak p177; Hurst Photo p83, p93, p101, p278; Hywit Dimyadi p83, p96; Iakov Filimonov p260; Ian 2010 p208; id-art p17, p274; Igor Dutina p242; Igor Normann p179; IgorAleks p82; Ildi Papp p65, p242; Image Point Fr p219; Imageman p164; Images by Maria p148, p154; images.etc p198; images72 p106; India Picture p215; Indigo Fish p242; InnaFelker p24, p81; Irantzu Arbaizagoitia p79; Irina Barcari p207, p212; Irina Nartova p199; Iulian Valentin p204; Ivaylo Ivanov p163; jabiru p98, p150; Jacek Chabraszewski p60, p97; Jackthumm p89; Jane Rix p83; jeehyun p79; Jeeranan Thongpan p164; Jetrel p86; Jiri Hera p169; JL-Pfeifer p176; JoannaTkaczuk p163; Joe Gough p18, p81, p83, p84, p91, p96, p168, p227, p240; JOSEPH S.L. TAN MATT p24; Joshua Resnick p80, p156; joshya p23, p73; jreika p3; Jubal Harshaw p117; Kamira p190; KANIN.studio p259; Karl Allgaeuer p79, p242; Kate Grigoryeva p122; Katerina Belaya p29; kay roxby p272; kazoka p91, p95, p179, p209; Keith Homan p170; Kenneth Sponsier p56; Kharkhan Oleg p207, p257; Kheng Guan Toh p156; KieferPix p75; KIM NGUYEN p82; Kjetil Kolbjornsrud p86, p288; Knorre p169; Kondor83 p94, p101, p186; Konrad Mostert p270; Konstantin Gushcha p143, p154; Konstantin Shevtsov p271; Korta p181; koss13 p80; kostasgr p282; KPG_Payless p207; kreatorex p280; Kristina Stasiuliene p93, p100; Kritchanut p181; Krzysztof Slusarczyk p14, p80, p91, p95, p96; kubais p155; KuLouKu p173; kungverylucky p92, p98; Lack-O'Keen p227; Lakeview Images p278; Lanav p123; LarsZ p178; Leah-Anne Thompson p326; Lee Torrens p50; Lenscap Photography p221; Lesya Dolyuk p12; Lightspring p31, p73, p79; Lilyana Vynogradova p56, p130, p197; Lisovskaya Natalia p78; littlekop p80, p179, p233; Liv friis-larsen p78; Liz Van Steenburgh p98; Login p308; lsantilli p79; LuapVision p154; Lucky Business p327; Luisa Leal Photography p195; Lukas Hejtman p49; Macrovector p259; MAHATHIR MOHD YASIN p11, p127; MaraZe p18, p106, p115, p295; margouillat photo p3, p24, p80, p99, p172, p173, p187, p245; MARGRIT HIRSCH p178; Marie C Fields p147, p154; marinini p232; Mariyana M p190; Mark Yuill p167, p281; Markus Mainka p242, p282; Marzia Giacobbe p242; Mathisa p191; matin p188; Matthew Bechelli p14, p80; mayakova p3; mgfoto p78, p176; Michael C. Gray p96; Mike Brake p207; Mike Focus p256; mimagephotography p231; Minerva Studio p50; Monika Wisniewska p288; Monkey Business Images p76, p93, p100, p176, p184, p205, p206, p326; monticello p295, p299; Moving Moment p82, p84, p274; mpessaris p100; MR. WATCHARA POOTO p180; MShev p20, p312, p315; MSPhotographic p92, p97, p191; muph p256; mypokcik p71; naka-stockphoto p43; Narattapon Purod p173, p176; Nata-Lia p83, p84; Natalie Board p207; Nataliya Arzamasova p214; Natasha Breen p155; nbriam p119; NDT p317; neil langan p96; Nicram Sabod p258; nikkytok p5; Niloo p206; Nitr p43, p67, p312; O.Bellini p156; oknoart p141; Oksana Kuzmina p209, p210; Oktava p3; Okyay p264; Olaf Speier p165, p166, p167; Olga Miltsova p27; Olga Nayashkova p66; Olha Afanasieva p98; Oliver Hoffmann p82, p309, p310; Only Fabrizio p147; Owl_photographer p18; Ozgur Coskun p112, p154; P.Jirawat p260; PANYA KUANUN p219; Pat_Hastings p287; Patricia Marroquin p264; Paul Cowan p84, p242; Paul Orr p273; paul prescott p256; paulista p12; pcruciatti p185; Peter Kim p4; Peter Zijlstra p82; Petr Malyshev p86, p177; Philip Lange p276; PHILIPIMAGE p190; phloen p280; Phonlamai Photo p197; photomaster p322; photopixel p4; Phovoir p86; phstudio p111; picturepartners p245; PiggingFoto p208; Piotr Adamowicz p86; pirtuss p227; Pixelbliss p216, p233; Psisa p211; purplequeue p191; R_Szatkowski p12; ra3rn p170; racorn p66, p76, p206; Radu Bercan p74; rangizzz p172, p200; Riccardo Mayer p270; Richard Griffin p92, p99, p212; Richard M Lee p28; Richard Peterson p161; Richard Thornton p275; Richard Waters p270; Rido p291; riopatuca p178; Rita Robinson p260; Rob Hyrons p76; Robert Adrian Hillman p241; Robin Stewart p124; Robyn Mackenzie pvii, p23, p25, p64, p75, p78, p79, p116, p127; rocharibeiro p82; Romiana Lee p208; Roobcio p78; RosieYoung p4; rprongjai p86; RTimages p24, p27, p65, p72; Rudmer Zwerver p179; Ruta Production p167; Sabphoto p326; sakhorn p269; sarsmis p5; sasimoto p3; sciencepics p18; Scott Bolster p287; Sebastian Crocker p181; Sebastian Kaulitzki p171; Seregam p156; Seregam p17; SergeBertasiusPhotography p193; Serghei Starus p242; sergign p81; Sergio Stakhnyk p179; Shaiith p92, p97, p106; Shebeko p315; Sheila Fitzgerald p225; showcake p137; shtukicrew p82; Silberkorn p22, p31; simez78 p180, p268; Simon Booth p232; Sipandra p80; Slawomir Fajer p81, p96; Sleepbird p202; smart.art p281; Solphoto p17, p34, p187; SpeedKingz p180, p185; spline_x pvi; Squareplum p127; stanga p234; Stankevich p296; Stefanina Hill p308, p313, p316, p331; stefanodinenno p280; Stepanek Photography p14, p176; Stephanie Frey p4; Stephen Clarke p221; stockcreations p4, p78; StockLite p51; StockPhotosArt p194; Stockr p256; Stocksnapper p173; stocksolutions pv, p3; Story p169; stuart.ford p177; Subbotina Anna p212; Sukpaiboonwat p258; Suwin p266; Svetlana Lukienko p80; svry p84; Syda Productions p13, p59, p60, p72, p194, p249; TaraPatta p208; tarapong srichaiyos p19; Tefi p276; Tequiero p277; TFoxFoto p275; thailoei92 p89; thatreec p4; Thinglass p216, p233; Tikta Alik p190; Tim Belyk p189; Tim Large p190; Tischenko Irina p11, p25; tiverylucky p91, p96; Tom Tom p34, p176; tommaso lizzul p249; Tomophafan p128; Toni Genes p218; travellight p5, p8, p123, p156; TristanBM p248; Tyler Olson p280; urbanbuzz p83, p218, p221, p224, p233, p285; Valentin Valkov p257; Valentina Razumova p248; Valentinash p271; Valentyn Volkov p3; Valentyn Volkov p12; Vasin Lee p115; verchik p214; Veronika Synenko p12; Viktor1 p66, p84; VLADGRIN p296; Vladimir Wrangel p264; Vladislav S p86; Volina p237; Voyagerix p247; Vytautas Kielaitis p208, p266; Warren Price Photography p108; Warut Chinsai p190; Wasant p137; Wasu Watcharadachaphong p32; wavebreakmedia p36, p74, p101, p203, p267; winnond p181; withGod p271; WitthayaP p258; WOLF AVNI p265; worker p179; Ye Liew p219; Yeko Photo Studio p22; Yulia K p43; zcw p3; Zeljko Radojko p276; zi3000 p144; ziashusha p99; Zigzag Mountain Art p188; **SPL:** St. Mary's Hospital Medical School p25.

Index